Contents

Sponsorship

The conference organisers gratefully acknowledge financial contributions towards the conference from the Royal Commission on the Ancient and Historical Monuments of Wales and the Welsh Mines Society.

NAMHO

National Association of Mining History Organisations

Preface

The 2014 conference of the National Association of Mining History Organisations, hosted by the AditNow Mining History Society, was held at Bangor University, Gwynedd, Wales, 25–27 July. Titled 'Mining Technology', the conference theme was technical innovation in the extractive industries. This volume presents the conference proceedings and includes papers related to metalliferous mining, slate quarrying and stone extraction.

Over the last four thousand years mining technology has progressed from antler picks and stone hammers, through the mechanical developments of the medieval period and the nineteenth-century industrialisation of mining, to the large laser-guided and computer-controlled mining machinery of the present day. The papers in these proceedings examine some of the technical developments that have facilitated the winning of material from the ground and the social effects of those innovations.

As can be seen in these proceedings, the history of technical innovation in the extractive industries of mining and quarrying can be traced via three distinct sources: the surviving technical artefacts such as tools and machinery remnants, evidence of mining methods and equipment left in the accessible parts of mines and quarries, and the pictorial and written record.

Tools (or remnants thereof) and other remains survive from the earliest period of mining in the shape of stone hammers, antler picks, wooden launders and similar objects. As well as informing us about the mining methods in use they provide a direct and emotive connection with the individual early miner. As far as more recent mining is concerned, most equipment of any value, even if only for scrap, was removed when operations ceased. However, there are still a few impressive survivals of machinery in situ underground.

The mined passages themselves may show traces of the technology used for their excavation. Picks and other tools, fire-setting and explosives all leave distinctive evidence of their use. Transport methods may also leave their mark in the shape of barrow ruts, rail sleeper impressions or modifications to underground passages in the shape of sockets for structures and machinery or attachment points for hauling.

Written and pictorial records exist, albeit sparsely for the early years, from the Roman period onward. Gaius Plinius Secundus (23–79 CE, better known as Pliny the Elder) described gold mining, including the large-scale use of water to scour alluvial gold deposits, in his *Naturalis Historia*, published towards the end of his life.

Georgius Agricola's (Georg Bauer's) *De Re Metallica* (published a year posthumously in 1556) seems to have been the first attempt to systematically catalogue the state of the art of prospecting, mining, refining, and smelting metals. The written descriptions tell us of the techniques of mining at the time, and the numerous wood-cut illustrations not only portray the machinery used but also give insight as to the occupations and dress of the men and women involved in the work, and bring the world of the medieval miner alive on the page. However, Agricola was not the only recorder of mining at this time. The artist Heinrich Gross sketched the silver mines of St Nicholas at La Croix-aux-Mines in sufficient detail that the construction of barrows and trucks can easily be seen. Earlier depictions of mining also exist such as the title-page illustration in the Kuttenberger Kanzionale of c. 1471, which includes a horse gin, jack rolls and ventilating machinery.

Although the art of the Romantic period can be seen as a reaction to the Enlightenment and the early Industrial Revolution, some of the landscape artists of the time included mining-related features in the landscape such as engine houses and transport of product by land and water. Whilst in some instances the accuracy of such images is questionable, they still provide evidence of the technology in use at the time and its general visibility. In addition, business letters, account books, estate records, newspapers and travellers' written descriptions form an important documentary record from this period onwards.

The aftermath of the Industrial Revolution in the late nineteenth and early twentieth century provides far more documentary evidence than is available for previous times. Photography developed during this period and was used to record both surface and underground scenes. The development of the modern patent system ensured that technical drawings of many inventions related to mining (not all of them successful) survive to the present. Other sources include articles in commercial and learned journals, official reports, text books and personal memoirs.

From the Bronze Age mines of Mynydd Parys and Great Orme to the nineteenth- and twentieth-century developments in the slate quarries of Snowdonia, north-west Wales provides evidence and illustration of many technologies related to mining and the extractive industries generally. Bangor and its university therefore provided the ideal venue for a conference which brought together mining historians, archaeologists and other persons interested in the field to share their work and their experiences, to socialise and to enjoy a rich mining and quarrying heritage. The venue was particularly appropriate, as a feature of the university's foundation was the voluntary contributions made by local people, including quarrymen, from their weekly wages over a period of time.

In producing these proceedings I would like to acknowledge the professional copy-editing expertise and generous amounts of time provided by Pam Cope.   *Dave Linton*

Prehistoric Mining Technology: Archaeology and Experimental Reconstruction

Simon Timberlake

Abstract: Over the last 10–15 years, investigation of firesetting and rock removal using stone, bone/antler, and wooden tools has been undertaken at a number of Copper Age/Bronze Age mines. Similar sites have been shown to exist worldwide – suggesting the parallel development of fairly utilitarian and adapted 'Stone Age' technologies. Study sites include those in Wales and England, Turkey, Georgia and South America (Chile).

Archaeological experiment has proved to be by far the best way to understand how the various different methods of mining and also the processing of occasionally complex and 'low-grade' ores was achieved when one allows for the necessary time (and patience), attention to detail, and sheer effort required. Case studies involving copper mining and smelting, gold/tin separation and recovery from hard-rock ores and iron pigment extraction will be discussed.

Introduction

Over the last twenty years the discovery and excavation of some twelve Bronze Age metal mines or prospecting sites, and the probable identification of at least eight others within England and Wales (Fig. 1), have provided a suitable timeframe for the first exploitation of metal within the UK (Timberlake 2009). This activity consisted of a widespread phase of early prospection taking place between 2000 and 1650 BC followed by production at a very limited number of sites (such as the Great Orme in North Wales: see Dutton & Fasham 1994; Lewis 1996), which continued right up until the Late Bronze Age. All of these archaeological investigations, except for those undertaken on the Great Orme, form part of a long-term programme of study currently being undertaken by the Early Mines Research Group (EMRG).

A good summary account of the actual mines themselves (in particular the ten Bronze Age copper mines in Wales) can be read in the paper 'New investigations and new ideas on Prehistoric-Roman metal mining and smelting in Wales' which was presented by the author at the 2013 NAMHO Mining Legacies Conference held in Aberystwyth, and which is currently in press.

The current paper deals mostly with the experience of recognizing and understanding the use of prehistoric mining tools through artefact analysis and experimentation, with most of the quoted evidence for this coming from work carried out in Britain, especially Wales. However, some of the most recent investigations by the author of prehistoric mining and ore processing took place thousands of kilometres to the east in Georgia, yet the tools used in each case appeared identical. This reflects the utterly utilitarian and opportunistic nature of primitive mining technology, with similar solutions to similar problems being encountered across the globe.

Prehistoric stone mining tools

Recognition and study

The earliest mention of finds of stone hammers within the ancient mines of Britain was of a discovery made at Twll y mwyn (Cwm Darren) Mine in Cardiganshire, Central Wales, in 1742. Lead miners working for Lewis Morris (who was

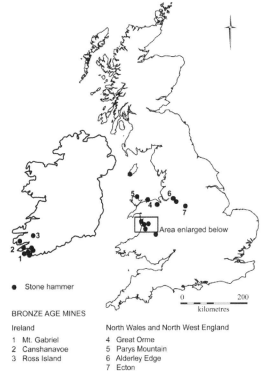

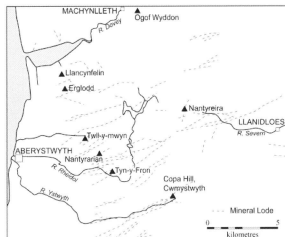

Fig. 1   Cobble stone mining tools and Bronze Age mines in Britain and Ireland. Inset shows the prehistoric mines and mineral veins of Central Wales. (S. Timberlake and B. Craddock)

the Crown Mineral Agent for the Manor of Perfedd, but also an antiquarian and a man of letters) re-opened the old trench and found traces of burning and broken cobble tools, which Morris described as follows '… the wedges were sea stones, with one end nipped off to an edge, and there is an impression on the other end where they used to strike on them … it seems [to me] the mine was worked before man knew the use of iron …' (Bick & Davies 1994). Just over a century later in 1874, William Boyd Dawkins (the curator of the Manchester Museum) described the finding of similar, though in this case grooved, examples of cobble stone tools within the pit workings at Brynlow Mine on Alderley Edge. These he described '… as perhaps belonging to the Bronze Age, when the necessary copper was eagerly being sought throughout the whole of Europe', noting the similarity of these to the Egyptian ones he had seen from the Sinai (Dawkins 1875).

Sixty years on from this a rather more broad-ranging study of stone tools and primitive mining in Britain was undertaken by Oliver Davies for the British Association for the Advancement of Science Section H (Davies 1937). Davies visited a number of the mines in Wales that had been referred to in *Mining Journal* reports as being ancient ones in which stone tools had been found, with the intention of trying to date them more accurately. However, in the days long before radiocarbon dating he was quite unable to date the charcoal he found, and with no pottery or artefacts, he ended up referring to all of these stone hammer mines simply as '… Roman or old Celtic in age'. Nevertheless, he did recognize that the cobbles must have been either 'pounding stones' or 'anvil-querns', yet erroneously considered them to have been '… broken to give better grip' (Davies 1947).

Arguably the first modern study, or classification, of these artefacts was undertaken by John Pickin in 1989/90. His typology consisted of 6 classes of cobble tools: unmodified (Type 1), surface-pecked (Type 2 a–d), edge-notched (Type 3 a–b), partially grooved (Type 4 a–b), single-grooved (Type 5) and multiple-grooved (Type 6 a–d) (Pickin 1990). As a very simple classification of these tools, this typology still stands. Around the same time David Gale was undertaking work for his Ph.D. at Bradford University. This was a functional study of stone tools which examined both use-wear and cobble morphometry (Gale 1995). Although quite comprehensive in its analysis, this work preceded the findings of most of the more recent archaeological work, and involved no experiments or tool reconstructions.

Occurrence and context

The current distribution of cobble stone mining hammers at metal mines across the British Isles correlates with some (but not all) of the areas of near-surface copper deposits, particularly along the west coast of Britain (see Fig. 1). Furthermore, the results of recent fieldwork indicate the generally good survival of these, even where they have become dispersed as a result of re-deposition by later mining. In general an assessment of the location(s) and scale of Bronze Age mining comes down to skill in the recognition of what sometimes are little more than fragments of unmodified cobbles used in a small way as percussion tools.

To date, all of the archaeologically excavated sites associated with *in situ* finds of cobble stone hammers have proved to be Bronze Age, despite the assertions of some sceptics that these tools, therefore the mines, may have been medieval, even modern, perhaps worked by poverty-stricken miners (Briggs 1988, 1993). Nevertheless, fully-grooved hammer stones, which are elsewhere commonly accepted as being the diagnostic type of prehistoric mining tool, are rare in Britain; in fact within the British Isles these tools have only been found at Ross Island, Killarney in Ireland (O'Brien 2004), and at Alderley Edge, Cheshire in the UK (Timberlake 2005a). Significantly there are no fully-grooved mining examples from Wales. In fact the numbers of unmodified (or only minimally modified) cobble tools found at these mines may help to explain why so many of these sites went unrecognized in the modern era, at least until the beginnings of more systematic and critical fieldwork, such as that carried out during the last two decades.

During field investigations the discovery of splinters and flakes alongside larger fragments of hammer stone within sections cut through ancient mine spoil indicates those places where prehistoric mining was well localized (i.e. where it occurred very nearby). Therefore this association can be considered as a good test of the *in situ* status of stone mining tools, particularly in those cases where one might be attempting to date this mining both above and below ground. Normally such tools are found broken up and re-used, either deposited within the mine spoil, as purposeful backfill, or as spoil slumped down from the surface into underground workings. Hammer stones (or fragments of hammer stones) are pretty much indestructible, in some cases surviving any amount of later reworking. Indeed in most of the cases examined the fragments of these tools never disperse far from source, even after reworking and redeposition. Our experience suggests that a complete range of broken tool fragments within mine spoil is a good indication for the survival nearby of other prehistoric mining remains and/or working areas.

Terminology

Most people interested in the study of ancient mining will be aware that stone mining tools are typically rather rudimentary but also universal in their form and global distribution. By and large they tend to be a product of utilitarian need rather cultural design. Given their universal nature it is perhaps surprising that there is no so little standardisation in functional analysis and terminology. These tools (some of them with quite specific functions) are variously described in the literature as stone mining mauls, hammer stones, stone hammers, stone mallets, pounders, crushing stones, stone picks etc. – often with little or no clear knowledge of function. So in order to refer to them in a more appropriate and relevant way it is proposed here that these assemblages of stone tools should be described using the generic and collective term 'cobble stone mining tools', a term which more accurately reflects their origin as waterworn cobbles (or sometimes rounded weathered lumps of rock) selected for a range of interchangeable mining tool tasks (see also Timberlake & Craddock 2013, 39). Only in one sense of the word are all of these tools artefacts. All show some signs of having been used, though only a small percentage of them have intentionally been artefacted (or, as I would prefer to say, modified).

Recording

The tasks of object recording/illustration, functional analysis and experiment are all closely linked in the process we have now adopted for interpreting the use and significance of these stone mining toolsets. When dealing with thousands of cobble stone mining tools we have found it absolutely essential to develop some sort of simple analytical, yet quite standardized method of recording that can easily be undertaken in the field. For this reason a standard two-page hammer stone recording sheet has been developed by the EMRG (Jenkins & Timberlake 1997, 66; Timberlake 2003; Timberlake & Craddock 2013, 41–42: see Fig. 2).

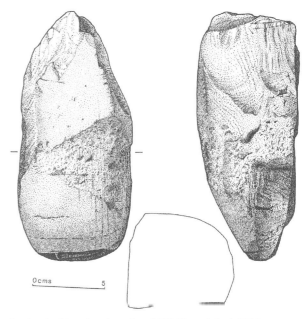

Fig. 3   Archive drawing of tool CH 89, weight 1.475 kg

Two site-specific studies from Britain: Cwmystwyth and Ecton

Cobble stone mining tools have been studied in some detail from the Early Bronze Age copper mine on Copa Hill, Cwmystwyth (426 m above sea level), and a summary is included here. At least 79% of the cobbles brought to this site for use as hammer stones had degrees of polish/smoothness similar to beach (littoral) pebbles, whilst 36% had roundness indices exceeding those of local river (fluvial) pebbles (Gale 1995). The average weight for near-complete examples of cobble stones found within the mineworking was between 2 and 2.25 kg, whilst for the larger fragments found on the tips outside it was less (i.e. between 1 and 2 kg). In fact most of the cobbles were 15–25 cm long and 8–13 cm wide, and cylindrical to flat-sided/sub-rectangular, all of this suggesting a moderate amount of size and shape selection at source. There appeared to be some selection of the finer grained and generally harder rocks amongst the greywacke cobbles (although this was less obvious); in fact 42% of these greywackes were of quartz-cemented sandstone types. Even so, there was little evidence to suggest any sort of vigilant selection to eliminate potentially flawed cobbles – although this might just as likely reflect the difficulties in detecting incipient joints within very well-rounded stones.

A survey of potential cobble sources within the Ystwyth valley was undertaken over the 25 km stretch between the mine and the sea. The results of this survey indicated a 'best match' with pebbles taken from the storm beach shingle bars located near to the mouth of the river Ystwyth (Jenkins & Timberlake 1997, 69–70). This probable source was determined by measuring three different parameters: (1) the amount of 'flattening' of the pebbles, (2) the degree of smoothness/polish of the surface, and (3) the presence or absence of beach pebble attrition (or 'chatter') marks. Natural selection of pebbles on a storm beach ensures that hard, competent, flawless cobbles predominate. From amongst these, the more cylindrical pebbles were preferentially chosen. By contrast, unworn glacial erratic cobbles collected from inland sources near to the mine were rarely

7: WEAR ANALYSIS – 1 Hammering							
End wear				Edge wear		Side wear	
Single ended (1)		Double ended (2)					
Primary	secondary	Primary	secondary	Primary	secondary	primary	secondary
Bruising				Bruising		Slight bruising	
Slight pounding						Bruising	
Moderate pounding						Indentation	
Heavy pounding				Heavy pounding	Heavy pounding		
Flaking							
Heavy flaking							
Faceted area				Faceted area		Faceted area	
Mineral residue		Mineral residue		Mineral residue		Mineral residue	

7.2 Grinding		7.3 Crushing anvil use		7.4 Re-use as flake
Location	Primary		Secondary	
Faint		Slight bruising		Hammering end
		Strong bruising		Chisel end
Strong		Indentation		
				Degree of use
Grinding marks – striations	Location			Slight
	Flake surface			Moderate
Faceted area/	Pebble surface			Heavy
Mineral residue	Mineral residue			Scratch markings

8: MODIFICATION (for hafting/handgrip)									
Position	Primary				Secondary				
mid girth	Edges	Side	Semi-continuous	groove	Edges	side		Contemporary scratch/ Scoring	Evidence for haft wear?
Towards narrow end	Scratch notching				Rounded sharp edge of Flake		Use of Natural indentation in Pebble		
Towards broad end								certain	
Centre of gravity					Notching			Possible	

9: SUMMARY DESCRIPTION OF TOOL (Estimate)
- well used
- poorly used
- long survival of usefulness
- hammering
- crushing
- small hammer for other tool
- anvil stone
- re-used
- recommend for detailed drawing
- recommend retain collection

10: PHOTOGRAPHS
(3 views: digital or print)

11: DRAWINGS
(annotated field drawings with outline 1:1 profiles: longitud. and transverse)

Fig. 2   Example of completed EMRG hammer-stone recording sheet

For each tool a combination of morphometric, petrological and wear analysis data is now measured and recorded in order to try and determine a possible source for the cobbles, alongside any indication of selection based on shape, weight and cobble type. Additionally we need to determine evidence for primary and secondary tool use, artefact modification and tool use-wear history (for example recycling as a similar or different tool, caching or final discard).

One of the most important tasks in recording is accurate illustration. Subtle details of modification or use-wear are best shown in fine ink drawings, many of which have since been reproduced in publication (Fig. 3).

found used as tools, alongside less than 30% of 'good fit' re-worked river pebbles.

Some 99% of the cobbles used as tools were composed of greywacke sandstones – all of them geologically local to this area of mid-Wales. However, most of the beach pebble sources contained at least 5% of igneous and metamorphic rocks from North Wales, the Lake District and Scotland, the latter brought to this coast as glacial erratics by the Irish Sea Ice. Although hard and heavy enough for use as tool material, these 'exotics' were only rarely found as hammers – most likely because of their rarity as suitably sized and shaped cobbles. In general, therefore, lithology seems to be of secondary importance to cobble shape, size and weight. Nevertheless, some 66% of the hammers used (or re-used) as anvils were composed of the harder quartzitic sandstones and coarser-grain-size lithologies.

Tool functions represented amongst the used cobbles were assessed in the following proportions. The largest group (67%) consisted of the mining tools themselves (rock-breaking hammers), with the crushing anvils (used or re-used) at 13%, mallets or chisels 8%, hand-held crushing tools 6%, and re-used flake tools 6%. Meanwhile the study of 1203 cobble stone tools revealed that only 9% showed indisputable evidence of modification for the purpose of hafting (this included 75 edge-notched hammers but only 4 semi-grooved examples). Meanwhile 41% of tools appear to have been re-used following initial breakage – some of them at least three or four times.

In contrast to Copa Hill is the Bronze Age mine of Ecton in north-west Staffordshire. Stone mining tools are altogether less frequent here, with the great majority, even the rock-breaking hammer stones, being hand-held implements. Of tool types that are common to other sites, only the disc-shaped cobbles used for crushing (Type C3) share similarities with those found at Alderley Edge, and to a lesser extent some of the mid-Wales mines. In fact Ecton is unique for the small and rather unsophisticated nature of its stone mining tools, most of which probably had a very short span of use. For example, there are no examples of grooved tools, but instead we see a new category of implement, the pointed pebble or pestle (Type C4), which may have been used as a small hammer to crush the mineral (such as copper carbonate) adhering to the outcrop (Timberlake 2014, 24–26). Despite these differences, we still find 35% of these tools showing some evidence for multiple function and re-use.

The geological origin of the two main types of cobble used as mining tools at Ecton is interesting, since both can be matched with identifiable sources (Timberlake 2014, 28). Most of the rounded-rectangular patinated river cobbles of quartzitic-sandstone, gritstone, and siltstone found at the mine can still be collected today from the river bed and flood plain of the river Manifold between Hulme End and Ecton Hill. These cobbles make up 75% of the stone tools found at Stone Quarry and the Lumb mines. Most will have been derived from the erosion of individual sandstone and proto-quartzite sandstone units (such as the Minn, Hardlow, Lum Edge, and Longnor sandstones) within the Upper Carboniferous Edale Shale Group, the outcrops of which have been eroded away by the incision of the river less than 2 km upstream of the mine (Ford 2000, 2, 6). Meanwhile, the second type of used cobble is a metaquartzite, examples of which may have been collected a little further afield. All

of these originate as glacial erratics, significant numbers of which appear to have been deposited within Neogene sand pockets found infilling solution features and other erosional features in the top of the Carboniferous Limestone. The nearest significant sand pocket and source of glacial erratics to the Ecton mine lies a few kilometres to the north and west of the nearby village of Hulme End. Given that there is no evidence that any of these ended up as river cobbles in the river Manifold, the most likely explanation is that all of these stones were collected at source from the weathered surface of the limestone.

Tool functions and types
Tool types reflecting the utilitarian nature and interchangeable functions of the mining and beneficiation process have been found at all of the prehistoric mines investigated. Whilst types do vary slightly from mine to mine, the tool functions they represent are universally relevant (Timberlake & Craddock 2013, 43–49). Figs. 4 and 6 below illustrate some of the tool types identified from Copa Hill together with interpretations of how they were used (Figs 5 and 7). These interpretations are based partly on use-wear study and partly on experimental archaeology.

Single and double-ended (ungrooved) mining hammers (Type A and Type AA)
These were unmodified or poorly modified (lightly notched) elongate cobbles used primarily as rock-breaking tools (Fig. 4). Some of these appear to have been hafted for use (Fig. 5: a, b), whilst others (for example most of the Ecton hammer stones) would have been hand held (Fig. 5: c). The double-ended hammers (Fig. 4: A) which are shown used in Fig. 5: b might have been used at alternate ends either for picking or smashing rock, for heavy pounding, or else as mallets for use with other tools (see Fig. 5: d). Many of these could have been hafted given our success with recent experimental reconstructions (Timberlake 2007, 30).

Picks or chisels (Type D)
These were used both for levering-off rock and for small extraction work. Commonly these tools are found modified (notched) and re-used (Fig. 4: E). Typically the cobble edges will have been removed through use; the chisels are often flakes detached from hammers which are re-used (Fig. 5: d), but sometimes they are remnant cores. Most were probably held in a short haft and used with or without a mallet (Fig. 5: e). Flakes re-used as small chisels or wedges can generally be recognized from the rounding of the fracture surface.

Pecking stones (Type F)
Rarely found, these were not mining tools, but instead were used for notching (modifying) the hammer-stone cobbles (Fig. 6: F). The few found were small (5–8 cm diameter) round and hard rocks – typically a vein quartz or quartzite pebble.

Crushing tools (Type C)
These were hand-held tools (8–20 cm long) used for breaking-up ore and crushing mineral (Fig. 6). Common amongst these are the broken-off ends of mining hammers (Type C1) re-used as crushing stones (Fig. 6: A, B), whilst another common type (Type C3) is a small cobble which has been

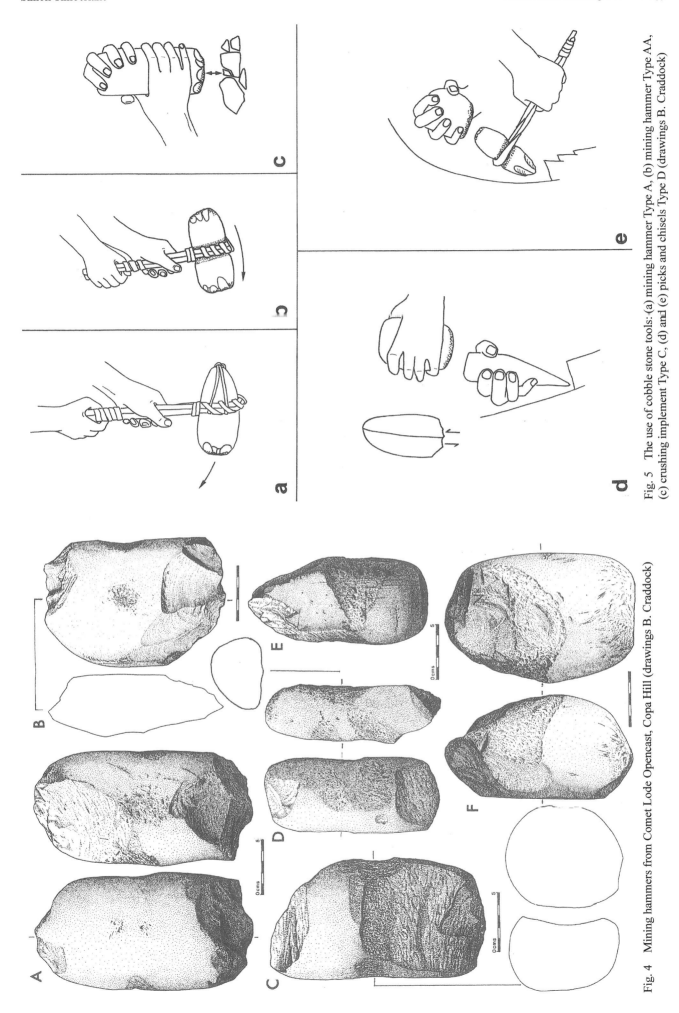

Fig. 5   The use of cobble stone tools: (a) mining hammer Type A, (b) mining hammer Type AA, (c) crushing implement Type C, (d) and (e) picks and chisels Type D (drawings B. Craddock)

Fig. 4   Mining hammers from Comet Lode Opencast, Copa Hill (drawings B. Craddock)

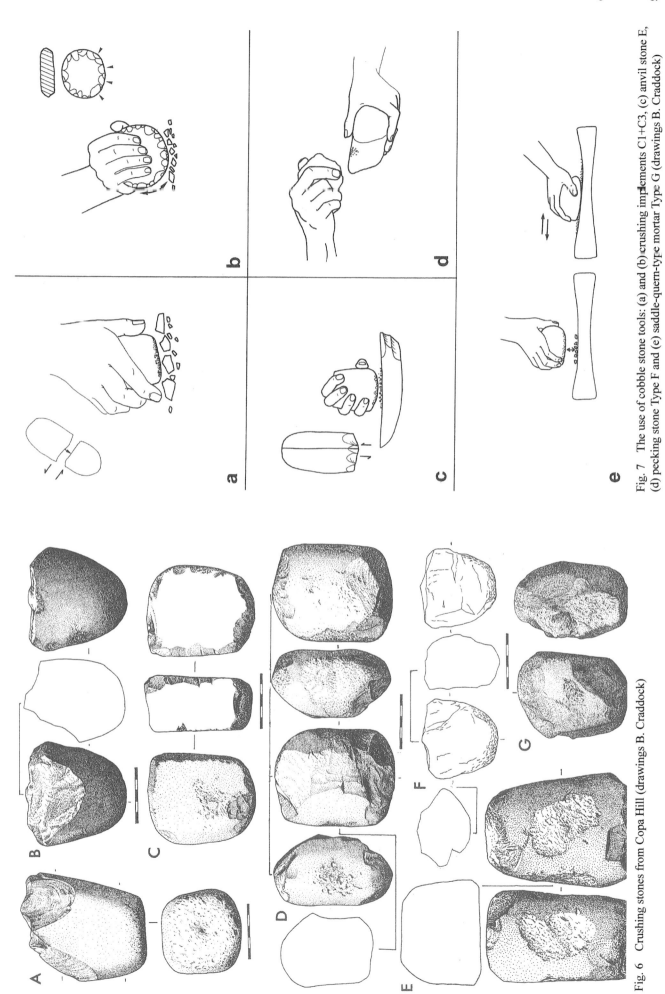

Fig. 7 The use of cobble stone tools: (a) and (b) crushing implements C1+C3, (c) anvil stone E, (d) pecking stone Type F and (e) saddle-quern-type mortar Type G (drawings B. Craddock)

Fig. 6 Crushing stones from Copa Hill (drawings B. Craddock)

worked around its outermost edge (Timberlake 2005a and 2006). Because of how these were held and worked these tools often ended up being discoid in shape (Fig. 7: b). Typically they would have been used for crushing small pieces of mineral. Larger hand-held hammer stones (up to 1.5 kg) were probably also used as crushing stones (Fig. 7: a).

Crushing anvils (Type E)
These were used for crushing small pieces of ore on (Fig. 7: c). Depending upon the degree of use, and the type of work carried out, these anvil stones might have been flat, or else have developed slightly indented surfaces (e.g. Fig. 8). More than 50% of these tools were actually fractured and split mining hammers which had been re-used on their flatter surfaces as anvils.

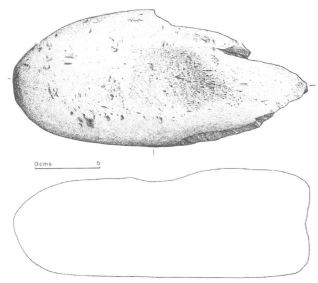

Fig. 8   Type E crushing anvil from Copa Hill. A recycled mining hammer, weight 2.25 kg (Drawing B. Craddock)

Grinding stone (Type G)
Usually a large stone slab used like a saddle quern for the fine grinding of an ore mineral mix (Fig. 7: e). Another use of these might be to crush pieces of smelting slag to release the entrapped metal prills. These querns are very rare finds from mining sites in Britain and Ireland, single examples coming from Copa Hill (Fig. 9) (Timberlake 2003, 98D) and from Ross Island, Killarney (O'Brien 2004, 359).

Grooved mining hammers (Types 2A and 3A)
The prehistoric mines of Alderley Edge are unique in Britain given that some 93% of the cobble stone mining tools from there show clear evidence for haft modification, either notched or partially grooved (referred to as Type 2) or fully grooved (Type 3) (Fig. 10). Grooved hammer stones are also found within the mines of Ross Island.

Some of the Alderley Edge hammers show extensive haft wear around the median groove, as well as the insertion of a butt-end groove over the broader top end. Butt-end grooves and additional lateral grooves were probably inserted as a response to wear-related movement in the haftings, and perhaps also because of problems with the geometry of the cobble(s) when the narrower 'pick' end of the tool was used.

The cobble source for the Alderley hammer stones appears to be the local glacial drift which contains large

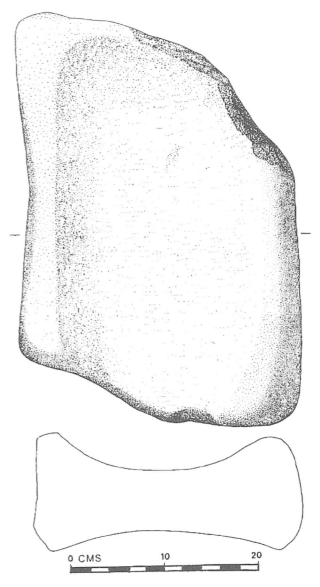

Fig. 9   A double-sided grinding stone (Type G) from Copa Hill (drawing B. Craddock)

numbers of rocks from the Lake District and northern England. Amongst these are hard greywackes, Shap granite, and a range of andesites, basalts and tuffs originating from the Borrowdale Volcanic Series (Browne 1995). On Alderley Edge, as elsewhere, we find a high level of recycling – though perhaps less so than at the upland Welsh mines. The cobbles may well have been grooved because

Fig. 10   Grooved mining hammer from Engine Vein, Alderley Edge, composed of Ennerdale granophyre (photo AELP archive, the Manchester Museum)

they survived for much longer without fracturing when used against the softer sandstone/conglomerate country rocks.

Boulder battering stone (Type L)

Typically these are large (or oversized) utilised cobbles (usually >8 kg in weight) which were probably used as rock-battering implements to remove larger amounts of rock. They would have been slung from a rope on a tripod, then swung against the rock face. The effectiveness of this arrangement was aptly demonstrated during experiments carried out with such boulders on the Great Orme in 1989 (Lewis 1990a). Cobbles or boulders of this large size were also found used as implements within the prehistoric mine (Lewis 1990b, 6).

Ethnographic evidence – comparative studies of stone mining tools from around the world

Archaeo-ethnographic evidence can be helpful in understanding how stone tools were made and used, but use of this has been limited. One important find was that of a stone mining toolkit belonging to 'Copper Man', a 1500-year-old Pre-Columbian Indian miner who was found preserved as a mummy in 1899 inside an ancient working at the Restauradora mine, Chuquicamata, northern Chile (Bird 1979). Just as interesting for us was the study and experimental replication by Brenda Craddock of another complete hammer from Chuquicamata (Fig. 11), one loaned to the British Museum in 1995 by William Wray (see B. Craddock *et al.* 2003).

There are also rare examples of stone mining tools still being used today. Worthington & Craddock (1996) describe a crushing tool and mortar stone for grinding gold-bearing quartz in Uganda, whilst similar 'hand maul' type crushing stones have been found within gold workings at Tembelini in Mali which date from the fourteenth century AD up to the present, and in the Ashanti goldfield (Laffoley 1998). Paul Craddock (1995, 162) illustrates the use of stone anvils/mortars for the crushing of lead/zinc ores at Ishiagu in southern Nigeria.

Yet interestingly the use of cobble stone tools purely as mining implements only seems to pre-date the introduction of high quality wrought iron into sub-Saharan Africa at the beginning of the nineteenth century. Though poorly dated, it seems likely that stone mining tools were still being used within the copper mines of Zimbabwe, alongside the use of iron, prior to the arrival of Europeans. However, the exceptional continuation of much earlier and outdated practices is equally intriguing. For example, there are a number of well-documented contemporary images of Kenyan smiths using hafted stone tools to forge iron (Brown 1995). Similar tools over 6 kg in weight have also been found within some of our own Bronze Age mines. This is hardly the same process, yet it is a revelation to see such large cobble stone tools being handled accurately, and apparently with ease.

Experimental archaeology: making and using stone mining tools

One of the most interesting aspects of this work has been the undertaking of archaeological experiments, such as making and using hafted cobble stone mining hammers (B. Craddock *et al.* 2003; Timberlake 2007). Brenda Craddock of the EMRG undertook a workshop in making and using grooved stone tools at Alderley Edge in 1997.

Fig. 11   Mining hammer with hafting from Chuquicamata, Chile (photo British Museum, W. Wray)

Using a small pecking stone, a groove 1–10 mm deep and 15–20 mm wide was cut around the circumference of a 100 mm diameter cobble in approximately one hour (Timberlake & Craddock 2005). In retrospect what we found following their hafting and use was that we did not need to peck much of a groove on the flat surfaces. We found the same thing on some of the archaeological examples. Making the handle for the tool involves bruising and twisting a hazel withy (approximately 1.2 m long) and then bending and tying this around a cobble and binding it with rawhide. In reconstructing the Alderley Edge tools, similar cobbles to those we find archaeologically were collected from the local boulder clay deposits. Archaeological experiments such as this can help us to understand the manufacture, function, and use-wear on these tools. They can also be used to predict archaeological findings.

Our original experiments using these tools with ropes and leather bindings were carried out in 1988 and 1989 at our Penguelan experimental site at Cwmystwyth where we had also been firesetting on the vein (Pickin & Timberlake 1988; Timberlake 1990). Later we tried using hammers hafted with freshly cut green willow handles (B. Craddock 1990). These proved to be too flexible, which made it difficult to accurately direct the tools against the rock. Following this, unmodified or else notched (but ungrooved) cobble stone mining hammers using a hafting modelled on the 'Chuquicamata-type' were experimented early in the 1990s (B. Craddock *et al.* 2003). These were more successful, one of them removing 1.5 tons of rock without any serious breakage of the cobble.

It was noted that very little breakage of these river or beach cobble hammers occurred whilst they were being used against already fire-weakened rock. The characteristic flaking or splitting of the ends of these cobbles (the splinters from which are commonly seen in prehistoric mine spoil) began only after the zone of rock unaffected by firesetting was reached. Inevitably the miners continued to use their tools against this until the rate of breakage and difficulty of progress prompted them to re-fireset. Therefore the batter or pounding marks that we find preserved on some areas of rock reflects the actual limit of mining. This was first proved experimentally, but was later recognized within the roof of the small Bronze Age mine gallery on Copa Hill (Fig. 12).

Fig. 12   Roof of mine gallery within Copa Hill Bronze Age mine worked with stone tools (photo S.Timberlake)

The wear facets and flaked/fractured surfaces produced on cobbles as a result of their experimental use as hammers have since been examined with an eye to recognizing the same types of wear amongst those tools recovered from the Bronze Age mine(s). During the experiments we also noted that we had scratched or pecked rather similar types of bilateral notches into the sides of these cobbles whilst attempting to haft and rehaft them in withy handles. Quite similar also was the impression we created from using/re-using these mining hammers as ore-crushing anvils. In general though these were not quite so developed as the examples we found in the mine(s).

In 1997 we experimented with the properly grooved cobble stone mining hammers at Alderley Edge, mining with these against previously fireset sandstones and conglomerates (Timberlake 2005b). Not surprisingly the haftings appeared to hold a bit better on these than on the completely unmodified cobbles. What was more important though was to remember during the experiments to swing these tools underarm against the rock face, using the weight and momentum of the hammer (as well as the bounce of its return) to help loosen joints and cleavage planes, including those previously weakened by firesetting.

We soon realized that repairing the broken hammer hafts and retightening the bindings where they had worked loose was an essential, though necessarily repetitive, part of the mining process (Timberlake & Craddock 2005). In fact we estimated that somebody would be needed every half hour or so to repair the tools: somebody with these skills would have been an essential member of any mining team.

The most recent mining experiments using these type(s) of tools have been carried out at Sakdrissi in Georgia (Fig. 13).

Fig. 13   Mining using prehistoric stone tools in 2011 at Sakdrissi, Georgia (photo S.Timberlake)

Mining tools of antler and bone

Small mining implements made from conveniently utilized fragments of split and broken animal bone (perhaps from the food brought to the site for the miners) have been recovered from the Bronze Age mines of Ecton, Ross Island and the Great Orme. The surface and underground workings on the Great Orme have produced thousands of this type of tools, since studied in some detail by Sian James (2011). Most of these tools seem to be made from cattle long bone shafts,which have been work-fashioned into gouges, chisels or bone points, although cow rib bones have also been found as scrapers at Ross Island and on the Orme; most of these tools have been used for working soft, typically secondary, copper ores such as malachite within dolomite or limestone. The much smaller assemblage of tools from Ecton has been classified as follows (Timberlake 2014):

Type 1 Heavy cattle-size tibia, distal end; naturally rounded joint end forms handle; facetted point has obliquely cut into interior bone hollow making pointed tool that also functions as a scoop (two examples: Fig. 14: 27, 44). No signs of ever having being hammered with another tool, therefore probably not used as chisels.

Type 2 Points, chisels, or scrapers made from axially split limb bones (Fig. 14: 36, 45, 53).

Type 3 Scoops made from axially split limb bones cut to make a chisel end (Fig. 14: 37, 53–55).

Type 4 Scoop, with chisel end opposed by broad scoop formed by natural splayed flake of articular end of limb bone (Fig. 14: 31).

Type 5 Long bone shaft; hollow triangular section cut obliquely at an angle as a gouge (Fig. 14: 30).

Type 6 Red deer antler tine point (Fig. 14: 34); probably end of a pick from he Lumb Trench C2 (219).

Mining picks made from red deer antler (with the first tine used as a pick and the antler crown used as a hammer) have been found during excavations on Copa Hill (Fig. 15). However, most of these are quite fragmentary, suggesting considerable wear and breakage as a result of being used against previously fireset but still hard quartz-veined rocks (Timberlake 2003). Fragments of antler pick have also

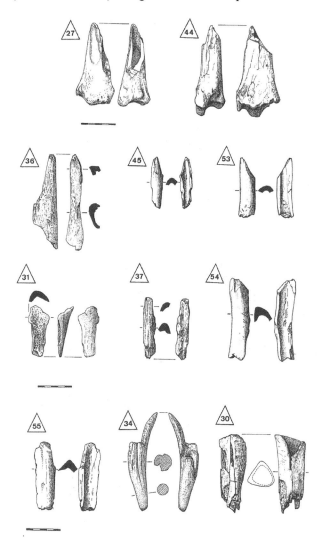

Fig. 14   Prehistoric mining tools of bone (bovid) and antler (red deer) from Stone Quarry and the Lumb, Ecton (drawings B. Craddock)

been found at the Nantyreira mine, Plynlimon (Timberlake 1990) and at Derrycarhoon in Co. Cork, Ireland (O'Brien 2013), whilst single antler points have been found within the limestone mines of the Great Orme and Ecton. The one illustrated in Fig. 14 (34) has two scored lines or grooves in it which were probably cut with a flint, perhaps to make a needle, but perhaps also to assist the hafting of this in a wooden handle. The other Bronze Age antler point found at Ecton in 1995 also seems likely to have been 'modified': it had been chamfered around the proximal end of the tine in order to insert it (perhaps) into some sort of pick handle (Timberlake 2014; Barnatt & Thomas 1998). Antler picks are commonly found within Neolithic flint mines, where they experience a slower rate of wear and survive better. As regards the copper mines of the Early Bronze Age period there are several examples from the 'Beaker' mines of El Aramo and Milagro in Asturias, north-west Spain (Rovira and Montero-Ruiz 2013).

Fig. 15   Antler pick hammer, Comet Lode Opencast, Copa Hill (photo S.Timberlake)

Experiments using antler picks

Picks of red deer antler were first used in mining experiments at Penguelan, Cwmystwyth, to test their effectiveness against hard rocks (Timberlake 1990). To do this they were used in a very different way to metal picks, instead functioning as mallets to knock out freshly fireset rock, or as levers to prise away blocks after the rock had first been fractured and loosened-up by hammer stones. Approximately 1.5 tons of fireset rock was removed with just one of these antler tools.

This alternation between the use of stone and antler tools proved such an effective combination that we suggested picks may once have been used within the Bronze Age mine, even though none had been found to date. However, we did not have to wait long. Sure enough, an example of one of these 'hammer picks' was discovered the following year within the opencast (Timberlake 2007). As predicted, this had been used on the tine as a pick, then on the crown as a mallet, in exactly the same way as we used these ourselves in the experiments. It was estimated that each pick could have assisted in the removal of between 15 and 25 tons of rock, and that between 100 and 300 antlers may have been brought up to the site during the history of working the mine.

Wooden tools

Examples of wooden mining tools from Bronze Age mines in the British Isles include crudely carved examples of 'spade-like' shovels such as the half-burnt one made of alder wood from Mine 3 on Mt Gabriel, Co. Cork (O'Brien 1994), and

Fig. 16 The Alderley Edge shovel – an oak shovel found at Brynlow Mine, Alderley Edge, in 1874 and dated to c. 1750 Cal BC (photo courtesy of The Manchester Museum)

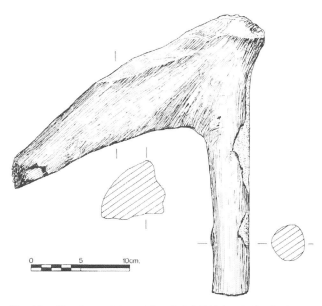

Fig. 17 Wooden pick from Mine 3-4, Mt Gabriel, Co. Cork (reproduced from O'Brien 1994)

Fig. 18 Excavating part of a broken withy handle, Copa Hill, Cwmystwyth (photo S. Timberlake)

the more complete oak shovel which was found in a Bronze Age mining pit at Brynlow Mine, Alderley Edge (Sainter 1878; Garner *et al.* 1994). The Alderley Edge shovel (Fig. 16) survived for more than a hundred years following excavation without any form of conservation treatment, thanks to its high metal content (chiefly of copper and arsenic), as has been shown by the study of this artefact using the Daresbury synchnotron (Smith *et al.* 2011). This revealed considerable evidence for its use in the Bronze Age, with high copper levels on the tip of the blade and on the handle where it had been held – the latter the result of ingrained contamination from the hands of ancient miners. Shovels of similar appearance have been found within the pre-Columbian (c. 1500 years old) copper mines of Chuquicamata and San José del Abra in the Atacama Desert of northern Chile (Figueroa *et al.* 2013).

Wooden 'mining picks' have been found both on Mt Gabriel (Fig. 17; O'Brien 1994, 148–149) and in the mines of the Mitterberg, Austria (Pittioni 1951), as have 'prise sticks' and 'wedges', the latter thought to have been used to assist in the removal of cleaved fireset rock (O'Brien 1994, 150).

Broken examples of the twisted hazel withy handles used to hold hammer stones have also been found in Ireland at Mt Gabriel (O'Brien 1994, 151–152) and at Derrycarhoon (O'Brien 2013), although the best preserved example was excavated at Cwmystwyth in 1994 – the two broken ends of a failed withy handle (Fig. 18) being found side by side where these were dropped onto the working floor of the mine nearly 4000 years ago (Timberlake 2003, 72).

Other wooden objects
Wooden stemples, pit props and planks survive wherever waterlogged conditions have persisted over time, the form of many being very similar in appearance to historic or modern examples. Small axe-cut stemples of oak were found in the mine on Copa Hill (Timberlake 2003, 71), whilst in the Middle Bronze Age workings beneath the Arthurstollen, on the Mitterberg, large *in situ* timbers of fir and larch were found still supporting the walls and roofs of the ancient stopes (Stöllner, Thomas *et al.* 2012).

Pine lighting splints used for illumination were one of the other finds recovered from the mining sediments within Mines 3 and 4 on Mt Gabriel, dating from around 1700–1600 Cal BC (O'Brien 1994, 158–160). However, much

larger numbers of these were found within the much deeper Middle and Late Bronze Age mines of the Mitterberg (Stöllner, Thomas *et al.* 2012). These may have been burnt when tied together as bunches, so as to provide much better illumination.

Other finds of note include the basket made of simply woven hazel that was excavated within the entrance to the mine on Copa Hill (Fig. 19a and b). This 'kreel type' basket, presumably used to carry ore or waste rock out of the mine, clearly must have broken, then been discarded onto a fire and partly burnt before becoming buried on the damp floor (Timberlake 2003, 72–73). This re-use of discarded wooden objects as fuel perhaps explains the low survival of such tools in this mining environment.

A wooden drainage launder
Another find unique to the Copa Hill mine was the discovery of three wooden launders: two less well-preserved ones of oak, and a better preserved one of alder. The latter is a 5-metre-long split and hollowed-out half log (Fig. 20), which had clearly been used as a gutter to carry water across the floor of a rock-cut trench to the outside of the opencast (Timberlake 2003, 69–70, 74). The radiocarbon date (2400–1750 Cal BC) suggests an already long history of use within the mine before its final abandonment around 1600 BC. When found, the launder was still in its last functional

Fig. 19a   Bronze Age miner's withy 'kreel type' basket being excavated, Comet Lode Opencast, Copa Hill

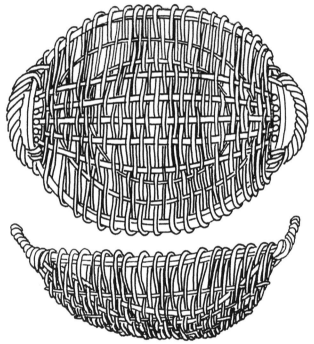

Fig. 19b   Conjectural reconstruction of miner's basket found at Comet Lode Opencast, Copa Hill (drawing B. Craddock)

Fig. 20   Section of Early Bronze Age alder wood launder left *in situ* within 1995 excavations of Comet Lode Opencast, Copa Hill (photo S. Timberlake)

position, inclined and supported upon laid out branches and stones, whilst on its sides were the cut marks of the flat copper or bronze axes and wooden wedges used during its manufacture on site. It seems likely that this and the other (once) interconnecting gutters had been placed here to tap the spring water issuing from the fault – so perhaps this is one of the very earliest known examples of mine drainage. An alternative, or possibly additional function of this wooden gutter may have been to wash the crushed ore, separating the lighter oxidised minerals such as malachite from the sulphides chalcopyrite and galena. Certainly the evidence here is that some ore crushing was taking place within this area, and that alternating lead-rich and copper-rich waterlain sediments were then being deposited, and a large proportion discarded.

Mining with firesetting

Most of our understanding of this technique comes from the experimental work we have undertaken. Although firesetting was never a universal practice, it was nevertheless a commonly used mining technique in prehistory, and in some places for thousands of years after that.

Firesetting experiments

To try and understand what we had found at Cwmystwyth we undertook our first firesetting experiments at the nearby Penguelan Shaft in 1987, and since then this site has been used on more than eight different occasions (Timberlake 1990; 2005b, 188). Over this period of experimentation the size of the pieces of firewood we used reduced from 3 m to 0.5 m split logs as we began to experiment with thinner and faster-burning branchwood. This matched the growing body of archaeological evidence that suggested the use of smaller hearths and oak branchwood as a fuel for firesetting in the mine (Nayling in Timberlake 2003, 63).

Typically 100–250 kg of firewood was used in each of our experimental firings, and by the end of this period the wood (fuel) to stone extraction ratio had improved substantially from about 1:1 to 1:2. This reflects an increase in skill, more economic use of fuel, and a much better understanding of the properties of the rock.

Experimentation has provided us with at least one important realization: that dousing the hot rock with water was not necessary. Whilst 'quenching' might help to shatter the rock surface, this practice did not significantly increase the yield of rock extracted. However, two interesting sets of reactions were observed when firesetting the shale and quartz veined rocks: firstly a decrepitation of the slate brought about by thermal shock as the temperature of the rock-face rose rapidly to 800°C, explosively ejecting debris (<0.01% of the total mass of extracted); and secondly, the splitting open of joints/cleavage by steam as water already present within the pervious rock became super-heated. The latter could lead to the collapse of some parts of the rock during firing, but more typically it would leave the rock weakened, allowing for its easy removal in large blocks using tools.

The area of maximum heat penetration of the rock, as suggested by the changed profile of the rock face after mining with stone tools for several hours, was 0.5 to 1 m above the level of the hearth floor. As a result this left a prominent rock step or 'heel' at the base of the rock face. This type of concavity is one of the most distinctive signatures of firesetting (Timberlake 2003). Though less evident in shale rocks than in the granular sandstones and limestones, a rather good example of a hearth step, and characteristic arched profile of firesetting, was observed within the small Bronze Age mine gallery found within the mine on Copa Hill. However, in other places Bronze Age miners managed to sink shafts or vertical trenches in the mines with nothing more than fire and stone tools. We can witness considerably more complex shafts and galleries of this kind within the mines of Kestel, Turkey (Willies 1990), Zawar in Rajasthan (Willies 1987), and the Early Bronze Age gold mine at Sakdrissi in Georgia (Stöllner *et al.* 2008). However, more recent experiments at Penguelan, Cwmystwyth, have shown that the use of much smaller fires, and the covering of these with heavy wood or stone to reduce air-flow, not only improves fuel efficiency, but slows the burn and helps direct heat penetration downwards.

Recent firesetting and mining experiments carried out at Sakdrissi Mine, in Georgia (Stöllner, Craddock *et al.* 2012) have proven the use of this technique in breaking-up some of the hardest rocks imaginable – in this case silicified rhyodacitic volcanics. In 2011 and 2013 repeated firesets using dried brush scrub and cut seasoned oak firewood were carried out on quartz-hematite veins exposed within the side of a mining road on the edge of the ancient mine (Fig. 13). In the most efficient fireset 255 kg of wood was burnt (the hot rock being doused with a very small amount of water at the end of two hours) to give 279 kg of rock, this being removed using hafted cobble stone tools and antler picks.

Processing the ore
Early Bronze Age ore recovery, at least in Britain, depended upon the careful hand-picking of an enriched ore composed mostly of secondary (usually oxidized) copper minerals following the crushing of selected ore lumps. This produced a concentrate sufficiently rich for simple reduction smelting within a crucible or small-scale furnace. Processing tools would probably just have consisted of stone anvils and crushing stones, a grinding stone, and bone or wooden spatulas for the separation of grains; a concentration mechanism which may have been assisted, in some cases, by the use of a wooden launder and a flow of water.

When 'mass production' of copper began in Europe during the Middle Bronze Age, more sophisticated means of gravity separation were developed. As part of a series of experiments in ore processing and smelting carried out by the Deutsches Bergbau Museum (DBM), work was undertaken to try to work out the function of a square wooden sluice box found in 2013 at the Middle Bronze Age ore processing site of Troiboden, close to the Main Lode workings near the Arthurhaus, Mitterberg (Stöllner et al. 2010, 6–18).

The sluice box was reconstructed by a Bronze Age wood technologist using bronze tools (axes and chisels), and then buried on the edge of a watercourse, within an equivalent context to the archaeological example (Fig. 21). It could be shown that holes cut into opposite sides of this box allowed for a controlled flow of water across its floor, which could be used for gravity separation of the finely crushed lighter waste from the heavier ore minerals, and the production of a richer concentrate of chalcopyrite from an otherwise poor-grade ore.

This Middle Bronze Age development of more sophisti-

Fig. 21   Experiments on the Mitterberg: the recovery of copper ore using a sluice box (photo S. Timberlake)

cated methods of mining, processing and smelting enabled these more abundant, less rich copper ores to be worked. This revolutionized the overall scale and importance of copper production within the Alpine zone, resulting in a trade in copper which ultimately ended up as recycled metal as far afield as the British Isles. These still-continuing experiments have helped to reveal how this earliest known example of wet processing and gravity separation worked: specifically the invention of the buddle.

Experiments in gold processing
In 2011 and 2013 experiments were carried out at Sakdrissi, Georgia at the site of a late fourth to early third millennium BC gold mine of the Kura-Araxes culture, a site currently being excavated by a joint German-Georgian archaeological team as part of the 2007–2011 Bochum Caucasus project (Stöllner *et al.* 2008). My own and Brenda Craddock's role in this role in this project was to try and reconstruct the gold mining, milling and washing process suggested by the archaeological evidence.

Crushing of the gold-bearing quartz-hematite was undertaken on mortar stones, the fine milling of it on grind stones recovered from the excavations, whilst the concentration and recovery of the gold itself was undertaken by panning (washing) the powdered ore to recover the gold (Stöllner, Craddock *et al.* 2012).

Sakdrissi Mine has been claimed, with some justification (Stöllner *et al.* 2008), as being the earliest example of (hardrock) gold mining in the ancient world. Its greatest enigma is that the gold grains present within the quartz-hematite veins are so tiny (<0.5 mm) as to be invisible to the naked eye in hand specimen. Although it is possible that the source of this gold was once traced by progressive alluvial recovery along the bed of the nearby Maschawera river, it remains difficult to comprehend how this particular deposit, consisting of quartz veins carrying only 10–100 ppm of gold in a very finely disseminated form, was identified from amongst hundreds of other less enriched ones. Moreover, how did they come up with an effective strategy to work it?

Crushing and separation
All the potential gold-bearing rock mined was carefully separated out from the rock waste, the hematite:quartz:waste

rock ratio ranging from 1:2:3 to 1:3:2 (by weight). The quartz-hematite contact samples were then processed separately from the quartz vein material, in part because we knew that the Soviet-period assays suggested considerable variation in the gold values within and between individual veins, and partly because we could see that the prehistoric miners had followed certain veins, or parts of veins, but not others. It was decided therefore to experiment with assaying each metre of the vein by milling and panning in order to see how practical it was to visually determine where the richest gold values lay. Were they close to the vein contacts, within the hematite, or perhaps in the white quartz?

To do this, we arranged different individuals to work on different parcels of ore: first crushing the quartz on anvil stones, then milling it in hollows on mortar stones using small pounding stones or flat-sided crushers, the goal being its reduction to a grit-size consistency (2–3 mm).

Parcels of this crushed ore were then fine-ground to a powder on large saddle-quern-type grind stones using suitably flat or slightly convex-worn rubbing stones (Fig. 22). Our washings of these residues showed that a grain size of between 0.25 and 0.5 mm was probably the best fraction for gold recovery. By increasing this to >1 mm the gold values of the same samples did not improve, but in some cases tailed-off. As it turned out these large grind stones proved to be ideal for the final stage of milling the ore.

Fig. 22   Grinding quartz-hematite to powder prior to gold washing at Sakdrissi in 2013 (photo S. Timberlake)

Gold washing and recovery
Samples of pulverized ore weighing 0.5–1 kg were panned using water raised by bucket from an anciently cut rock cistern perched on the edge of the adjacent opencast. This cistern had been uncovered during the archaeological excavation of the mine, and was interpreted by the excavators as a small reservoir which might have been used for gold-washing assays (Stöllner pers. com.). It was believed such assaying would have been an essential practice in helping to determine the direction of mining, and thus the advancement or perhaps abandonment of the veins. Pan washing these samples for 10–15 minutes removed the quartz and produced a dark concentrate of hematite. This was much harder to pan away, yet a number of the samples with significant hematite and goethite contents (30–40% Fe_2O_3 + FeO(OH)) yielded some of the best heads of gold – the

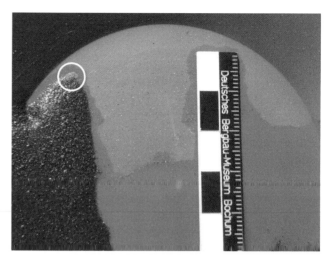

Fig. 23   Gold 'head' (circled) washed out of hematite, Sakdrissi (photo S. Timberlake)

latter composed of fine yellow flakes, the largest of these grains being only 0.5 mm in diameter (Fig. 23).

Some assistance with the visual assessment of these assays in terms of their modern economic grade (i.e. in parts per million gold) was provided by a local gold panner who was familiar with the assays undertaken on these veins during previous exploration attempts. What we could deduce from this was that the typical range of gold values present within the ore we had mined ranged between 5 and 20 ppm. However, the best result we achieved (perhaps >50 ppm gold) came from the milling of a sample taken from the hematite-rich portion of a 200 mm width quartz vein exposed within a boulder recovered from the excavations. Almost certainly this would have come from one of the veins worked in prehistory.

It seems feasible that a team of five to ten skilled people could have assayed the ore using some sort of open-ended wooden scoop for gold washing. (Perhaps this is also an explanation of the purpose of the scoop recovered from the underground Roman workings at Dolaucothi in South Wales (Davies 1936, 54).) At Sakdrissi intensive wash-assaying may have been a viable method for rapidly monitoring the produce of each mined heading. Rather than focusing on processing the ore at the mine site itself, assay checking the size of the gold head against the dark concentrate in a 'pan' would have been all that was required to know whether the cut-off grade had been reached within each small area of the vein(s) worked. In other words, this would help determine whether the ore in any one part of the mine was richer, equal to, or poorer than the rest, thus whether it worth continuing with, or possibly even developing, thereby diverting resources from one part of the mine to another.

However, there were other things to consider, such as the creation of passages, leaving structural supports between the footwall and hanging wall of the veins, and the creation of suitable openings for ventilation. A much more complex system of underground ventilation would be needed to permit firesetting to be carried out without having to abandon the mine. As regards gold recovery, the most likely scenario is that the worthwhile ore was being taken down to the Maschawera river, or perhaps to the nearby Kura-Araxes settlement of Balitschi-Dzedzwebi for processing (Stöllner *et al.* 2008, 278).

Concluding comments

In Britain during the Early Bronze Age beach cobbles were preferentially transported inland for up to 25 km from the coast for use as tools within the mines. These cobbles were largely unmodified, yet experiments have shown that even without proper grooving they could still be hafted and used as mining hammers or as hand-held tools, many of them being recycled, often for use as anvils or as crushing stones. Alongside this was the commonplace use of bone tools and antler picks and also a range of wooden tools and other objects, many of which do not survive mining, particularly when firesetting was used.

In all probability this represents a completely utilitarian technology which could, and almost certainly did, develop spontaneously and independently across the globe at the very beginning of the first metal working period(s). It was a product of environmental determinism rather than diffusionism.

Given the obvious similarities between the assemblages of cobble stone mining tools found in the 5000-year-old gold-bearing hematite mine in Georgia and a 4000-year-old copper mine on Copa Hill, Cwmystwyth in Wales, what then are the differences? The former should have implements for the fine grinding of hematite, but beyond that, it should be possible to see some of the same functional types of tool appearing at both; this being the result of similar utilitarian needs associated with the development of a 'primitive' fireset mine, and the ensuing wear and fragmentation of the stone tool sets.

The collection and use of such tools reflects the continuation of what was effectively a stone age technology employed in the earliest extraction of ores and the production of metal. In general terms, the stable ergonomics of stone tool use pre-dates the arrival into general circulation of bronze in sufficient abundance to become expendable as tools; this is particularly the case where it was individuals of modest status who are undertaking the mining (Shennan 1999). This may well have been the situation in Europe right up until the Middle to Late Bronze Age expansion in metal production.

As regards the various mining and ore processing techniques experimented with in this study, we can be pretty certain that most prehistoric miners used only a very basic toolkit, but used it in a way that sometimes involved quite skilled and complex processing sequences. Most impressive of all was the ingenuity of these people, their intuitive geological 'knowledge', and also a completely different approach to timescale, economy and the effort of collective labour.

Acknowledgements

I would like to acknowledge the various archaeological sponsors (including the Royal Commission for Ancient and Historical Monuments in Wales, the National Museum of Wales, English Heritage, British Academy, the Leverhulme Trust, The Manchester Museum) who have supported this research in the UK, but most importantly the excavation team of the Early Mines Research Group who made these archaeological excavations possible. Thomas Stöllner and Irina Gambaschidze invited me to work on their projects in Georgia and Austria, for which I am grateful. Brenda Craddock provided some of the drawn graphics illustrated in this paper.

References

Anreiter, P. *et al.* (eds), 2013. *Mining in European History and its Impact on Environment and Human Societies: Proceedings for the 2nd Mining in European History-Conference of the SFB-HIMAT, November 2012* (Innsbruck: Innsbruck University Press)

Barnatt, J., & Thomas, G., 1998. 'Prehistoric mining at Ecton, Staffordshire: a dated antler tool and its context', *Mining History: Bulletin of the Peak District Mines Historical Society* 13(5), pp. 72–78

Bick, D.E., & Davies, P.W., 1994. *Lewis Morris and the Cardiganshire Mines* (Aberystwyth: National Library of Wales)

Bird, J.B., 1979. 'The "Copper Man": a prehistoric miner and his tools from northern Chile', in E.P. Benson (ed.), *Pre-Columbian Metallurgy of South America* (Washington), pp. 105–132

Briggs, C.S., 1988. 'The location and recognition of metal ores in Pre-Roman and Roman Britain and their contemporary exploitation', in J. Ellis-Jones (ed.), *Acta of British School in Athens Centenary Conference on Ancient Mining and Metallurgy* (University of Wales, Bangor), pp. 106–114

Briggs, C.S., 1993. 'Early mines in Wales again: a reply to Budd *et al.* 1992', *Archaeology in Wales* 34, pp. 13–15

Brown, J., 1995. *Traditional Metalworking in Kenya*, Cambridge Monographs in African Archaeology 38 (Oxford)

Browne, T., 1995. 'The Mysteries of Alderley Edge', *The North West Geologist* 5, pp. 18–21

Craddock, B., 1990. 'The experimental hafting of stone mining hammers', in Crew & Crew 1990, p. 58

Craddock, B., Cartwright, C., Craddock, P.T., & Wray, W.B., 2003. 'Hafted stone mining hammer from Chuquicamata, Chile', in P. Craddock & J. Lang (eds), *Mining and Metal Production through the Ages* (London: British Museum/ Archetype), pp. 52–68

Craddock, P.T., 1995. *Early Metal Mining and Production* (Edinburgh University Press)

Crew, P., & Crew, S. (eds), 1990. *Early Mining in the British Isles*, Plas Tan y Bwlch Occasional Publication 1 (Maentwrog, Snowdonia)

Davies, O., 1936. 'Finds at Dolaucothy', *Archaeologia Cambrensis* 91, pp. 51–57

Davies, O., 1937. 'Mining sites in Wales', *Report of Annual Meeting of the British Association for the Advancement of Science Section H4*, pp. 301–303

Davies, O., 1947. 'Cwm Ystwyth mines', *Archaeologia Cambrensis* 100, pp. 61–66

Dawkins, W.B., 1875. 'On the stone mining tools from Alderley Edge', *Proceedings Manchester Lit. and Phil. Soc.* 14, pp. 74–79

Dutton, L., & Fasham, P., 1994. 'Prehistoric copper mining on the Great Orme, Llandudno, Gwynedd', *Proceedings of the Prehistoric Society* 60, pp. 245–286

Figueroa, V., Salazar, D., Salinas, H., Núñez-Regueiro, P., & Manríquez, G., 2013. 'Pre-Hispanic mining ergology of northern Chile: an archaeological perspective', *Chungara Revista de Antropología Chilena* 45(1) (Tarapacá, Chile), pp. 61–82

Ford, T.D., 2000. 'Geology of Ecton and other north-east Staffordshire mines', *Mining History: Bulletin of the*

Peak District Mines Historical Society 14(4), pp. 1–22

Gale, D., 1995. 'Stone Tools Employed in Prehistoric Mining' (unpubl. Ph.D. thesis, University of Bradford)

Garner, A., Housley, R., & Prag, A.J.N.W., 1994. 'The Alderley Edge shovel: an epic in three acts', *Current Archaeology* 137, pp. 172–175

James, S., 2011. 'The Economic, Social and Environmental Implications of Faunal Remains from the Bronze Age Copper Mines at Great Orme, North Wales' (unpubl. Ph.D.thesis, University of Liverpool)

Jenkins, D.A., & Timberlake, S., 1997. 'Geoarchaeological Research into Prehistoric Mining for Copper in Wales', a report to the Leverhulme Trust (unpubl.), University of Bangor

Laffoley, N., 1998. 'Primitive mining tools from Tembelini, near Syama, Mali, West Africa', *Mining History: Bulletin of the Peak District Mines Historical Society* 13(6), p. 6

Lewis, A., 1990a. 'Firesetting experiments on the Great Orme's Head 1989', in Crew & Crew 1990, pp. 55–56

Lewis, A., 1990b. 'Underground exploration of the Great Orme copper mines', in Crew & Crew 1990, pp. 5–10

Lewis, A., 1996. 'Prehistoric Mining at the Great Orme: criteria for the identification of early mining' (unpubl. M.Phil. thesis, University of Bangor)

O'Brien, W., 1994. *Mount Gabriel: Bronze Age Mining in Ireland*, Galway University Press

O'Brien, W., 2004. *Ross Island: Mining, Metal and Society in Early Ireland*, Bronze Age Studies 6 (University of Galway)

O'Brien, W., 2013. 'Copper mining in Ireland during the later Bronze Age', in Anreiter *et al.* 2013, pp. 191–200

Pickin, J., 1990. 'Stone tools and early metal mining in England and Wales', in Crew & Crew 1990, pp. 39–42

Pickin, J., & Timberlake, S., 1988. 'Stone hammers and firesetting: a preliminary experiment at Cwmystwyth Mine, Dyfed', *Mining History: Bulletin of the Peak District Mines Historical Society* 10(3), pp. 165–167

Pittioni, R., 1951. 'Prehistoric copper mining in Austria: problems and facts', *Institute of Archaeology Seventh Annual Report* (Institute of Archaeology, London), pp. 16–43

Rovira, S., & Montero-Ruiz, I., 2013. 'Iberia: technological development of prehistoric metallurgy', in S. Burmeister *et al.* (eds), *Metal Matters: innovative technological and social change in prehistory and antiquity* (Leidorf), pp. 231–239

Sainter, Rev. J.D., 1878. *The Jottings of Some Geological, Archæological, Botanical, Ornithological, and Zoological Rambles round Macclesfield* (Macclesfield: Swinnerton & Brown)

Shennan, S., 1999. 'Cost, benefit and value in the organization of early European copper production', *Antiquity* 73(280), pp. 352–363

Smith, A.D., Green, D., Charnock, J.M., Pantos, E., Timberlake, S., & Prag, J., 2011. 'Natural preservation mechanisms at play in a Bronze Age wooden shovel found in the copper mines of Alderley Edge', *Journal of Archaeological Science* 30, pp. 1–9

Stöllner, T., Gambaschidze, I., & Hauptmann, A., 2008. 'The earliest gold mining of the ancient world? Research on an Early Bronze Age gold mine in Georgia', in *Ancient Mining in Turkey and the Eastern Mediterranean*

(proceedings of the above-titled conference in Ankara, 15–22 June 2008), ed. U. Yalçin *et al.* (Ankara: Atilim University), pp. 271–288

Stöllner, T., Breitenlechner, E., Fritzsch, D., Gontscharov, A., Hanke, K., Kirchner, D., Kovács, K., Moser, M., Nicolussi, K., Oeggl, K., Pilcher, T., Pils, R., Prange, M., Thiemeyer, H., & Thomas, P., 2010. 'Ein nassaufbereitungskasten vom Troiboden', *Jahrbuch des Römisch-Germanischen Zentralmuseums Mainz* 57, pp. 1–32

Stöllner, T., Craddock, B., Timberlake, S., & Gambaschidze, I., 2012. 'Feuersetzen im frühesten Metallerzbergbau und ein Experiment im frühbronzezeitlichen Goldbergbau von Sakridissi, Georgien', in *Der Geschichte des Bergbaus in Tirol und seinen angrenzenden Gebieten: Proceedings zum 6 Milestone-Meeting des SFB HiMAT 2011* (University of Innsbruck), pp. 65–76

Stöllner, T., Thomas, P., Hanning, E., Gontscharov, A., Röttger, K., & Pils, R., 2012. 'Mitterberg Kampagne 2011: Neue Ergebnisse aus der Geländearbeit', in *Der Geschichte des Bergbaus in Tirol und seinen angrenzenden Gebieten: Proceedings zum 6 Milestone-Meeting des SFB HiMAT 2011* (University of Innsbruck), pp. 33–43

Timberlake, S., 1990. 'Firesetting and primitive mining experiments, Copa Hill, Cwmystwyth', in Crew & Crew 1990, pp. 53–5

Timberlake, S., 2003. *Excavations on Copa Hill, Cwmystwyth (1986–1999): an Early Bronze Age copper mine within the uplands of Central Wales*, British Archaeological Reports (British Series) 348 (Oxford: Archaeopress)

Timberlake, S., 2005a. 'Stone mining tools from Alderley Edge', in Timberlake & Prag 2005, pp. 58–78

Timberlake, S., 2005b. 'Experimental mining on Alderley Edge. Part 1: A firesetting and mining experiment at Church Quarry in 1997', in Timberlake & Prag 2005, pp. 188–192

Timberlake, S., 2006. 'Excavations of early mineworkings at Twll y Mwyn (Cwm Darren) and Erglodd, Ceredigion', *Archaeology in Wales* 46, pp. 79–86

Timberlake, S., 2007. 'The use of experimental archaeology/archaeometallurgy for the understanding and reconstruction of Early Bronze Age mining and smelting technology', in S. La Niece, D. Hook & P. Craddock (eds), *Metals and Mines: studies in archaeometallurgy* (London: British Museum/ Archetype), pp. 27–36

Timberlake, S., 2009. 'Copper mining and metal production at the beginning of the British Bronze Age', in P. Clark (ed.), *Bronze Age Connections* (Oxford: Oxbow), pp. 95–122

Timberlake, S., 2014. 'Prehistoric copper extraction in Britain: Ecton Hill, Staffordshire', *Proceedings of the Prehistoric Society* 80 [on-line http://dx.doi.org/10.1017/ppr.2013.17] (Cambridge University Press), pp. 1–48

Timberlake, S., & Craddock, B., 2005. 'Experimental mining on Alderley Edge. Part 2: The manufacture of stone mining hammers – the record of a communal experiment on Alderley Edge', in Timberlake & Prag 2005, pp. 192–197

Timberlake, S., & Craddock, B., 2013. 'Prehistoric metal mining in Britain: the study of cobble stone mining tools based on artefact study, ethnography and experiment', *Chungara Revista de Antropología Chilena* 45(1) (Tarapacá, Chile), pp. 33–59

Timberlake, S., & Prag, A.J.N.W., 2005. *The Archaeology of Alderley Edge: survey, excavation and experiment in an ancient mining landscape*, British Archaeological Reports 396 (Oxford: Archaeopress)

Willies, L., 1987. 'Ancient zinc-lead-silver mining in Rajasthan, India: interim report', *Mining History:*

Bulletin of the Peak District Mines Historical Society 10(2), pp. 81–123

Willies, L., 1990. 'Kestel Tin Mine, Turkey: interim report', *Mining History: Bulletin of the Peak District Mines Historical Society* 12(5), pp. 51–71

Worthington, T., & Craddock, B., 1996. 'Modern stone tools', *Mining History: Bulletin of the Peak District Mines Historical Society* 13(1), p. 58

Deep Mining Technology:
Devon and Cornwall in the Eighteenth Century

R.J. Stewart

Abstract: In the late seventeenth and early eighteenth centuries miners in Devon and Cornwall were working at increasingly greater depths in search of copper ore. With greater depth came the twin challenges of hard ground and water, requiring a transition from the essentially artisanal techniques of the tinners to a capital driven and increasingly industrial approach to mining. This paper examines the technological responses in the increasing challenge of deep mining.

Introduction

Arguably there are two key events which define pre-twentieth-century mining in the south west of England: firstly the transition from tin streaming to working lode tin which took place during the Tudor period and, secondly, the transition from this relatively shallow lode mining to deep lode mining which took place during the late seventeenth and early eighteenth centuries. The transition from shallow to deep mining is largely, although not exclusively, associated with the birth of 'modern' copper mining in the region from the 1690s onwards.

Given the importance of copper to the English economy it comes as something of a surprise that, in spite of the best efforts of the Company of Mines Royal in the 1580s, copper mining did not become established in the South West until the eighteenth century. There are a number of reasons why copper mining did not start to take root until the 1690s. These can be briefly summarised thus:

- smelting technology
- the impact of the Glorious Revolution of 1688
- The physical challenge of deep mining and advances in mining technology

The primary copper ore in the South West was chalcopyrite which requires quite a complex, multi-phase smelting process which was ill understood by English miners. The Company of Mines Royal neatly side stepped the issue by importing German mining masters such as Ulrich Frosse, who ran the Company's smelter at Neath in the 1580s and understood the process. The problem was finally solved by 1688 when the Clerkes successfully smelted copper ore using a coal fired reverberatory furnace (Morton 1985).

The Glorious Revolution of 1688 and the accession of William III and Queen Mary had a significant impact on English economic life. Under William and Mary the English economy was deregulated, Tudor and Stuart monopolies being swept away. Amongst these monopolies was the Company of Mines Royal's monopoly on copper mining in Devon and Cornwall. Probably more important, although less tangible, was the creation of a spirit of free enterprise that had been singularly lacking under the Stuarts, particularly during the reign of James II. Nowhere was this liberalisation more keenly felt than in Bristol, the centre of the English brass and copper industries. Indeed it was the Bristol merchant class who would provide the extensive capital required to initially develop deep mining in Devon and Cornwall.

Physical challenges of deep mining

To understand the physical challenges faced by late seventeenth and early eighteenth century copper miners one needs to consider characteristics of a 'typical' (if such a thing exists) copper lode as shown in Fig. 1. The upper section of the lode, known as the gossan, is heavily weathered by the percolation of surface water. The gossan is denuded of copper which is leached out of this upper zone and re-deposited as secondary copper minerals at depth. Cassiterite is less susceptible to leaching and tends to remain in the gossan. Below the gossan lies the un-weathered copper zone containing both primary and secondary copper minerals. The boundary between the upper tin zone and the lower copper zone is typically marked by the level of the water table.

This zonation of and the transition from tin to copper was well understood by the pioneering copper miners. Writing

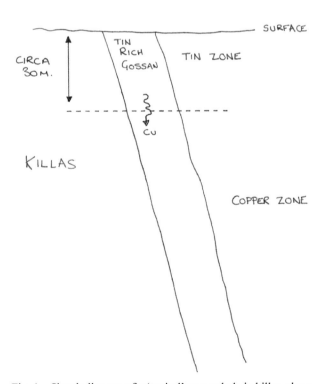

Fig. 1 Sketch diagram of a 'typical' copper lode in killas, showing the relationship between the upper tin zone and the lower copper zone. The dotted line represents the water table, typically the boundary between the two zones.

in the mid 1720s Henric Kalmeter, a Swedish industrial 'spy', comments:

> … these mines were taken up and worked for tin until, when they came further and deeper down on the lode, the former diminished or disappeared, and copper ore came in instead. (Brooke 2001)

The tinners had the distinct advantage that they could extract cassiterite from the weathered ground which lay above the water table. In contrast the would be copper miner was working below the water table in hard, un-weathered ground. If copper was to be mined successfully in Devon and Cornwall the twin challenges of drainage and breaking hard ground had to be addressed.

John Coster II and the emergent domestic copper industry

Key to the development of copper mining in the South West was John Coster II (1647–1718) who has rightly, in the current author's opinion, been described as the 'father of Cornish copper mining' (Barton 1961; Day 1977). John Coster II had been involved with Clement and Talbot Clerke's pioneering work on reverberatory copper smelting in the late 1680s, being described as the 'chief technical man' of that concern (Day 1977). John Coster II was also intimately concerned with the establishment of a very early copper smelter at Upper Redbrook in the Wye valley; acquiring a sixty year lease for a site in July 1691 (Day 1977).

Whilst there is a suggestion that Upper Redbrook was getting a supply of copper ore from the Forest of Dean (Jenkins 1942), the Upper Redbrook smelters primarily looked to the South West for their copper ore. From the outset they appear to have been content to buy copper ore via agents. However it soon became apparent that the quality of ore being dispatched from Cornwall was at best variable and, at worst, unusable. To secure better ore John Coster II started buying direct from Cornwall. Initially buying on behalf of Upper Redbrook, he soon became the agent for a consortium of Bristol brass and copper interests usually referred to as the Bristol Company (Brooke 2001; Morton 1985).

Chacewater mine

It appears that Coster's main source of supply was 'the copper mine near Truro' (Cletscher 1696). The mine in question was at Chacewater and was owned by Hugh Boscawen. When Thomas Cletscher, another Swedish industrial 'spy', visited the mine in 1696 he noted that ' the mines are 40 or 50 fathoms deep' and were suffering from water problems. Consequently output was suffering and skilled miners were deserting the mine for the copper mine at North Molton. Boscawen had started to drive an adit, but, as Cletscher observed, it was 'not yet half carried on' (1696). Indeed it would appear that draining the Chacewater mine was too great a challenge for Boscawen and the mine was subsequently abandoned, depriving the emergent copper industry of one of its major sources of supply.

To make the transition from shallow to deep mining required a technological step forward and to take this step required increased capital investment. A similar transition had taken place in the Tudor period when the focus moved from alluvial tin to lode tin. In terms of capital tin stream-

ing was within the realm of the working tinner whilst lode mining was, comparatively, capital intense. The capital to develop lode tin mining came from within the South West, from wealthy tinners, merchants and local gentry; men like Hugh Boscawen. Whilst the resources of Boscawen and his ilk would have been sufficient to exploit lode tin at shallow depths, working copper below the water table was a game too rich for local pockets alone. This is, of course, where the mercantile strength of Bristol becomes important.

The Bristol Company and mining in the South West

In order to secure the Chacewater ore the Bristol Company acquired the lease of the Metal Work and Pittslooarn / Wheal Busy sections of the mine from Hugh Boscawen (created Viscount Falmouth in 1720) at dues of 1/9th (Brooke 2001), thus becoming directly involved in mining in Cornwall.

The Bristol Company would go on to dominate copper mining in the South West during the first third of the eighteenth century, their interests largely being represented in Devon and Cornwall by the Coster family. To better superintend the Bristol Company's interests in the South West John Coster III (1688–1731) took up residence in Cornwall by 1714, initially living in Redruth and latterly in Truro (Woodcroft 1862; Brooke 2001; Day 1977; Coster 1731).

The application of adit drainage

To dewater Chacewater mine the Bristol Company used adits. By the 1690s the use of adits was well known in the region, having been in use as early as 1309 in the Bere silver mines in Devon (Claughton 1994). Carew in his *Survey of Cornwall* notes that tin works were frequently drained by adits (Carew 1602). What makes the Chacewater adits stand out is the scale of the undertaking, which dwarfed anything which had gone before. Henric Kalmeter visited the mine on 4 December 1724 and wrote:

> To these works twin adits have been driven, the first an old one [presumably Boscawen's part finished 1696 adit] and the later one, which is no deeper than the first but has cost about £11,000. Because they intended to survey the ground they have sunk shafts in many places and continued working in the level at numerous places, by which the work has gone on rapidly. It became dreadfully expensive because of the many shafts and the many workmen who are employed to work on both sides of the shafts and towards each other. Thus they have in less than three years driven an adit over a mile long begun in the lowest ground they could find. What otherwise makes the work expensive is that they have to keep men to pump the water up the shafts instead of driving the level so that the water runs out on its own and without further expense. (Brooke 2001).

Such huge expenditure, which would have been way beyond the means of the previous generation of adventurers, demonstrates both the level of investment required to develop a deep copper mine on this scale and the vast financial resources the Bristol Company was able to draw on. Whilst financial resources were key to the driving of long adits such undertakings would not have been technically feasible without the adoption of gunpowder in the South West post 1689 (see below).

The ability, both technical and financial, to drive long adits reached its apex in the County Adit. Commenced in

1748 the adit was conceived by William Lemon (a Coster protégée) and John Williams, initially to drain Poldice mine. The adit rapidly developed beyond its original goal and ultimately extended to nearly 40 miles of underground tunnels draining most of the Gwennap copper district (Buckley 2000).

Working below adit

Whilst undoubtedly successful, the driving of adits was only a partial solution to the problem of water and it was inevitable that copper miners would want to chase their lodes below adit level, necessitating mechanical pumping. The need to pump was nothing new, the challenge having been addressed, to a degree, by the tinners as they honed the techniques of lode mining. Carew notes:

> For conveying away the water they pray in aid of sundry devices, as adits, pumps, and wheels driven by a stream and interchangeably filling and emptying two buckets, with many such like, all which, notwithstanding, the springs so encroach in these inventions as in sundry places they are driven to keep men, and somewhere horses also, at work both day and night without ceasing, and in some all this will not serve the turn. (Carew 1602)

William Pryce, in his seminal work *Mineralogia Cornubiensis* of 1778, echoes Carew's observations:

> With all the skill and adroitness of our Miners, they cannot go any considerable depth below the Adit, before they must have recourse to some contrivance, for clearing the water from their workings. The hand pump, and the force pump, will do well for small depths, and are necessary in the first sinkings into the Lode, before the Stopes can proceed. Next to these the water is drawn to adit by small water barrels, in a core of six or eight hours, they give over drawing by hand, and erect a Whym, which is a kind of horse engine to draw water or work …
>
> Another water engine is the Rag and Chain … Several of these pumps may be placed parallel upon different Stulls, Sallers or Stages of the mine, and are usually worked by hand like those in our navy. The men work at it naked excepting their loose trowsers, and suffer much in their health and strength from the violence of the labour, which is so great that I have been witness to the loss of many lives by it. (Pryce 1778)

The inadequacy of existing technology, as highlighted by Carew and Pryce, is well illustrated by the example of the Marquis copper mine in the Tamar valley:

> She was first discovered seventeen years ago [1707] on the bank of the river, when some workmen got together, took a set or lease of 20 fathoms from the water's edge from the owner of the land, and drove a level from the lowest point. They found some copper ore, and the work or place was called Bedford. Immediately after this some enterprising adventurers formed a company and took a sett of the ground above Bedford. They drove a level, which is vertically seven or eight fathoms above the former one, and more than sixty fathoms long, though it was driven in such a way that it was made parallel with the first level. Thereupon both workings were united and were and still are called the Marquis. When those holding the second sett or tack note began work they first found tin ore upon the back of the lode, or upmost in the

ore ground. But when they sank on it they found copper, and that in much larger quantities and of a better kind than in the first level. The ore shoot runs exactly east and west, and up the hill from the river. Probably as the water took the upper hand, they had sixty men employed to pump it out, but the labour became too great and was abandoned … (Brooke 2001)

The use of large overshot waterwheels

The Marquis lay idle until 1723 when the lease was acquired by the 'Copper Company in Bristol' who promptly installed a 'water engine' at the end of the upper level. The engine was an overshot waterwheel; recent archaeological investigation suggests that the wheel was in the region of 30 feet in diameter and three foot breast (R.E. Waterhouse, pers. comm.). The water was laundered in along the upper adit level; tail race water and the water pumped from below deep adit went out via the deep adit to the river. At the time of Kalmeter's visit on 13 November 1724 a shaft had been sunk to a depth of 16 fathoms, the intention being to put in pumps once they had cut paying ore ground (Brooke 2001).

The use of waterwheels to drive pumps was far from unknown in the west of England, waterwheel driven pumps having been in use on the Bere Ferrers mines since 1480 (Claughton 1994). What was innovative was the use of large, overshot wheels, an innovation credited to John Coster II. In this context William Pryce wrote:

> About four score years back, small wheels of twelve or fifteen feet diameter, were thought the best machinery for draining the Mines; and if one or two were insufficient, more were often applied to the purpose, all worked by the same stream of water. I have heard of seven in one Mine, worked over each other. This power must have been attended with a complication of accidents and delays. However, soon after the above date, Mr John Costar, of Bristol, came into this country, and taught the natives an improvement in this machinery, by demolishing those petit engines, and substituting one large wheel of between thirty and forty feet in their stead. (Pryce 1778)

In addition to the Marquis wheel Kalmeter recorded details of other overshot wheels being erected on mines with a Coster / Bristol Company connection:

On 3 December 1724 Kalmeter visited Tolgus Downs copper mine run by Thomas Coster (1684–1739, the elder brother of John III (Day 1977)) and a Captain Miners. Kalmeter noted that Tolgus Downs was one of the oldest copper mines in Cornwall, having been 'worked continuously for copper for nearly thirty years'. At the time of Kalmeter's visit an 'engine to draw water' was being installed to pump water from the bottom of the mine to adit. The engine itself comprised a 34 foot diameter overshot waterwheel, typical of the Costers' thinking and practice. A pair of cranks attached to the axle drove two sets of pumps. In December 1724 the bottom of the engine shaft lay 11 fathoms below adit although the engine had the potential to pump from a depth of 24 fathoms (Brooke 2001).

John Coster III was responsible for installing 'water engines' at the extensive North Molton copper mine in north Devon. Kalmeter, who visited the mine on 28 December 1724, described the engines in some detail:

In both workings water-engines were put in by the afore-mentioned John Coster, and the mine is worked by the so-called Bristol Company. To put these machines to work they have water flowing from the river a good bit higher upstream. In the western working it consists of a wheel 20 feet in diameter, to the end of whose axle is fixed a crank or double iron cranks, which lifts two sets of rods 4 fathoms long and deep, being cast of iron in such a way that when one rod is lifted up by the one crank the other is forced down by the other crank. Each one of these rods or bars works a so-called bob or arm 4 fathoms underground, which as mentioned goes up and down, and these arms also work two pumps and pump-rods in the excavation, which is 16 fathoms deep. The water which comes out of the pumps goes into two cross-pipes or pump launders, which lead across into a larger pipe running into the level, by which means it is led of to the stream.

The machine in the eastern work is of the same design and construction suited to its work, except that the water wheel is 24 feet in diameter; the working iron rod also has the rods and bobs, or arms at 20 fathoms depth. But in addition there are two half-wheels on the side of the shaft, which are moved up and down by two iron rods, which are attached at one end to the iron crank, and at the other end to the half wheel; they are thus in constant motion upwards and downwards. The one of these half-wheels works in the same way as mentioned under Chasewater Mine, a pump at 30 feet and another at 40 fathoms, or down to the bottom of the mine.' (Brooke 2001).

Constraints of large overshot wheels

Where appropriate the large overshot water wheel was an ideal solution to the problem of mine drainage as is demonstrated in their wide scale application during the nineteenth century. However they were by no means a universal solution. Pryce summarises the problem elegantly:

Happy it would be for the mining interest, if our superficial streams of water were not so small and scanty; but the situation of our Mines, which is generally in hilly grounds, and the short current of our springs from their source to the sea, prevent such an accumulation of water, as might be applied to the purpose of draining the Mines; and of course the value of the water is the more enhanced. There are very few streams, which are sufficient to answer the purpose in summer, as well as in winter, so that many engines cannot be worked from May to October. (Pryce 1778)

As Pryce suggests, some mines with inadequate water supplies often had to be abandoned periodically. Kalmeter cites the example of 'Frenches Work' near Roseliddon:

Mr Coster now runs the work on tribute … The water is pumped up by hand from the bottom to the aqua duct [adit], and it can be noted that this is one of the workings called a summer work, since it can only be worked in summer, water hindering them in winter.(Brooke 2001)

The Coster's patent water engine

Whilst abandoning mines on a seasonal basis was sometimes the only option, the situation arose when a mine which lacked a sufficient water supply to drive a large over-shot wheel was so rich that abandoning it for months on end was not a viable option. The Costers' response to this problem was to develop an ingenious water engine which required less water than a large overshot wheel.

John II and his son John III patented their water engine in 1714:

AD 1714 … No 397
Coster and Coster
Engine for drawing water out of mines.

Anne, by the Grace of God &c. To all to whom these presents shall come, greeting: Whereas Our trusty and wellbeloved John Coster, of Redbrooke, in Our county of Gloucester, gentleman, and John Coster, junior, of Redruth in Our county of Cornwall, gentleman, have by their humble petition represented unto Us, that they have with great paines and expenses invented an brought into perfection an engine for drawing water out of deep mines, much cheaper and more effectuall that the usual ways, by water wheeles; in which new invented engine the water that drives it is carried down the shaft or pit to the adit in bored elemes and mettall cillinders, and by that means circulates a chain with bobbs through the said cillinders, which chain, depending on a peculiar sort of wheele, workes a cranke at each end of the axell thereof; which said engine, with the application thereof for the drawing water with sucking plumps, chaine plumps, and forcing plumps, is a new invention not formerly known and practised in England, and being made for lesse charge than water wheeles, and requiring much less room underground, as well as less charge to keep it in repair, and that it will wit the same stream of water draw at least one third part more water in quantity from the same depth, or one third in depth more than water wheels with the same stream can or will do, the said engine will be of great use for such mines as have been left off for want of ability to draw the waters off them, the recovery and working of which will be of great advantage to the nation in generall as well as to the Lords of the Royalties and persons adventuring in such mine; and having therefore humbly prayed us to grant them Our Royal Letters Patent for the sole use of their said invention for fourteen yeares. (Woodcroft 1862)

The Costers' water engine was, in effect, a rag and chain pump albeit, in an elegant display of lateral thinking, used as the prime mover rather than as a pump.

A description and illustration of the Costers' water engine appeared in Desaguliers' technical encyclopaedia of 1744:

The late Mr Costar, (I believe without having heard of Francini's Machine) considering that sometimes from a small Stream, and sometimes from little Springs or Collections of Rain – water, one might have a pretty deal of Water above Ground, tho' not a sufficient Quantity to turn an Overshot Wheel; thought that if a sufficient Fall might be had, that Water might be made useful in raising Water from the Bottom of the Mine to the Adit, and thereby save the Expense of Men and Horses use for that Purpose: The Fall to be had appear'd to him to be CL; that is, from the Grass or Mouth of the Pit down to the Adit, which here we'll suppose is 25 Yards. Then he contriv'd to Place a Rag Wheel RR, with its Chain or Bucket-Pump at the Mouth of the Pit at Cc, much after the manner of Francini, receiving the superior Waters brought into a collection cistern W, thro' a Pipe A, leading into the Buckets B, making them go the reverse way (because in the common Chain-Pump the Rag-Wheel carries the Buckets, but here the Buckets carry the Rag Wheel) down as far as the Adit, into which they discharge themselves at bb; and there turning another Rag-Wheel rr, the whole Axis works an Engine bringing the Water from the Bottom which is also delivered into the Adit which caries away both the Waters to the Delivery at the Bottom of the Mountain at Z, which we suppose at a great distance from the Mine. Any kind of Engine may be work'd by this lower Rag-Wheel, whose Axis is HI; as for Example a common Chain-Pump, like that at D, Fig 2. By making the Rag-Wheel sufficiently deep; or Cranks, as I have represented it at Gg in the Figure, working two Pump-Rods KK moving in the Barrels MM, and delivering their Water into the Trough leading into the Adit. N.B *There must be a Wheel fix'd to the Axis of the upper Rag-Wheel at C, to carry a Pinion or smaller Wheel D, having a Fly FF, in order to regulate the Motion of the Whole Machine, and prevent Jerks.* (Desaguliers 1744, pp. 457–458) (Fig. 2)

One of these engines, possibly the prototype, was erected on the Pittslooarn / Wheal Busy section of Chacewater mine, possibly as early as 1712–1714. We are indebted to Henric Kalmeter who recorded comprehensive details of the engine, which he examined on 4 December 1724. As described by Kalmeter the Chasewater engine worked on the Costers' rag and chain principle applied on a large scale; the 'working column' extended to a depth 18 fathoms. The flywheel was similarly impressive being 13 feet in diameter and carrying 1,100 pounds of lead on its rim. The engine pumped from a depth of 11 fathoms below adit. The water engine proved an immense saving over manual pumping, reportedly saving £500 to £600 a month (Brooke 2001).

At the time of Kalmeter's 1724 visit an 80 fathom long drive had been put in from the shaft containing the water engine to a further shaft in 'the old Metal Work'. The original water engine was connected via a flat rod run along this new level to a pair of pumps pumping the Metal Work shaft. The new pumps raised water from a depth of 7 fathoms deeper than the pumps in the Wheal Busy shaft. The Metal Work pumps delivered the water to the original Wheal Busy pumps which, in turn, delivered the water to adit. Kalmeter noted that the machine was constructed by Mr John Coster of Truro (John Coster III) who 'has for his expenses in construction received 8s. for each ton of ore brought up, being, however, still in debt over it' (Brooke 2001).

John Coster III is also noted as being the builder of the water engine at Polgooth. Polgooth was a tin producer which, at the time of Kalmeter's visit on 9 December 1724, was divided into three works: Polgooth or Cock's Head, St Margaret's and St Martin. The St Martin work was leased by 'Messers. Coster and company' 'not over three years since' (i.e. 1721) from 'Mr Edgcumbe of Mount Edgcumbe' and it was on this section of the lode that the Polgooth water engine was erected. Initially the mine had been drained to a depth of 24 fathoms by an adit. When the water engine was installed it was found expedient to drive another adit, a mere 3 fathoms below the first, to accommodate the new engine, the new adit costing £8,000 (Brooke 2001). With regard to the water engine Kalmeter notes:

The machine is the same kind as the one at Chacewater, but only has a head of nine fathoms. There are four

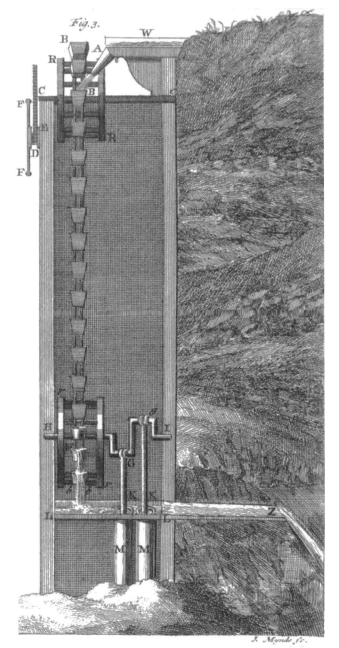

Fig. 2   Plate from Desaguliers' *Course of Experimental Philosophy*, vol. 2, demonstrating the concept of the Costers' patent water engine. Whilst Desaguliers' illustration shows buckets the actual engines as built would have used a rag and chain pump column.

pumps, of which the upper work 22 fathoms below the last level, to which they raise the water, which runs out through it to the stream down the valley. The other two lower pumps raise the water two and a half fathoms. (Brooke 2001)

Relistian mine on Gwinear Downs was visited by Kalmeter on 1 December 1724 at which time it was being worked to a depth of 20 fathoms for both tin and copper. At its peak Relistian had been a major tin producer; Kalmeter noted that it produced 200,000 pounds of tin metal in 1717 and that the lode had been 40 feet wide in places. At its greatest extent Relistian had reached a depth of 75 fathoms and had been drained by a water engine of 'the same kind as the one at Chasewater mine'. Unfortunately the lode at depth was found to be weak and narrow and by 1720 the water engine had been removed (Brooke 2001).

Fire engines

Whilst the Costers' patent water engine did, to a limited extent, address the problem of lack of surface water the real solution to the problem lay in the application of steam to mine pumping. 1712 saw the successful introduction of Thomas Newcomen's atmospheric engine for mine pumping at Dudley Castle, arguably the single most important event of the history of technology.

The early history of atmospheric engines in Cornwall is obscured by the distance of time and will no doubt be argued over for generations to come. Suffice to say the earliest contemporary reference to an atmospheric engine in the South West dates from 1716 when the following advertisement appeared in the *London Gazette* of 11 August 1716:

> Whereas the Invention for raising Water by the impellent force of Fire, authorized by Parliament, is lately brought to the greatest Perfection; and all sorts of Mines &c. may be thereby drained, and Water raised to any Height with more Ease and less Charge than by the other Methods hitherto used, as is sufficiently demonstrated by diverse Engines of this Invention now at Work in the several Counties of Stafford, Warwick, Cornwall and Flint. These are therefore to give Notice, that if any person shall be desirous to treat with the Proprietors for such Engines, Attendance will be given for that Purpose every Wednesday at the Sword Blade Coffee House in Birchin lane; London, from 3 to 5 of the Clock; and if any Letters be directed thither to be left for Mr. Elliot; the Parties shall receive all fitting satisfaction and Dispatch. (*London Gazette* 1716)

Of obvious interest is the reference to an engine at work in Cornwall. This engine was, in all probability, erected at 'Wheal an Vor', at that time a rich tin producer. It is probable that the engine was erected at the instigation of the Godolphin family who may have trialled a Savery engine at Wheal an Vor as early as the 1690s. We are very lucky that Kalmeter includes details of this engine:

> The mine is said to be 55 fathoms deep and 80 fathoms in the length of the level. The lode is sometimes twelve to fifteen feet wide, sometimes not more than two or three feet, but all in killas, a black slate. As this work was one of the deepest in the county and therefore very wet, a fire engine was erected about seven years ago [c. 1717] to draw up the water. It worked for about four years, but as this type of machine, particularly at that depth, is a mass of difficulties and subject to repairs, it is too costly. The engine was therefore removed, and the mine lies largely idle … (Brooke 2001)

As with any new technology, and especially such an innovative one, it is not surprising that it was not an overwhelming success and also not surprising that did not spawn any immediate imitators.

It has been suggested that an atmospheric engine was erected on Wheal Fortune at Ludgvan in 1720; however this claim has been comprehensively demolished by the late Justin Brooke (Brooke 1996).

The next three engines erected in Cornwall appear to have been the work of Joseph Hornblower (1696?–1762) who founded something of a dynasty of steam engineers. Evidence for his activities in Cornwall in the 1720s comes from a book, published in 1833, written by his great grandson Cyrus Redding and entitled *Yesterday and Today*. This appears to be the key source for most later writers, the current author included. Given Redding's distance from the events he was describing a degree of caution is probably advisable:

> He [Hornblower] had visited Cornwall for the purpose of erecting some of Mr Newcomen's engines at the mines about 1725 … It could not be many years after 1720, that the first engine was erected in Cornwall, near the North Downs at Huel Rose, seven or eight miles from Truro, and Mr. Joseph Hornblower, thus mentioned was the engineer, who had been sent for into Cornwall on purpose. (Redding 1833)

Regarding the second Joseph Hornblower engine, Redding cites the views of his cousin:

> Mr Moyle, of Helston, an eminent medical practitioner there, and my first cousin, said in reply to a letter of mine on the above subject, in 1833: – 'I think it is probable that the above engine was erected above a hundred years ago (referring to that at North Downs, Huel Rose, I believe). My uncle Mathew says he has often heard that the *second* engine was erected at Huel Busy, or Chacewater mine, and that our great grandfather Joseph was the engineer … (Redding 1833)

Redding concludes:

> After erecting these two engines it appears that my great-grandfather erected a third at Polgooth Mine. He then left the County entirely … (Redding 1833)

Thus if we accept Redding's account, and certainly more eminent historians than the current author do, post 1725 three Newcomen engines were erected in Cornwall by Joseph Hornblower. Rolt and Allen suggest the following dates for these engines: Wheal Rose 1725, Chacewater 1725–1727 and Polgooth 1725–1727 (Rolt & Allen 1997).

The erection of a Newcomen engine at Chacewater (Fig. 3) marked the beginning of a history of engines on the mine which would, in microcosm, encompass the history of steam pumping engines in Cornwall.

It is highly significant that all three mines were Coster / Bristol Company mines (Brooke 2001), demonstrating the Costers' readiness to embrace new technology. The fact that both Chacewater and Polgooth had previously employed the Costers' patent water engine suggests that these engines had reached their limit by 1725–1727.

By 1733, when the patent which covered atmospheric engines had expired, the Newcomen engine had established itself in many British mining fields and, indeed, abroad. Rolt and Allen suggest that somewhere in the region of one hundred engines had been erected by this date (Rolt & Allen 1997). In contrast maybe as few as four atmospheric engines had been put to work in Cornwall.

Whilst blessed with seemingly endless mineral wealth Devon and Cornwall are particularly bereft of coal, which had to be imported from the South Wales coalfields; consequently coal was an expensive commodity. Unfortunately for the mine adventurers in Devon and Cornwall Newcomen engines had a voracious appetite for coal. This was a direct consequence of the thermally inefficient operating cycle of the engine which required the alternate heating and cooling of the cylinder, a problem not satisfactorily resolved until Watt's introduction of the separate condenser. Massive coal consumption was not a huge issue for engines erected on coal mines which had an almost inexhaustible supply of cheap or even free coal; indeed on some coal mines Newcomen engines continued in use in the late nineteenth or even early twentieth century. However for the West Country adventurer the cost of coal was of paramount importance. Writing in the 1770s William Pryce observed;

> The vast consumption of fuel in those engines, is an immense drawback upon the profits of our Mines. It is a known fact, that every fire engine of magnitude consumes to the amount of three thousand pounds worth of coal in every year. This heavy tax upon Mining, in some respects, amounts to a prohibition. (Pryce 1778)

The cost of coal was compounded by an import tax on sea borne coals apparently introduced in 1698 during the reign of William III to help meet the costs of the Nine Years' War / War of the Grand Alliance (1688–97) (Howard 1999; Pole 1844). Pole, in his *Treatise on the Cornish Pumping Engine* of 1844, notes that 'the duty on coal alone required for one engine only amounted to nearly £350 per annum'.

In response to the tax on sea borne coal a group of mine adventurers, foremost amongst whom was William Lemon who has already been encountered in connection with the driving of the County Adit in Gwennap, prepared a 'memorial' on the subject which was submitted to Parliament. Unfortunately the memorial is not dated but probably dates from the late 1730s:

> The Case of the Gentlemen Adventurers in Tin and Copper Mines in the County of Cornwall, and the Inhabitants of the said County.
>
> For these many years past, there have been no new lodes or veins either of tin or copper discovered; and by the extraordinary and indefatigable labour of the miners, the county has been so entirely tried, that there is not the least reason to expect there will be any, so that unless some means can be found out to work the old mines at advantage, there is the greatest probability that the commodities of tin and copper will in a few years greatly decrease.
>
> This has obliged us humbly to desire Parliament to encourage fire engines by granting a draw back of the duties upon all coals consumed in working them, the only method we know of by which the old mines can be worked, the greatest and most considerable part of them being so deep that all other means for draining water out of them have already proved ineffectual.
>
> The advantage is so apparent that we humbly hope this will meet with no opposition. It is evident the revenue cannot be lessened by it, because there are at present no coals at all consumed in that way; but on the other hand, if the mines remain unworked, the revenue must greatly suffer, since the duties on coals consumed in making tools and engine materials for working the mines, on iron, candles, gunpowder, foreign timber, and deals, great quantities of which are consumed in the mines, will be considerably diminished, as well as his Majesty's duties arising from tin exported.
>
> It is therefore humbly desired, in consideration of the great expense the adventurers must necessarily be at, that this encouragement may be given, (as well as a further encouragement by a draw-back of the duties on all coals used in the calcining of tin ore,) to preserve the said valuable commodities so very advantageous to the public, and without which thousands of families now employed in the several branches of these manufactures will be thrown out of business, and the greatest part of the county entirely ruined; or that such other methods be taken as Parliament in their wisdom shall think most meet. (Pole 1844).

Of particular interest is the assertion that no engines were at work. Pryce, in considering the duty on seaborne coal, notes that 'thirty-six years ago, this county had only one fire engine in it' (1778); given that Pryce's book was largely completed by 1774/75 this places his statement at 1738/39.

Lemon's memorial appears to have been successful for in 1741 Parliament passed the astoundingly named 'Act for granting to His Majesty the sum of One Million out of the Sinking Fund, and for applying other sums therein mentioned for the service of the year one thousand seven hundred and forty-one; and for allowing a Draw-back of the duties upon Coals used in Fire Engines for draining Tin and Copper Mines in the County of Cornwall; and for appropriating the supplies granted in this session of Parliament; and for making forth Duplicates of Exchequer Bills, Lottery tickets and Orders, lost, burnt otherwise destroyed; and for giving further time for the payment of duties omitted to be paid for the Indentures and Contracts of Clerks and Apprentices' (cited in Pole 1844).

The abolition of the duty on sea borne coal appears to have had a significant effect on the adoption of fire engines in Cornwall. Pryce comments:

> The drawback upon coal used in our smelting houses and fire engines, has been attended with such happy consequences for the publick, that we may venture to affirm, not one-fifth of the fire steam engines now working, would ever have been erected without such encouragement. Thirty-six years ago, this county only had one fire engine in it: since which time above three score have been erected, and more than half of them have been rebuilt, or enlarged in the diameter of their cylindrical dimensions. (Pryce 1778)

Borlase similarly notes that:

> … without this bounty, fire engines would not have been erected, nor could these mines … ever have been worked … (Borlase 1758)

As Pryce observes, the 'post draw back period' saw a massive expansion in the use of atmospheric engines in Cornwall (although none in west Devon); indeed it is probable that Pryce's estimate of 'three score' engines errs on the conservative side.

As engineering and manufacturing skills developed so did the power and size of the engines being erected. The account books of Thomas Goldney, a shareholder in the Coalbrookdale Company, which cover the period 1741/42 to 1769 have been examined by K.H. Rogers and are of particular interest in that they contain details of cast iron cylinders supplied to Cornish mines (Rogers 1976). Table 1, extracted from Rogers, illustrates the increasing size of cylinders employed on Cornish mines.

An alternative to ever greater cylinder size was multiple engines pumping the same shaft, as was the case at Chacewater:

There were formerly two atmospheric engines working on this mine; one a 64 inch cylinder, the other a 62 inch; both six feet stroke. These two engines were stated to consume 16½ bushels of coal an hour. The quantity of water they raised to keep the mines drained, was 80 cubic feet per minute, in summer and 100 cub. ft. per min. in winter.

One of these engines worked the lower column of pumps, 18½ inc. diam., and 24 fathoms lift, and the other engine worked the upper column 17½ inc. diam. and 26 fathoms lift; so that one engine raised the water to the other, and that engine raised it up high enough to run away, by the subterranean level or adit, which was 24 fathoms below surface. In the whole the water was raised 50 fathoms.

This was a common arrangement for draining the large mines in Cornwall, which required more power than one engine usually possessed; this plan was called shammaling. (Farey 1827)

Enlarging cylinder size or, as an alternative, shammaling, whilst allowing greater depths to be attained were very expensive solutions to the problem of draining deep mines. The great expense of keeping increasingly deep mines drained must have exercised the minds of Cornish adventurers, particularly in the light of the onslaught that Cornish copper mining was experiencing from Anglesey. The solution was obvious, at least to the polymath engineering genius John Smeaton (1724–92): improved efficiency.

Smeaton had turned his attention to the atmospheric engine in the mid 1760s, studying its operation and foibles in the same meticulous way that he brought to all his endeavours. To better understand the engine's workings Smeaton constructed a small, portable experimental model. As part of his work Smeaton collected data on working engines in both the North East and, of particular interest in this context, Cornwall (Rolt & Allen 1997). In Cornwall Smeaton recorded details of fifteen engines at work in 1769 at Wheal Virgin, Poldice, Wheal Maid, Dolcoath and Wheal Chance (Rolt & Allen 1997; Farey 1971).

Smeaton concluded that both engines and boilers were often poorly engineered and operated. In the light of his experience Smeaton went on to build a number of much improved atmospheric engines. In summing up Smeaton's contribution to the evolution of the atmospheric engine Pole, writing in 1844, concludes:

> He does not seem to have added anything new to the machine, or to have invented any thing connected with it which can be easily particularised; but by a careful study of its action, and an accurate theoretical consideration of the several relations of its parts one to the other, he so contrived to improve their proportions as to increase the duty by this means alone nearly fifty per cent. (Pole 1844)

In 1775 Smeaton erected what many regard to be the finest atmospheric engine ever built, on Chacewater mine. Smeaton's Chacewater engine (Fig. 3) had a 72 inch cylinder cast and machined by the Carron foundry. Barton (1966) comments that this was the largest engine erected in Cornwall in the eighteenth century. Smeaton noted that he expected the engine, working at nine strokes a minute, to raise 880 hogsheads of water from a depth of 51 fathoms, burning 13 London bushels of coal per hour (Smeaton 1837). Writing in the 1860s Smiles says of the engine that it was 'the finest and most powerful work of the kind which had until then been constructed …' (Smiles 1866).

Whilst the Chacewater engine must have been a magnificent machine Smeaton had, arguably, reached the limits of the technology. What he had not addressed was the intrinsic flaw of the atmospheric engine: the massive thermal inefficiency inherent in the repeated heating and cooling of the cylinder. In Cornwall, where economic use of coal was fundamental, this would prove to be the final nail in the coffin for the atmospheric engine. The man who drove that nail would be James Watt and, to stretch the metaphor to breaking point, the hammer he used to drive the nail was the separate condenser. Boulton and Watt started erecting engines in Cornwall in 1777, the first being a 30-inch at Chacewater. The following year Smeaton's 72-inch was rebuilt by Boulton and Watt as a 63-inch, the original cylinder serving as a steam jacket: a new era had begun (Dickinson & Jenkin 1927).

Table 1   Cast iron cylinders supplied to Cornish mines

Year	Mine	Cylinder diameter (inches)
1744	Trevenson	40 (estimated)
1745	Trevenson	40 (estimated)
1746	Ludgvan Lease	47
	Roskear	47
	Dolcoath	40
	Lemon & Co. (mine unspecified)	40 (estimated)
1747	Polgooth	40 (estimated)
1748	Pool Adit	60
	Drannack	55
1749	Lemon & Co. (mine unspecified)	52
1750	Chacewater	54
1753	Dolcoath	54
	Herland	70
	Wheal Rose	60
1756	North Downs	60
1758	Wheal Virgin	60
1763	Wheal Oula	70
	Poldice	60
1765	Wheal Virgin	60
1765	Tresavean	60
1766	Chacewater	66
1767	Wheal Virgin	60
1768	New Dolcoath	63

(Rogers 1976)

Breaking ground

Whilst it is generally accepted that gunpowder was introduced into mining in the South West in 1689 its adoption was not immediate nor its application universal through the industry. The early part of eighteenth century may be seen as a period of transition as far as breaking ground is concerned. On the one hand techniques widespread amongst tinners, such as the use of picks and wedges, were adopted by copper miners. However due to the greater depths at which the copper miners were working they were encountering harder, unweathered ground which required more aggressive techniques such as firesetting and powder work which, arguably in the case of firesetting, were not part of the tinners' repertoire.

Picking and wedging

The use of picks, hammers and wedges and would have been familiar to anyone involved in early eighteenth century mining. In his *Survey of Cornwall* published in 1602 Richard Carew notes with regard to the tinners' tools:

> Their ordinary tools are a pickaxe of iron about sixteen inches long, sharpened at the one end to peck, and flat-headed at the other to drive certain little iron wedges wherewith they cleave the rocks. They have also a broad shovel, the utter part of iron, the middle of timber, into which a staff is slope wise fastened. (Carew 1602)

Tools (and presumably techniques) had changed little by the 1670s as attested by a very interesting, although unfortunately anonymous, paper published in the *Philosophical Transactions of the Royal Society* for 1671:

> The instruments commonly used in Mines, that serve for ripping the Loads and breaking the Deads, and landing both the Ore and the Deads, are; (1.) a Beele or Cornish Tubber (i.e. double points), of 8l. or 10l. weight, sharped at both ends, well steeled and holed in the middle. It may last in hard Country 1 year, but new pointed every fortnight at least. (2.) A sledge, flat headed from 10l. to 20l.

weight; it will last about 7 years, new ordered once a quarter. (3.) Gadds, or Wedges of 2l. weight, 4 square, well steeled at the point; will last a week; 2 or three days then sharpened. (4.) Ladders. (5.) Wheelbarrows, to carry the Deads and Ore out of the Drifts or Adits to the Shambles. (Anon. 1671)

The use of such apparently simple tools was widely adopted by the eighteenth century copper miner. As an example Kalmeter records that hammers and wedges were being used to break ground in the Marquis copper mine in November 1724:

> There are twenty workmen here, of which the miners who work with hammers and wedges enjoy 28s. a month, with free tools and candles … (Brooke 2001)

In spite of the utility of such techniques miners employing them in hard ground must have been very frustrated; Carew was fully aware of the limitations of picks and wedges:

> … To part the rocks they have the forementiond axes and wedges, with which, mostly they make speedy way, and yet (not so seldom) are so tied by the teeth that a good workman shall hardly be able to hew three feet in the space of so many weeks' (Carew 1602)

In such circumstances more aggressive techniques were required:

Firesetting

One response to hard ground as encountered by the early eighteenth century copper miner was firesetting (Stewart 2014). Although demonstrably an ancient technique, firesetting does not appear to have been widely used by the miners in the South West prior to the emergence of copper mining in the 1690s. Certainly archaeological and documentary evidence is very limited. The current author is only aware of one contemporary reference to firesetting in the South West. This is contained in the Tonkin manuscripts and was written at some time between the 1710s and mid 1730s:

> When they meet with Rocks and very hard Ground as sometimes they doe such that requires not only three weeks but three months to hew through the same they formerly burnt furze faggots, & C. to break the rock, but that proving insufficient, & very often fatal to the workmen by the sudden changing of the wind & driving the smoak down upon them. (Tonkin MS B, p. 62)

One might argue that firesetting was not an appropriate technique as far as working lode tin was concerned and would have had a very limited application. Most lode tin works were sunk close to surface in the weathered 'tin zone' above the water table, in which picking and wedging would have been more than adequate to break ground. That said tin works had started to go deep by the end of the Tudor period. Carew notes that mines were working to depths of 40 or 50 fathoms, at which sort of depths very hard ground was being encountered in which miners could drive no more than a foot a week using conventional techniques (Carew 1602). If firesetting was used by tinners arguably this would be the situation in which the technique would have been of most use. However Carew makes no mention of firesetting in these deep works and it is tempting to suggest that at these depths the complexities of ventilation, as suggested by Tonkin, precluded the use of firesetting.

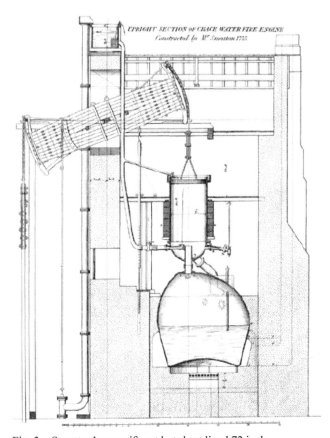

Fig. 3   Smeaton's magnificent but short lived 72 inch Chacewater engine

Recent archaeological work in west Devon has identified at least five sites with convincing evidence of firesetting. Three of these sites can, with a degree of certainty, be co-related with documentary evidence relating to early eighteenth century copper works, namely the Providence, the Success and Virtuous Lady (Stewart 2014).

Firesetting appears to have been employed as a strategy to deal with the exceptionally hard, unweathered ground often encountered in the hanging and footwalls of west Devon sulphide lodes in the 'copper zone'. Such ground often contains quartz, chlorite and iron pyrite which, experiment has demonstrated, is incredibly difficult to break even with modern steel picks and chisels or indeed compressed air tools. It is worth noting that whilst quartz does not yield easily to mechanical techniques it is particularly susceptible to firesetting. Willies observes that some minerals, most notably quartz, 'undergo rapid crystallographic rearrangement when heated or cooled through various critical "inversion" temperatures'. With regard to quartz the key temperature is 575°C. At this temperature, which is easily obtained with a wood, or indeed a furze, fire, quartz simply disintegrates (Willies 1994). A crude experiment, undertaken in August 2009, using a wood fire and a sample of quartz from Virtuous Lady, has satisfied the current author as to the destructive effects of heating quartz.

One question that intrigues the current author is where did these early eighteenth century copper miners get the technique from? Given that a significant number of copper miners would have had direct experience of tin working, was firesetting a technique already established in the South West and simply adopted and adapted by copper miners? There is a possible alternative to this 'indigenous adoption' argument: it is possible that, like the use of gunpowder, firesetting was imported from the Mendip lead mines rather than being adopted from the tinners' repertoire. Firesetting was certainly in use on Mendip prior to the eighteenth century. Gough, in his scholarly work on Mendip mining, is of the opinion that on Mendip firesetting was a technique which had been used from at least Elizabethan times. Gough quotes a letter from the philosopher Joseph Locke dated 5 May 1666:

> … when they meet with hard rocks in their way, they make a fire upon them, that they may dig through the easier … (Gough 1967)

Given the direct links that both mining in the South West and on Mendip had with Bristol and also the direct diffusion of the use of gunpowder from Mendip to the South West, the suggestion, and it is no more than a suggestion, that firesetting in the South West was imported from Mendip, rather than adopted from tin mining, should not be dismissed out of hand.

With regard to firesetting in the South West it is probably too early to draw any firm conclusions. The only documented archaeological evidence for firesetting demonstrates that the technique was employed by west Devon copper miners during the first quarter of the eighteenth century. Tonkin's reference to the technique suggests that it had been employed in Cornwall, although whether in copper or tin mines is obscure. It is the current author's contention that firesetting was much more appropriate to copper mining than tin mining. One might tentatively suggest that fire-

setting in the South West was in vogue from (possibly) the 1690s, when miners started seriously exploiting the copper zone, to the 1720s, when the widespread adoption of gunpowder rendered the technique obsolete; as such firesetting was very much a transitional technique.

Gunpowder

As noted above it is generally accepted that gunpowder was introduced into mining in the south west of England in 1689, possibly at the instigation of the Godolphins. The first documentary evidence for its use is to be found in the Breage parish register:

> Thomas Epsley Senior of Chilchumpton pish [parish] of Bath and wills [Wells] in Sumersitsheers [Somersetshire] he was the man that brought that rare invention of shooting the rocks which came here in June 1689 and he died at the ball [bal] and was buried at breag [Breage] the 16 day of December in the year of our lord Christ … 1689' (cited in Earl 1978)

Given the Somerset connection it would be reasonable to assume that Epsley acquired his knowledge in the Mendip lead mines. The date is very suggestive.

Of interest is a paper read to the Royal Geological Society of Cornwall in 1830. John Hawkins, the Vice President of the society, notes that he and Davies Gilbert, the then President of the society, had taken an interest in the subject as early as 1792, possibly making Hawkins and Davies Cornwall's earliest mining historians. On 3 June 1792 Davies wrote to Hawkins:

> On the subject of blasting, what I have been able to pick up, is far from satisfactory. I only learn, in general, that it was first introduced by a German, and used at St. Agnes. It strikes me as highly probable, that this German was Becher. (Hawkins 1832)

A further letter from Davies to Hawkins dated 22 September 1792 contains the following:

> I have seen the old man from Zennor, and although the information he has to give, is far short of what we hope to procure, yet even this little may be esteemed curious. He remembers having heard from his father and other old men, that blasting had been first introduced by Germans, into the eastern part of this county; and it was bought to the west (i.e. Lelant, Zennor, and St.Ives) in their time, by two eastern men called Bell and Case, and was used by them in Trevigha bal; and they affected to keep the mode of operations secret, suffering no one to see them charge the holes; till a man of Zennor, hiding himself under a bolt, saw what they were about. This he thinks must have happened about ninety years ago. He observes that, for a long time, baked clay was constantly used for tamping, till at last other materials were found to answer just as well. (Hawkins 1832)

The earliest account of the use of powder in Devon is to be found in Thomas Cletscher's account of his visit to North Molton mine in 1696:

> Here are used only national [local?] workmen, who are so unaccustomed to mining that they lay off the mine as soon as the lode or vein is lost, without further searching

for it. They are working in the German manner, first hacking out the rock and then blasting it. (Cletscher 1696)

If, as Cletscher suggests, the North Molton workforce were inexperienced local men it seems strange that they were employing such an advanced technique as blasting at a comparatively early date. The answer may be that the technique was introduced to North Molton by the Chacewater miners who had been displaced by the water issues which plagued Chacewater.

Kalmeter describes the technique as used in the 1720s:

The work in the mine is performed either with hammers and wedges, or, when the country rock is very hard, they blast it with gunpowder, boring the hole seventeen or eighteen inches deep or more, and filling above the gunpowder with clay. In some places they find it best to tamp it with the fine gravel which comes out when boring the hole, which is mentioned here because instead of this they recently began the practice of using an iron bar between the plug and the wall of the level so that the plug should not spring out. (Brooke 2001)

Writing at a similar time to Kalmeter Tonkin observes:

They had of late had recourse to Gunpowder by boring holes in them, in the nature of mining: and this devise has been likewise attended with many fatal accidents, by powder taking fire too early by a spark from the rod; which hath been of late much remedied by a new method, introduced from abroad, by Major Joseph Sawley as used in mining in sieges, by not making use of the rod at all, but covering the powder and fuse with fine earth, which answers full as well as if it was rammed in. (Tonkin MS B, p. 62)

As to the source of powder used in the South West: Earl notes that the earliest reference to gunpowder being made in Cornwall is 1809; prior to that he suggests that powder was supplied by London or Somerset mills (Earl 1978). It comes as no surprise to learn that Bristol and its hinterland was an important centre of gunpowder production during the later seventeenth and early eighteenth centuries (Buchanan 2000). Given the Bristol connection one does wonder if it was the influence of the Bristol merchant class that inhibited the development of an indigenous gunpowder industry in Devon and Cornwall during the eighteenth century. The source of gunpowder used in mines in the South West is a subject worthy of further study and one suspects that the Port Books might prove illuminating.

Conclusions

Mining in the South West experienced rapid technological advances during the late seventeenth and early eighteenth centuries in response to the challenges of deep mining, mainly associated with the development of copper mining. Technological innovation was directly linked to the growing involvement of 'out adventurers', particularly the Bristol merchant classes who had access to much greater capital resources than were available to 'in adventurers' who had driven mining up to that date. This in itself was facilitated by the increasingly liberal, deregulated economic landscape which developed as a consequence of the Glorious Revolution of 1688.

References

Anon., 1671. 'An accompt of some mineral observations touching the mines of Cornwall and Devon', *Philosophical Transactions of the Royal Society*, pp. 2096–2113

Anon., 1976. 'The Hornblower family, pioneer steam engineers', *Journal of the Trevithick Society* no. 4, pp. 7–44

Barton, D.B., 1961. *A History of Copper Mining in Cornwall and Devon* (Truro: D. Bradford Barton Ltd.)

Barton, D.B., 1966. *The Cornish Beam Engine* (Truro: D. Bradford Barton Ltd.)

Borlase, W., 1758. *The Natural History of Cornwall* (Oxford)

Brooke, J., 1993. *The Cunnack Manuscript* (Trevithick Society)

Brooke, J., 1996. 'Wheal Fortune in Ludgvan', *Journal of the Trevithick Society* no. 23, pp. 63–67

Brooke, J., 2001. *The Kalmeter Journal* (Twelveheads Press)

Buchanan, B.J., 2000. 'The Africa trade and the Bristol gunpowder industry', *Transactions of the Bristol & Gloucestershire Archaeological Society* no. 118, pp. 133–156

Buckley, A., 2000. *The Great County Adit* (Penhellick Publications)

Carew, R., 1602. *Survey of Cornwall* (London)

Carne, J., 1828. 'On the period of commencement of copper mining in Cornwall: and on the improvements which have been made in mining', *Transactions of the Royal Geological Society of Cornwall* vol. 3, pp. 35–85

Claughton, P., 1994. 'Silver-lead – a restricted resource: technological choice in the Devon mines', *Mining History: Bulletin of the Peak District Mines Historical Society* vol. 12 no. 3, pp. 54–59

Cletscher, T., 1696. 'Relation of the European mines in the year of 1696', translation of that part covering his visit to England, typescript in Liverpool University, Harold Cohen Library MS 7.1(21)

Coster, J., 1731. Will of John Coster of Truro, National Archives, Kew, PROB 11/646/262

Day, J., 1977. 'The Costers: copper-smelters and manufacturers', *Transactions of the Newcomen Society* vol. 47 1974–1975 and 1975–1976, pp. 47–58

Desaguliers, J.T., 1744. *A Course of Experimental Philosophy*, vol. 2 (London)

Dickinson, H.W., & Jenkins, Rh., 1927. *James Watt and the Steam Engine* (2nd ed. 1981, Moorland Publishing)

Earl, B., 1978. *Cornish Explosives* (Trevithick Society)

Farey, J., 1827. *A treatise on the steam engine, historical, practical and descriptive* (Longman, Rees, Orme, Brown and Green)

Farey, J., 1971. *A treatise on the steam engine, historical, practical and descriptive*, vol. 2 (David & Charles)

Gough, J.W., 1967. *The Mines of Mendip*, 2nd ed. (David & Charles)

Hawkins, J., 1832. 'On the state of our tin mines, at different periods, until the commencement of the eighteenth century, *Transactions of the Royal Geological Society of Cornwall* vol. 4, pp. 70–94

Howard, B., 1999. 'The duty on coal 1698–1831', *Journal of the Trevithick Society* no. 26, pp. 30–35

Jenkin, A.K. Hamilton, 1927. *The Cornish Miner* (George Allen & Unwin Ltd.)

Jenkins, Rhys, 1942. 'The copper works at Redbrook and Bristol', *Transactions of the Bristol and Gloucestershire Archaeological Society* 63, pp. 145–167

Lemon, C., 1838. 'Statistics of the copper mines of Cornwall', *Transactions of the Statistical Society of England* June 1838; reprinted in R. Burt, *Cornish Mining* (David & Charles, 1969)

London Gazette issue 5459, 11 August 1716, p. 2

Morton, J., 1985. 'The Rise of the Modern Copper and Brass Industry in Britain 1690–1750' (Doctoral thesis, University of Birmingham)

Pole, W., 1844. *A Treatise on the Cornish Pumping Engine* (London: John Weale)

Polwhele, R., 1831. *Biographical Sketches in Cornwall*, vol. 1 (London: J.B. Nichols and Son)

Pryce, W., 1778. *Mineralogia Cornubiensis* (London: J. Phillips)

Redding, C., 1863. *Yesterday and Today* (Newby)

Rogers, K.H., 1976 *The Newcomen Engine in the West of England* (Moonraker Press)

Rolt, L.T.C., & Allen, J.S., 1997. *The Steam Engine of Thomas Newcomen* (Landmark Publishing Ltd.)

Savery, T., 1702. *The Miners Friend or an engine to raise water by fire described* (1827 reprint, London)

Smeaton, J., 1837. *Reports of the Late John Smeaton F.R.S.*, vol. 2 (London: M. Taylor)

Smiles, S., 1866. *Boulton and Watt, comprising also a history of the invention and introduction of the steam engine*, 2nd ed. (John Murray)

Stewart, R.J., 2014. 'Firesetting in west Devon – an initial discussion', in *50 Years of Mine Exploration, Proceedings of the 2011 NAMHO Conference* (Shropshire Caving & Mining Club), pp. 111–113

Tonkin MS B, Royal Institute of Cornwall collection

Tonkin MS H, Royal Institute of Cornwall collection

Willies, L., 1994. 'Firesetting technology', *Bulletin of the Peak District Mines Historical Society* vol. 12 no. 3, pp. 1–8

Woodcroft, Bennet, 1862. *Reference Index of Patents of Invention from March 2 1617 (14 James 1) to October 1852 (16 Victoria)* (London)

From Calley to Curr: the Development of the Newcomen Engine in the Eighteenth Century

Steve Grudgings

Abstract: The publication in 1790 of John Curr's guide to constructing Newcomen engines and their houses provides a major milestone in the development of the engine. From Newcomen and Calley's initial work around 1710, the materials and methods used for constructing boilers and cylinders underwent considerable change and refinement. Similarly the layout and proportions of the engine, its components and house were subject to considerable variety. This paper examines the issues and objectives underlying these developments and looks also at what can be gleaned of the skills and modus operandi of the engine wrights who built and operated these engines.

Introduction

The atmospheric engine introduced by Thomas Newcomen in 1712 was unique in that it harnessed fire as its energy source. It was termed 'atmospheric' because it derived its power from the condensation of steam inside a cylinder, creating a vacuum which allowed atmospheric pressure to push the piston down. This action, when connected to a pivoted beam, provided a reciprocating motion suitable for raising water, which could enable mine owners to access previously unworkable mineral reserves. It was a significant introduction and there is a strong case for Newcomen's engine being one of the main catalysts for the Industrial Revolution to which Britain owes much of its wealth and global status.

The take up of these 'fire engines' was rapid by the standards of the day, but the details of their builders and their construction are poorly documented and understood. There is a general perception that James Watt was the inventor of the first steam engine in 1776 but, whilst he made important contributions, Watt improved on Newcomen's work rather than being an originator. His innovation was to move the condensing process from the cylinder into a separate vessel (the subject of his lucrative patent), thereby improving dramatically the efficiency of the engine. Watt's partnership with the industrialist Matthew Boulton in the Soho engine works enabled engine making to start its transition from the remit of skilled artisans to what we can recognise as the start of the factory system.

The history of the Newcomen engine has received much attention over the years, resulting in many excellent papers and articles. However, with the exception of Rolt and Allen's work,[1] most studies have been concerned with specific engines or areas and as a result there are a number of gaps in the published research. One of these omissions is the study of the development of the skills, methods and technologies needed to produce the engines' components and assemble them into a robust and effective whole. This paper discusses the early engine builders, what they did, the context in which they did it and the challenges they had to meet.

Who were Calley and Curr?

Calley and Curr were chosen as the names for the title of this paper because their lives mark the start and end of the

Fig. 1   Although surrounded by later housing, the form of John Wise's c. 1739 engine house in Brislington, South Bristol, is distinctive. It is understood to be the oldest complete Newcomen engine house in the world.

period in question. Their contributions to engine building and what is known of them as individuals illustrate some of the changes that occurred over the eighteenth century.

John Calley (c. 1674–1717) was a plumber and glazier by trade and appears to have been Thomas Newcomen's main business partner during the development and construction of the early engines. The two were fellow Baptists, a faith shared by many of the men that Newcomen worked with. Little more is known of Calley other than that he died whilst putting up engines in Whitehaven and Austhorpe (Leeds).[2]

By contrast, we know more about John Curr (1756–1823). He was superintendent of the Duke of Norfolk's Sheffield collieries from 1781 to 1801 and was active in the engine building world by the end of the eighteenth century.

He is understood to have constructed a number of engines around Sheffield whilst in this employment. These were probably the basis from which his published standard table of dimensions and materials was derived. Curr's book *The Coal Viewer and Engine Builder's Practical Companion*[3] also contains details of his other technical innovations, including the L-section rail, often termed 'Curr rail'. In addition to his iron rail, he also took out patents for flat hemp rope and cage guides and was an early exponent of haulage by stationary engines.

Calley, like Newcomen, typifies the capable yet unsung artisan engineers of the early eighteenth century. Curr, whilst apparently a highly competent engineer, is better known because of his work setting out best practice for a number of colliery engineering matters, specifically dimensions of Newcomen engines.

The engine builders

Other than Newcomen himself, the early engine builders and their endeavours do not seem to have attracted the attention of many researchers. Until the advent of men such as Smeaton and Watt, the work of such engineering pioneers does not appear to have been thought important.

Who were they?

It is important to differentiate between the people that funded and commissioned the engines and those that built them. The selection of engine builders that appears below is highly subjective and based on the author's incomplete knowledge. It does however give a brief account of the more important ones.

RICHARD PARROTT (and son STONIER) and GEORGE SPARROW: These three are credited with constructing seven early engines between 1714 and 1736 in a small area of the Warwickshire Coalfield around Nuneaton. These engines included the well known Griff engines for Richard Newdigate.[4] The three men are also reported to have built other engines in Staffordshire.

CARLISLE SPEDDING was agent for James Lowther's Whitehaven collieries and was responsible for erecting and repairing a number of engines between 1717 and 1739, dealing directly with both Newcomen and Calley at first.[5] It is not clear whether he employed another engineer to assist these endeavours.

The HORNBLOWER family: Three generations of this family, originally from the west Midlands, were involved in putting up engines in the Midlands, Bristol and Cornwall from 1715 until the end of the century. JONATHAN is well known as the inventor of the compound engine around 1782; one of his forebears constructed the first engine in North America in 1753.

JOHN WISE: A long-lived engine builder, active between 1725 and 1770. Like the Hornblower family, he came from the west Midlands (Hawkesbury) and may have learnt his trade alongside Newcomen and Calley at Griff and nearby around 1715. Wise took out the first patent for converting reciprocating to rotary motion in 1742 and appears to have been a successful and widely respected engine builder, responsible for installations in London, Bristol and Cornwall (and most probably Warwickshire).[6]

WILLIAM BROWN: Reported by Matthias Dunn as having been responsible for erecting 22 engines in the north-east and a further three in Scotland between 1756 and 1776, Brown is cited as one of the first engineers to recognise the importance of adequate boiler capacity.[7]

The PALMER family: CHARLES and his son THOMAS built, moved and valued engines in the Bristol and Somerset coalfields between 1750 and 1790. Palmer's and others' bills have been used to highlight the materials, skills and costs involved in the construction of a 42" engine at Coalpit Heath in 1751, as reported in an account that lists all known references to engines with which the family were involved.[8]

JOHN NANCARROW and JOHN BUDGE: Both built engines in Cornwall, the former migrating to North America after 1760, the latter apparently working alongside John Wise from 1760 onwards and taking on his role at Dolcoath following his death in the early 1770s.

JAMES BRINDLEY: A millwright by trade, Brindley built a number of successful engines in the Staffordshire Coalfield in the 1760s before concentrating on building the first canals, an indication of the breadth of his engineering skills.[9]

JOHN SMEATON: Smeaton was originally associated with the Carron ironworks in the 1760s, when he is alleged to have installed the cylinder boring mill there, the results of which enabled the Carron Company to take a large share of the engine cylinder market. Smeaton is reported to have been one of the first engineers to take a systemic approach to improving the performance of the Newcomen engine, something he put into practice on Tyneside from the 1770s onwards.[10] He went on to build engines in Cornwall that were recognised as the most efficient of the pre-Watt engines.

FRANCIS THOMPSON: Thompson, who resided in Ashover, Derbyshire, is perhaps best known as the builder of the 1791 engine from Pentrich Colliery preserved in the Science Museum. He built engines in Derbyshire and Lancashire between 1780 and 1800 in addition to installing the first engine underground at Yatestoop lead mine. Like Hornblower and Heslop, he was one of the early exponents of compounding.[11]

How did they learn their trade and what were their prerequisite skills and experience?

Like many of the questions about these early engines, there is no clear or single answer and so we need to rely on educated guesswork. The main precedents for the use of massive timber machinery were probably in wind and water mills. Ship building and operating also involved similar skills and expertise. The skills of managing coal fires (ashpits, firegrates, flues to chimney, watertight and fire-resistant wrought iron platework) had probably first been developed in panhouse saltmaking – all but the last had recently been adapted to metalworking in the development of the cementation steel furnace and the various reverberatory non-ferrous smelting furnaces.

Having some of these skills would not have been sufficient to commence engine building. I suggest that the early engine builders also needed some of the following:

- a wide range of trusted colleagues and tradesmen in related trades
- the vision and ambition to undertake a task as challenging as engine building
- a good range of practical skills, as we might now expect of a 'good handyman'

- an excellent reputation for their skills and trustworthiness

We know, for example, that Newcomen was an iron-monger (a wholesaler of iron) travelling frequently to the West Country mines, and that Calley was a plumber and glazier, both skills that obviously were relevant. We can guess that because John Wise's father was a carpenter in Hawkesbury it is likely that he was skilled in this area too. Charles Palmer's family owned and apparently operated a windmill on Kingswood Lodge Hill in Bristol, an ideal trade and location from which to launch an engine building career. Brindley's first trade was also as a millwright and further research may reveal the background of others.

Some engine wrights probably started their acquaintance with these engines as engine men, in which role they would have developed the knowledge and capability to operate them efficiently and make the frequent running repairs required.

How were they engaged?
The men responsible for engaging the early engine build-ers were landowners and/or mine operators who wanted to increase their income by extracting more coal. Newcomen and Calley and the joint stock company The Proprietors of the Invention for Raising Water by Fire (the holders of Savery's 1698 fire engine patent after his death), were gen-erally reimbursed via a service contract whereby they were paid an agreed proportion of the value of the coal or ore that their engine had drained. Boulton and Watt's charges were based on a proportion of the fuel savings achieved by their engines. However, in the intervening period, it would appear that it was the norm for engine builders to be paid an agreed sum on satisfactory completion and commissioning of the engine; the funding for the engine was supplied by the mine owners themselves.[12] For example:

- the Chelsea Waterworks Company paid John Wise 60 guineas for building their 32" engine in 1742 – the total cost was £422 (excluding building materials)
- Jarrit Smith paid Charles Palmer £20 (in addition to his direct wages) for constructing the 42" engine at Coalpit Heath in 1752 – the total cost of the engine (excluding building materials) was £868

What was their role?
Perhaps the easiest way to understand the engine builders' role is to examine the lists of materials needed to build an engine. Our engine wright (or fire engineer as they were then known) would have needed to know enough about the materials involved to be able to organise their assembly into a reliable working unit. The main groups of materials were masonry (brick, stone and mortar); massive timbers for the engine, cylinder retaining beams, headgear and pitwork; cast and wrought iron components for cylinder, boiler and controls and the more expensive specialist metals such as lead, brass and solder.

Once the shaft depth and volumes of water to be pumped were known, our man would have had to develop and agree the overall design of the engine to perform the work needed. He would then have needed to translate this design into quantities of materials, some of which he may have had the skills to do directly; for other items such as blacksmiths' work, he may have had to rely on trusted specialists.

Once materials quantities were determined, they needed to be ordered. Bored castings, specifically the cylinder and pump barrels, would probably have had the longest lead time, whilst other items such as brick and stone would gen-erally have been available locally on demand. The funding for these materials was normally provided by the individual commissioning the engine and a level of trust and mutual understanding was needed between builder and commis-sioner for this arrangement to work effectively.

These early engine builders would probably have set out the majority of the specifications and material volumes on a verbal basis without reference to material standards or detailed drawings, something difficult for modern engi-neers to conceive. Quality standards were important too and would require liaison with suppliers prior to placing orders. It appears to have been the practice for engine builders to visit suppliers of critical components such as cylinders and bored castings to discuss their requirements and satisfy themselves of the supplier's capability to produce them

Why are they not better known?
It was not until the last century that Newcomen's role as the father of the steam engine was recognised, largely thanks to the efforts of the society that bears his name. Because skilled practical men such as Newcomen and his succes-sors were not members of the aristocracy, nor did they hold positions of importance in the military, judiciary or govern-ment, their endeavours were probably not thought worthy of record. Consequently they feature rarely in published materials unless they were the subject of legal proceedings or were featured in the accounts of travellers or historians.

It is notable that before the advent of Boulton and Watt's partnership and Brindley's and others' work on canals from 1770 onwards, the work of any engineers, civil or otherwise was rarely publicised.

The technical context
It has been argued that Newcomen's 1712 Dudley engine with its sophisticated self-acting valve gear was the result of a lengthy series of experiments and was preceded by three separate engines in Cornwall. The existence of these pre-1712 engines has been widely referenced but not rigor-ously analysed, something that is in the process of being addressed as this paper goes to press.[13]

The visual impact of these smoking, steaming early engines, particularly their harnessing of fire as an energy source, attracted much attention and the term 'fire engine' remained in use for most of the eighteenth century. The construction methods of these early engines and the sources of their components have, in my opinion, not received the attention they warrant. Whilst the dearth of reference mate-rials makes this understandable, it is not sufficient reason for the topic to be ignored.

The development of the technologies and skills needed to construct the engines' major components, such as the cyl-inder and boiler, will be examined later but first it is worth looking at some less obvious aspects of early engine building.

Design and layout: drawings
It may not be widely recognised that measured drawings of machinery in the classic plan and section views with which we are familiar were rare before 1750; such items were normally

drawn using an artistic and subjective three dimensional perspective. This may appear a trivial point until the following requirements of the engine builder are considered:

- specification and communication of shapes and sizes of items to be produced by suppliers (and subsequent checking that they were accurate)
- recording and communication of specific layouts and arrangements, such as hole locations, lever lengths and fulcrum points
- production of batches of items (nuts, bolts etc.) to a common pattern
- recording and communication of successful results of experimental arrangements

While there were others who may have gone before them, it was not until Boulton and Watt's engine building business was established in the 1780s that what we would now recognise as engineering drawings started to be widely used (Fig. 2). So we are left with the question of how early engine builders communicated their component specifications to their suppliers and workmen. The short answer, as with many of the questions posed in this paper, is that we do not know. It seems most likely that existing patterns would have been copied and direct instructions given, possibly supported by wooden models. It is also worth recognising that many early engine builders would have gone to great lengths to keep their skills and knowledge secret; their engine specifications and measurements are likely to have been committed to memory only.

Technology transfer

The technical context in which the early engines were constructed is easily misunderstood, as the standards that underpin all engineering related communications today were generally absent. The repeatable production processes that emerged in the Victorian era were made possible by a series of essential if unspectacular enabling developments, the most important of which were:

- the progressive introduction of machine tools that removed the need for bespoke blacksmithing expertise to produce specific shapes (the first was Maudslay's invention of the slide-rest lathe in 1797; planing and milling machinery were some of the important later developments)
- the progressive fixing of standards for weights and measures, which was an essential underpinning for the work of men such as Whitworth, who established the standards for screw measurements in 1841
- reducing quality variations in ferrous materials by improved and standardised manufacturing processes
- concentration of capital, driven by (amongst other things) the investment levels required to both produce and commission these new machines (Boulton and Watt's Soho engine works was probably the first and best known example of this)

During the period covered by this paper, the engine building profession went through a major transition. As previously mentioned, Newcomen and Calley were self-taught artisans and the components of their engines were bespoke items, specified by them. By contrast, Curr's exhaustively tabulated specifications for building engines of different sizes (Fig. 3) were usable because, by 1800, all the components needed could be purchased to the standards defined, something unknown ninety years previously.

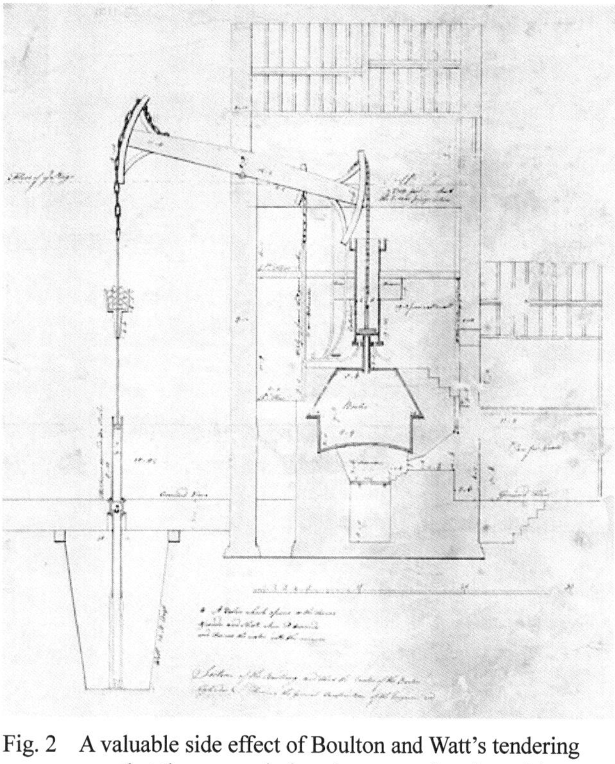

Fig. 2 A valuable side effect of Boulton and Watt's tendering process was that they commissioned a proper drawing of the engine they were being asked to replace. This example is the first of the Chelsea Waterworks engines, constructed by John Wise in 1742 with a 32" diameter cylinder. (Birmingham City Archives, MS3147/Portfolio/5/1103)

Diameter of Cylinders	BOILERS. page 43.		CROSS BEAMS Under Pillars. page 50.			CYLINDER BEAMS. page 51.				CISTERNS for the JACK HEAD. page 51.						
	Number.	Diameter.	Length.		Scantling.	Length.		Scantling.	Quantity.	Length.		Breadth.		Height.		Thickness of Planks.
In.		Feet.	Feet	In	In. by In.	F.	In.	In. by In.	F.	F.	In	F	In	F	In.	In.
25	1	8½	9	6	9 by 9	8	3	13 by 9	14	5	6	3	9	4	6	2
30	1	10½	10	0	10 by 10	8	3	14 by 10	16½	6	0	3	9	4	9	2
35	1	12½	10	0	10 by 10	8	6	15 by 11½	20	6	3	4	0	4	9	2
40	1	14	10	6	11 by 10	8	9	16 by 13	25	6	6	4	0	4	9	2¼
45	2	11	9	6	11 by 10	9	1	17 by 14½	32	6	6	4	3	4	9	2¼
50	2	12½	10	0	12 by 10	9	6	18 by 16	38	6	6	4	3	4	9	2½
55	2	13½	10	6	13 by 10	10	0	19 by 17	45	6	6	4	6	5	0	2½
60	2	14½	11	0	14 by 10	10	6	20 by 18	52	6	6	4	6	5	6	2½
65	2	16	11	4	15 by 10	11	0	21 by 19	61	6	9	4	9	5	9	2½
70	2	17	11	8	16 by 11	11	6	22 by 20	68	7	0	5	0	6	0	2½

Diameter of Cylinders.	ENGINE HOUSE DIMENSIONS. page 52. INSIDE.				STRENGTH of WALLS.			No, of Bricks. page 52.	Lime. page 52.	Sand. page 52.	Masons Bills. page 52.	Feeding Pipes for the BOILERS.	
	Length.		Breadth.		Front.	Sides.	End.					Number.	Inside Diam.
In	F.	In.	F.	In.	In. or In.	In.	In.	Thods.	Ch.	Loads	£.		In
25	15	6	7	0	29 or 30	19	15	48	16	32	20	1	2½
30	16	0	7	0	34 or 35	19	19	55	18	36	22	1	3
35	16	0	7	4	38 or 39	24½	19	65	21	42	24	1	3
40	16	0	7	6	38 or 39	24½	19	70	23	46	26	1	3½
45	16	4	8	0	43 or 44	24½	24½	80	27	54	32	2	3
50	16	8	8	4	48 or 49	24½	24½	90	30	60	39	2	3
55	17	0	8	10	53 or 54	29	24½	102	36	72	45	2	3¼
60	17	6	9	3	58 or 60	29	24½	120	40	80	55	2	3½
65	17	10	9	8	68 or 70	34	29	134	46	92	66	2	3¾
70	18	3	10	1	77 or 78	34	29	150	54	108	75	2	4

Fig. 3 Curr's book *The Coal Viewer* contains 25 pages of tabulated data for engine components. This is a typical example.

Engine building

There was a recognisable sequence in the construction of most engines, and the arrival of materials on site would have been phased accordingly. Examination of historical records suggests that six months was a typical minimum timescale for engine construction and that the sequence of work was as follows.

- The engine shaft was normally sunk or 'proven' before any other work commenced and this would also have included making arrangements for disposal of the pumped water, either into a convenient adit or stream or a specially constructed water channel.
- The shaft collar and foundations for the engine house are likely to have been constructed together and the location of the firing platform and ashpit incorporated.
- While the engine house walls were being built, the blacksmiths would probably have arrived and set up their smithy, remaining on site until the engine was functioning. Responsibility for sourcing the specialist iron and steel required for the engine is unclear but was probably shared by the smith and engine wright. The smiths had much to do and their work fell into four distinct groupings:
  - responding to demands for the individual links, levers, strapping and fixings needed to hold all the engine components together
  - dressing the major castings so they were fit for purpose and drilling and fixing the items necessary on and to them
  - making and assembling the engine's vital components, such as the piston, chains, straps and fixings that bore all the stresses and strains of routine operations
  - cutting, bending, drilling and riveting the wrought iron boiler plates to the predetermined shape and working with the plumbers to assemble the boiler, incorporate the pipework and make it water and steam tight
- When the bob wall was of the required height, the beam could be installed on a trunnion constructed for the purpose. The beam would have been constructed from massive baulks of carefully seasoned oak reinforced with wrought iron straps and chains. The outdoor beam end would have been coated with tar or oil to protect it.
- Once the bob wall and beam were in place, the cylinder could be positioned precisely and secured. To have had it in place before the beam was installed would have both obstructed the working area and risked damaging the cylinder.
- After this the engine builder had more latitude on the work that followed, this included installing the piston and arch heads, completing the walls, roofing the house, installing the boiler and pipework etc. The final months were concentrated on making and fitting the smaller components, ensuring the main components were properly linked and the whole engine watertight before steam testing. The stage at which brasswork, specifically valves and regulators, were installed is not clear but would be expected to have been during this period.
- Testing the engine would have needed care, with initial movements controlled probably by ropes to ensure alignment and clearances were correct. Water testing would have preceded testing under steam, leakages at each of these stages needing attention from the requisite craftsmen.
- Finally there would have been a period of tuning the engine so that it stroked as required and this is likely to have been combined with training the engine men – a skilled and sensitive task given the relative costs of the engine and the effects of any breakages on draining the underground workings.

Challenges

There was no shortage of technical challenges for the early engine builders. They included:

- casting and boring the cylinders
- specifying and sourcing the ironwork
- making the moving parts
- organising the water channels
- securing the engine in its house
- making the boilers
- connecting the boiler and cylinder
- connecting the other components

These are discussed in the following sections.

Making the cylinders

Casting the cylinders

Of all the engine components, the cylinder was the one that attracted most attention, probably because of its massive weight and cost, and also the skills and infrastructure needed to make it.

Early cylinders were of brass. Their sources are not recorded but the Bristol area with its burgeoning brass industry is a likely one. However, by the 1730s this material had largely been replaced by cast iron. Whilst brass had the advantage of conducting heat well and is easy to work, the downside was that it was more expensive and less robust than cast iron. The processes for making brass and iron cylinders were similar to those used for making cannon, but the maximum bore of a cannon rarely exceeded 12 inches; the methods used for boring needed to be scaled up considerably for cylinder manufacture. Similarly, as average cylinder diameters increased, the hearth capacity and mould making capabilities of the iron foundries were also stretched.

Until the 1740s, the charcoal-fired blast furnaces of the Kentish Weald supplied some cast iron cylinders, presumably drawing heavily on their cannon-making capabilities,[14] and it is possible that other foundries were involved with this trade. However, the majority of cast iron cylinders from the late 1720s onwards appear to have been supplied by Abraham Darby's Coalbrookdale company, a situation which persisted until John Wilkinson's Bersham (and possibly Willey and Bradley) foundries and the Carron ironworks were able to produce more accurately bored and cheaper cylinders.

The cylinders were the largest and heaviest single castings produced in their day and I have a strong suspicion that it was the need for greater engine power and hence cylinder size that was the main driver for increasing hearth capacity (the maximum weight of iron that could be produced in a single firing). The rationale for this is that a cylinder has to be cast from a single run of molten iron and larger quantities require increases in capacity of both the furnace and the casting floor. In parallel with this, the capability to make larger capacity moulds that were sufficiently robust to contain such a large quantity of liquid metal was also important.

Boring the cylinders

Boring cylinders accurately in three dimensions was always a challenge, which was not resolved effectively until the introduction by the Carron Company of its new boring machinery in the 1760s. Early cylinders were bored in the same way as the tree trunks used for water pipes (Fig. 4) and their final finishing and smoothing was often done by hand and eye. Apparently one early method for smoothing involved pulling a lead ball back and forth inside the cylinder in which sand was sprinkled with the cylinder rolled over as required.

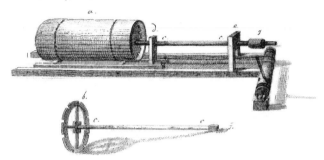

Fig. 4   Boring a cylinder at Coalbrookdale in the 1750s. (R.R. Angerstein, image courtesy of Peter Berg, reproduced with permission)

Specifying and sourcing the ironwork

Until the advent of Newcomen's engines, all large-scale machinery had been constructed in wood, including bearings, joints and connections. Careful examination of wind and water mills and the accounts of their builders make it clear that a variety of woods were used, each carefully selected on the basis of its characteristics for a specific function. So, for example, apple wood was normally used for the teeth of mill gears, oak for the main shaft, elm for the paddles and launders. The engine builders needed to use a similar approach to identify where cast and wrought iron engine components should be used. The loadings placed on the components of even the earlier, smaller engines would have exceeded the capabilities of the wood previously used, prompting the move to iron.

By the mid-nineteenth century, manufacturing and quality standards for wrought and cast iron had reached a high level of sophistication and consistency, which had not previously been the case. In the eighteenth century technical and quality standards for iron and the small amounts of steel produced appear to have been defined by the manufacturer: if you wanted something of consistent quality, you asked the maker to produce more of the same. There was a well established market for different grades of iron and steel and in the first half of the century Britain imported substantial amounts of high quality bar iron from Swedish charcoal iron forges, the organisation and quality control of which was highly sophisticated.[15] These supplies were supplemented later in the century by Russian iron as the demands of the UK exceeded the Swedish production capabilities. Charcoal-smelted bar iron had a high level of purity and therefore was ideally suited to the demands of the blacksmiths who forged the multiplicity of ferrous items needed to build an engine.

Records from 1751 for a 42" engine at Coalpit Heath[16] refer to both blister steel ('raw' cementation steel suitable for forging-up on site) and German steel (probably highly

Fig. 5   The cast iron piston assembly from the 54" engine Old Sarah (date unknown) which worked at J. & J. Charlesworth's Newmarket Silkstone Colliery near Wakefield until August 1917 and which was donated to the Science Museum by them. Note the central boss and webs and the retaining ring above the top lip of the piston used to compress and secure the piston seal.

Fig. 6   Old Sarah: the blacksmith-made components connecting piston rod and chains.

forged cementation steel from north-east England, but possibly genuine finery-process steel from Germany) being used and this was probably not an isolated occurrence. The applications of this steel are not described in the records, but are expected to have been where high tensile strength and the capability to withstand wear were important.

Because blacksmithing was a highly individualised craft, undertaken by widely distributed small-scale operators whose skills and knowledge were passed down by word of mouth and long apprenticeships, we are left to guess the details of their work on early engines.

Moving parts

In addition to requiring a number of large robust components, the mechanical arrangements of the new 'fire engines' required some new or adapted technology. Wind and water mills used similarly massive components, and the linkages between them were made by closely meshed cogs and gearing running for long periods in a single direction. The layout of the fire engine, however, needed to allow for the reversal of the engine's movements up to 12 times each minute, placing significant inertial loads on the connections between piston rod and indoor arch head and between outdoor arch head and pitwork. Perhaps the best way to understand these challenges is to examine the components making up these items.

Links between piston rod and indoor arch head

- The lower end of this assembly terminates in the piston, an iron casting with raised sides and a central boss into

Fig. 7   The indoor end of the beam of the 66" engine at South Liberty Colliery, Bedminster, Bristol, c. 1895, with the chains to the piston and the hot well pump. The winch (left foreground) is presumed to be for removing the piston for maintenance.

which one end of the piston rod was secured (Fig. 5). Examination of this feature on remaining engines indicates it was executed with a tapered cotter inserted through a hole in the lower part of the piston rod that corresponded with one in the boss cast into the piston. This linkage was not required to move other than for occasional adjustments and infrequent dismantling.

- The linkage at the top of the piston rod (Figs 6 and 11) presented different challenges. Whilst its predominant movement was vertical, the flexibility of the chains to which it was connected required some flexibility in horizontal directions. Illustrations of this linkage on early engines do not give a clear view of how it was executed and so we are left to examine this feature on later engines; these are described in the captions to above figures.

- The final stage between the top of the piston rod linkage and the indoor arch head was via chains which varied from single simple chains on smaller engines (as in Fig. 18) to multiple ones similar to bicycle chains on large engines (Figs 7 and 8). The links on these multiple chains were either cast or forged, the former probably being cheaper and the latter stronger. Individual links of both types appeared to wear at different rates and were replaced as required.

- The end of this chain was secured by one of a variety of methods to the upper extremity of the arch head and in alignment with it (Fig. 7).

Connection between pump rods and outdoor arch head

The links on the outdoor end of the beam were a little simpler but more heavily loaded as all the pitwork hung off the chains below the arch heads (Fig. 8). There was more latitude for movement here as the 'barrels' into which the pitwork descended were at minimum 30 feet below the arch head and so, as long as the chains were strong enough and linked effectively to the top section of the pitwork, the main risk was one of component breakage. The other linkage in this set was to the balance boxes or beams used to equalise the loading on either end of the beam.

Fig. 8   This photograph (taken at the same time as Fig. 7) of the outdoor end of the beam of the South Liberty engine shows how these massive items were constructed and the chains attached. The weight of the beam at around 10 tons made it too heavy for its proposed installation in the V&A Museum when it ceased work in 1900.

Other linkages and connections

In addition to the linkages to the beam, examination of other metal-to-metal linkages on the remaining Newcomen engines shows a surprising range of solutions, even though the earliest surviving engine, Fairbottom Bobs,[17] was built more than 50 years after the first engine. Figures 10, 12 and 13 show some of the approaches used.

Organising the water channels

Newcomen engines use a lot of water for their boilers and for condensing the steam in the cylinder and so the layout of the water pipes, channels and conduits needed considerable care.[18] The volumes of water needed for the condensing spray at each piston stroke were two to three times greater than that needed to maintain boiler water levels; whilst some waste condensate could be used for boiler feed the rest was surplus, needing disposal. So each engine needed a system of pipes or conduits for the following water feeds:

- a source of clean, cold water for the condensing spray and pipework to take it to the header tank at the top of the engine house

Fig. 9   The upper hot water conduit at the 1791 Serridge engine site. This image shows the size of the passage and the challenges of exploring and photographing it.

- a pipe from this header tank to the spray nozzle at the cylinder bottom
- a pipe for the waste condensate from the cylinder base to the hot well
- a pipe from the hot well for the boiler feed and an additional conduit to take the surplus off site, ideally into an adjacent drainage level (Fig. 9)
- a further pipe from the hot well to the cylinder top, which ensured there was always water above the piston to seal it and maintain the vacuum; this would be supplemented by a smaller drain pipe set into the cylinder lip to ensure that surplus water atop the piston did not overflow

Securing the engine in its house

A major challenge faced by the engine builders was how to fix the engine in its house and keep it stable. I believe the major issues were as follows.

- The 'bob wall' was the wall on which the beam pivoted on its trunnion. Because of the considerable weight of the beam (beams of 5 tons were common) and its continual movement this wall needed to be strong. This was normally achieved by making it thicker than the other walls. As a result, bob walls are often the only surviving masonry remains of early engine houses.
- Once the bob wall was built, the beam needed to be mounted on it. It is assumed that the practice of winching beams up in stages that was used for the Cornish engines was also used for these earlier engines.
- The massive beams that spanned the engine house and on which the cylinder was mounted (Fig. 21) would have needed careful preparation and location.

The engine house was an integral part of the structure of the engine and this led to its distinctive form (Figs 1 and 22).

It is worth recognising that the introduction of the external boiler and separate condenser meant that an engine could be built without a masonry engine house, using only a suitable bob wall, as with the Fairbottom Bobs engine. This arrangement dispensed with the walls and cylinder location beams, and must have been a lot cheaper to build.

Making the boilers

Precedents and challenges

The early boilers would have been difficult to make and maintain and the processes for both are poorly documented. Boilers were a relatively recent innovation in 1712; Savery's engine of 1700 had needed one but was the only direct precedent. Boilermaking appears to have developed from two earlier technologies: firstly the use of enclosed copper stills in the brewing industry and secondly the use of wrought iron pans for saltmaking. Copper and brass boilers would have been easier to make and conducted heat well but both materials were expensive and did not 'scale up' well, being weak when filled with large volumes of water. Wrought iron, whilst stronger and cheaper, was of inconsistent quality and not easily worked. In the longer term the advantages of wrought iron outweighed its drawbacks and by the end of the century the boilermaking industry had made good progress and was producing reliable products.

The use of wrought iron for boilers went through an intermediate stage involving the fitting of copper or lead tops to boilers until around the mid eighteenth century. The

Fig. 10   The hot well of the Pentrich engine showing the variety of fixing solutions employed by Francis Thompson. Note the square blacksmith-made nuts, the iron cross strap and the cast-angle bracket.

Fig. 11   The Pentrich piston, viewed from the cylinder top. This shows what appear to be three piston rods which are in fact the broken original central one and two additional ones on either side. It is not known what caused the breakage or how long it ran in this form but it exemplifies the ingenuity of the local engineers and the inherent tolerance of these simple machines.

Fig. 12   Control levers and their fixings and connections on the Pentrich engine were made by the blacksmiths, as is obvious from their slightly uneven shapes.

Fig. 13   Another view of the Pentrich engine again shows the range of items and fixings the blacksmiths were required to produce. Note the incorporation of weighting in the lever on the right.

reason for this combination is understood to be that contemporary ironworking skills were insufficiently developed for the range of shaped pipes and junctions needed for the connections with the top of the boiler and to make them steam tight. Hence copper and lead continued to be used for boiler tops and the numerous steam and water pipes and valves that fitted into the upper part of the boiler.

The rest of this section will examine the challenges presented by these early boilers.

Designing the boiler

During the eighteenth century the haystack (also known as haycock, circular, balloon or flange) boiler predominated, probably because the circular form was structurally the strongest and (apart from the flange) required no acute angles, which were difficult to make and prone to failure. Other shapes were tried but the circular boiler appears to have been the most common.

Once the basic haystack form was confirmed, the next challenge was to work out the capacity and grate size needed to produce the steam output required for the engine. This calculation can be summarised as follows.

i.   The weight of water x to be lifted to height y, multiplied by the number of working hours in the day, establishes the work needed from the engine (expressed in number of strokes per period).

ii.   The work needed can be converted into the volume of steam to be condensed which, when multiplied by the stroke rate, establishes the steam output required from the boiler over a specified period of time.

The calculation can be performed easily nowadays, but in the early eighteenth century it was unknown and very much a matter of trial and error. The obvious temptation was to build in some contingency and make boilers bigger than they needed to be; however, this increased costs and structural weakness. Even more fundamentally, while boilers were housed inside the engine house the dimensions of the latter placed an obvious constraint on boiler size.

Making the boiler plates

I have not been able to locate any information on the manufacturing process for copper and brass boilers and I assume they were made either from rolled plate or by the battery-ware method used for brass pots. Whilst the malleability of brass and copper made plates of this material relatively easy to produce, shape and fit, the same could not be said of wrought iron.

Iron is an unusual material in that its cast and wrought forms have different responses to tension, compression and heat. Cast iron could not be used for boilers because of its inability to cope with sudden temperature changes, leaving wrought iron as the only option. The characteristics of wrought iron were normally determined by the skills of the smith, a factor that did not easily lend itself to large-scale production of boiler plates. As a result, the quality of wrought iron plate varied greatly and the life of early boilers was severely limited by this and other factors.

As the century progressed it appears that specialist boiler plate makers emerged who were able to make plate consistently to the standards required. The process for producing boiler plate is unclear but would most likely have involved finishing with a trip or plating hammer (Fig. 16). The amount

of work that went into making boiler plates was reflected in their high cost, which was only slightly less than that of bored castings (both were sold by weight). The identities of the companies active in the boiler plate trade are unclear but it is known that John Willetts of Wednesbury[19] (one of the precursors of Spear and Jackson) was an important supplier of such plates, as was George Wilding of Framilode in Gloucestershire.[20]

Constructing the boiler

Boiler construction required considerable metalworking skill. Whilst the manufacture of copper and brass boilers cannot have been easy, the challenges of cutting bending and drilling tough wrought iron plate, up to half an inch thick, would have been greater still. Because I have not been able to find any accounts of the work entailed, most of what follows is conjecture. Further information would be most welcome.

It is probably easiest to visualise the boilermaking process by examining the drawing (Fig. 14) of a boiler produced for Isaac White's Nailsea Coal Company in 1836 by Rogers and Co. of Bristol. Although produced a century later than the early boilers, the basic shape and components would not have changed significantly. To understand the boilermakers' challenges we need to recognise that this 12 foot diameter boiler had 142 component plates of three different thicknesses.

The construction process was probably phased as follows:

a. Firstly it was necessary to convert the design into a series of templates for the various parts and then make up a framework against which to locate the plates of the boiler as they were made, possibly using a wooden framework in the form of the boiler.

b. Once plate sizes were known, with appropriate allowance for flange overlap, it would have been necessary to mark them up on the flat wrought iron sheet, probably using a paper template similar to a dressmaking pattern.

c. It would then have been necessary to cut the plates to shape and, whilst heavy duty shears may have been used for this in the nineteenth century, my guess is that for much of the preceding century this would have been done by punching or drilling lines of holes close together and filing through the remaining metal.

d. Cutting work could have been done with the plates flat on a suitable floor but this was not possible for the next stage, which brought the challenge of shaping them into three dimensions (probably by forging on a curved anvil, see Fig. 16). Handling these hot, bulky and heavy items throughout the process was probably done by a combination of hand work and crane.

e. At this stage I would expect each plate to have been offered up to its predecessor *in situ*, and again I suggest that a wooden framework would have been built to enable this. The boiler base plate or flange may have been the first item produced and positioned to provide a solid base for the work of building the boiler.

f. Once the plates had been offered up, found to be the right shape and size and lined up with their neighbours, I suggest the next step would have been to mark the locations of the rivet holes and then punch or drill them. I presume the preceding plate would already have had its holes formed, otherwise there would have been no reference point for locating its neighbour. I believe that the plates would have been heated again to facilitate drilling or punching, with the risk that their shape might change.

g. The result of these labours would have been a haystack-shaped boiler shell (Fig. 15) to which (until around 1750), it would have been necessary to fix a carefully made copper or lead top. Until all the boiler plates had been made and satisfactorily offered into position, I believe they would have been held together by wooden pegs or fixings through the rivet holes.

h. The process of riveting the boiler plates together would have been a challenging one, probably requiring simultaneous hammer blows by men working both inside and outside the boiler (Fig. 16).

i. Whilst I suspect that the joints between the plates of these early boilers would have been caulked, I do not

know whether any additional sealant was used here. Combinations of oakum, sacking, rope and cow dung are believed to have been used to seal some of the gaps that developed during the use of the boilers and it is understandable that chroniclers of the period were not drawn to document this process.

j. Once the boiler was complete, I suggest it would have been moved into its final position and (until external boilers were in general use) this may have been via a suitably sized hole left in the engine house wall (Fig. 22). To minimise damage, I imagine the lead boiler top would have been installed and sealed with solder once the rest of the boiler was *in situ*. It is also possible that the boiler may have been built up inside the house, but this would have required some working space, a luxury that was not normally available.

k. Once the boiler was *in situ*, the supporting masonry around the boiler would have been built, incorporating

Fig. 14   A drawing from the order book of Messrs. Rogers and Co., Boilermaker of Moorfields, Bristol, showing a typical 12' diameter haystack boiler for Messrs. White of the Nailsea Coal Company in 1836. (Image courtesy Robin Stiles)

Fig. 15   Haystack boiler from J. & J. Charlesworth's Rothwell Haigh Colliery near Wakefield. In the 1920s Henry Ford commissioned Herbert F. Morton, one of his Manchester-based employees, to purchase selected UK examples of early engineering machines. This boiler exhibit in the main hall of Ford's Dearborn museum, Detroit, is one such item.

Fig. 16   Forging by tilt hammer. A plating hammer would have been similar. (Denis Diderot, eighteenth century)

Fig. 17   Part of a heavily corroded (presumed) boiler flange showing small, closely spaced rivets, presumably used in the interests of structural strength. This was discovered during detailed investigations by the Shropshire Caving and Mining Club at the site of what is thought to be a Heslop compound engine at Pitchcroft, where a number of ferrous items have been uncovered.

the spiral flue around its sides to maximise the heating surface. This masonry served to reinforce and insulate the boiler as well as providing an extra heating surface.

l. The last task was to incorporate and connect all the pipework and then test the boiler, firstly with water and secondly by firing and steaming it.

Connecting the boiler and cylinder

Because the design of the atmospheric engine placed the boiler directly below the cylinder, it was not possible to mount the cylinder onto a stable masonry base. Instead it was fixed between a pair of large timber beams that ran across the engine house, with their ends set into the walls. Given that even a small cylinder weighed in excess of a ton and taking into account the regular movement of piston and beam, this arrangement was not particularly rigid. Recognising also that cylinder and boiler were connected by a lead pipe, a material of low structural strength and limited ability to withstand constant movement, this joint would have required constant attention and regular repair.

There is little information available regarding the arrangement for securing the cylinder to the beams and it is generally shown on contemporary drawings as a set of straps, presumably of wrought iron. The cylinder of the replica 1712 engine at the Black Country Living Museum (BCLM) has a pair of cast lugs that support the cylinder on the beams (Fig. 21) but it is uncertain that this refinement was within the founders' capabilities during the first half of the eighteenth century. This arrangement of mounting the cylinder continued until the boiler was moved outside the engine house, which enabled the cylinder to be mounted directly onto a masonry base.

Operating the engine

Stoking the replica 1712 engine at the BCLM has given the author a small insight into some of the issues involved with operating and maintaining these engines.

- Firing the boiler needs to anticipate the steaming demands of the engine: the fire needs building up when working hard and damping down when idle.
- The valves need setting by hand to ensure the engine is 'stroking' properly before transitioning to automatic operation (Fig. 20).
- The water feed into the cylinder top needs to be balanced to ensure that the piston is always covered but not so deeply as to deposit excess water over the cylinder top at each stroke.

More fundamentally, the engine men also needed to guard against the following more serious issues:

- ensuring the engine did not 'over stroke' and allow the piston to descend too far into the cylinder with the risk of serious damage to both – the reason why spring beams were incorporated into most engine houses
- ensuring that the pitwork did not break, leading to the same damage as overstroking
- making certain the water level was maintained so that the boiler did not run dry

It is understandable that engine men were carefully selected for their role, considering the value of the machine for which they were responsible and the consequence of its failure.

Maintaining the engine

Day to day maintenance

As may be imagined, running repairs on the early engines were often necessary and it would appear that solder was used extensively to repair and seal holes in lead pipes but, because of its low melting point could not be used near to the fire. Maintaining a good level of vacuum was also important: whilst air leakages into the cylinder were prevented by the piston seal, the water injection nozzle and condensate drains also needed to be properly sealed. The difficulty with air leakages is that they are not always easy to spot and require regular checks. The piston needed to be easily removable from the cylinder for repacking and inspection.

In addition to driving the engine, the engine man would probably have been responsible for minor maintenance tasks such as:

- attending to small leaks and blockages in the feed to the injection nozzle in the cylinder, which would have affected the engine's performance out of all proportion to their size
- adjustments to valve gear
- repairs to pipework
- lifting the piston for repacking the seal (Fig. 19)
- cleaning and adjusting the water injection valve

Maintaining, repairing and replacing the boiler

Boilermaking was a new skill for which there was little precedent, the early boilermakers having little to guide them as to optimum shapes, sizes and fire settings. In the same way there was little guidance for the subsequent maintenance of the boilers.

Whilst small water leakages in the boiler shell could be tolerated, larger ones needed attention and in many cases this would have required that the boiler be drained and the engine taken out of service for the duration. The materials used for sealing such leaks are likely to have included fibre, putty and possibly wood; apparently horse and cow dung make a good sealant too.

Early boilers appear to have failed frequently and the main reasons are thought to have been poor quality plates, bad maintenance, irregular heating and acidic water. Boiler failure would disable an engine and is understood to have been the main reason for introducing external boilers for back up purposes which, by definition, were located outside the house.

Whatever the reason for the failure, the boiler would have needed to be either repaired or replaced, either of which would have required that:

- the engine cease work (if this was for a protracted period the workings were at risk of being flooded, which would have been expensive because of lack of sales revenue and the need to repair the water damaged workings)
- the masonry surrounding the boiler be removed to give access to the area requiring repair which, if done *in situ*, would require that the damaged plates be carefully removed, possibly by drilling out the rivets

When replacement of the boiler was necessary, in the Bristol Coalfield at least, there seems to have been a practice of constructing large arches in the lowest storey of the engine house to facilitate this (Fig. 22). How this was addressed elsewhere is not known; it might have been by removing and replacing the appropriate masonry.

Fig. 18   The indoor arch head of the replica 1712 Newcomen engine at the Black Country Living Museum shows the effect of progressive warping in the main beam. Up to a point, movements like this can be tolerated because of the inherent flexibility of the design.

Fig. 19   The piston assembly during its removal from the BCLM replica engine. The removal took around five minutes with two men and simple lifting tackle.

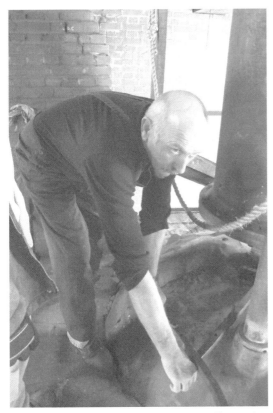

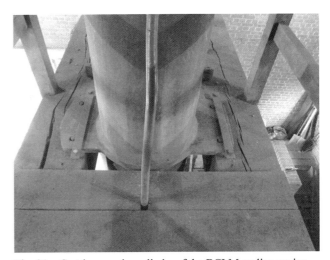

Fig. 21   Cast lugs on the cylinder of the BCLM replica engine and the straps used to secure it in position. It is likely that the early engines used similar arrangements.

Fig. 20   The steam inlet valve on the BCLM replica engine. This is lever operated and is worked manually for starting. Once the engine is stroking properly it can be changed to automatic action by a quick and simple connection to the plug rod and jack head pump. In this image the steam inlet lever is in Phil Pitt's right hand and his left hand is in the process of connecting it to the jack head pump.

Fig. 22   An engine house (converted to a dwelling) at Trooper's Hill, Bristol, showing the arch in the basement wall thought to have been used for boiler repair and replacement. No details of the engine are known. (Samuel Loxton, c. 1905)

Other maintenance and repairs
Significant warping of the beam (as can be seen in Fig. 18) would have required its realignment with cylinder and pit-work to keep the whole mechanism 'true'.

Conclusions
Recognising that much in the preceding sections is conjecture, in the ninety years between Calley and Curr the main developments in Newcomen engine building can be summarised as follows.

- Tentative experimentation with both engines and materials by a handful of bold engineers evolving to a point where both knowledge and materials for the construction and operation of Newcomen engines were freely available. It is instructive to recognise that despite the atmospheric engine being supplanted from the 1770s by Watt's invention, they continued to be constructed until at least 1823, with the last one at Elsecar passing out of service only 25 years before the last Cornish engine.
- Within this overall transition was a series of supporting and enabling developments, including better understanding of the properties of ferrous materials, the start of the demise of the blacksmith and the emergence of early machine tools, as well as more abstract but equally important developments such as measurement standards.
- Whilst it was in the Victorian period that the enablers of mass production emerged, their origins can be detected in the period in question: Curr's work in detailing material specifications would have been of no value if the items he described were not available on the open market.
- By 1800 the professional engineer was starting to be recognised; ninety years previously there had been no such recognition. Whilst some of this new status may have been driven by personal publicity initiatives, there is no doubt that most of it was due to public recognition of engineers' contributions to what would later be known as the Industrial Revolution.

For reasons given in this paper, there is a dearth of material describing how engine building skills evolved. Further field and desk research is needed to address what I believe to be an important area of research.

Acknowledgements
My sincere thanks go to everyone who has shared their knowledge of Newcomen related matters with me over the years, especially the South Gloucestershire Mines Research Group team working on the Serridge engine and Richard Lamb and Mike Potts for their diligent work on early engines. John Barnatt and Peak District Mines Historical Society colleagues have been endlessly helpful in sharing archaeological findings and theories on early engine sites. I am also grateful to Rick Stewart and James Greener for their inputs concerning early Cornish engines and David Cranstone and Peter King for their patient efforts in educating me on matters metallurgical.

Photographs of the replica Newcomen engine at the Black Country Living Museum and of the Pentrich and Old Sarah engines at the London Science Museum were taken with the permission of the respective institutions.

Notes
1   L.T.C. Rolt & J.S. Allen, *The Steam Engine of Thomas Newcomen* (Landmark Publishing, 1997).
2   *Ibid.* – numerous entries.
3   John Curr, *The Coal Viewer and Engine Builder's Practical Companion* (1797; reprinted Augustus M. Kelly, 1970).
4   A.W.A. White, 'Early Newcomen engines on the Warwickshire Coalfield 1714–1736', *Transactions of the Newcomen Society* XLI (1968–69), pp. 203–216.
5   J.S. Allen, 'The 1715 and other Newcomen engines at Whitehaven, Cumberland', *Transactions of the Newcomen Society* XLV (1972), pp. 223–226.
6   Steve Grudgings, 'John Wise – unrecognised engine builder and contemporary of Newcomen and Watt', *International Journal for the History of Engineering and Technology* vol. 82 no. 2 (2012), pp. 176–186.
7   Rolt & Allen, *The Steam Engine of Thomas Newcomen, op. cit.*, p. 107.
8   Steve Grudgings, *Jarrit Smith's 1751 Newcomen Engine* (South Gloucestershire Mines Research Group, 2012), pp. 52–53.
9   Victoria Owens, *James Brindley's Notebooks* (The Choir Press, 2013).
10   Rolt & Allen, *The Steam Engine of Thomas Newcomen, op. cit.*, – numerous entries.
11   David K. Hulse, *Two Engineers: Francis Thompson & Richard Trevithick* (TEE Publishing Ltd., 2008).
12   The Pentrich estate of the Duke of Devonshire appears to have funded the construction, movement and reconstruction of a number of different Newcomen engines in the 1816–1840 period as part of their planned infrastructure costs prior to the leasing of the respective mines to teams of miners (Cliff Williams, pers. comm., based on his extensive researches of the duke's archives).
13   James Greener is in the process of finalising a number of papers describing all that is known of Newcomen's pre-1712 Cornish engines.
14   The contribution of the Kentish foundries to Newcomen cylinder production does not appear to be widely recognised. The following three foundries (there may have been others) are recorded as having produced cylinders:
     William Bowen supplied a 28" iron cylinder to the Chelsea Waterworks Company in 1742 and had

supplied pipes in 1731 for an engine in Flintshire (see Grudgings, 'John Wise', *op. cit.*);

William Jukes or Jewkes is reported to have had a 32" cylinder at hand in 1746 when approached by the Chelsea Waterworks Company;

William Harrison supplied at least three large cylinders (1 x 38" and 2 x 42") to James Lowther for his Whitehaven collieries in the late 1730s (Peter King, pers. comm.).

15 C. Evans & G. Rydén, *Baltic Iron in the Atlantic World in the Eighteenth Century* (Brill, 2007).

16 Grudgings, *Jarrit Smith's 1751 Newcomen Engine, op. cit.*

17 The Fairbottom Bobs engine was used for drainage at Park Bridge Colliery near Bardsley, Ashton-under-Lyne. It is now preserved at the Henry Ford museum, Dearborn, Detroit.

18 Since 2005, SGMRG have undertaken protracted excavations and conservation of features at the site of the 1791 Newcomen engine at Serridge in South Gloucestershire. Although there are minimal surface remains, the largely undisturbed subsurface contains over 100 yards of carefully constructed small and large passages, many of which appear to have served as hot and cold water drainage and recycling systems for water from the engine. Similar arrangements are assumed to have existed on other Newcomen engine sites but do not appear to have been reported.

19 Paul Belford, 'Five centuries of iron working: excavations at Wednesbury Forge', *Post Medieval Archaeology* 44/1 (2010), pp. 1–53.

20 Amina Chatwin, 'Some Gloucestershire ironmasters', *Journal of the Historical Metallurgy Society* vol. 31 no. 1 (1998), p. 21.

Technological Innovation and Adaption: Tyndrum Lead Mine and the German Managers, 1838 to 1865

Catherine Mills

Abstract: In 1838 the second Marquis of Breadalbane, having failed to lease the mineral rights at Tyndrum lead mine on the Campbell family estate in the southern Scottish highlands, made a decision to work the mine himself. When he began his operation, the mine was nearing exhaustion and what little productivity remained was hindered by increasingly complex mineralisation. The Marquis, however, was convinced that the mine could still produce great wealth; he looked to Germany for expertise and employed a succession of German mining engineers to manage his ailing operation. The survival of their monthly progress reports and other documentation offers a unique perspective on the Scottish lead mining industry and the adaptive strategies, in terms of technological innovation and mining practices, that the Germans employed to prolong the venture's economic survival.

Introduction

It was Jacob Schmookler who first drew attention to the distinction between an invention and a sub invention when exploring the process of technological change. Sub invention, he argued, was an 'obvious change in a product or process' resulting from the application of engineering knowledge and/or acts of skill, and this included the notion of 'routine innovation', previously described by Merrill as a modification that a 'skilled practitioner' would be expected to make in a product or process to adapt it to suit minor changes (Schmookler 1966, 6). Burt described these processes in the early 1990s, specifically in relation to non-ferrous mining, as the 'straightforward application of engineering knowledge and or acts of skill by the workforce', and he used the idea, in part, to challenge the traditional view that the Germans established world leadership in the mining and metallurgical arts and subsequently brought their knowledge to Britain (Burt 1991, 251–254).

Rather than engaging with the question of who pioneered British non-ferrous metal mining (the focus on German engineers in this instance is purely coincidental), this study examines the process of sub invention or routine innovation as a strategy for economic survival at Tyndrum lead mine in the mid nineteenth century. Whilst the application of key inventions to rock removal, blasting, haulage and pumping ushered in the era of deep mining, it was often small adjustments and modifications to existing equipment and infrastructure that enabled mining companies to gain further economies in extraction. The fickle nature of lead ore deposits and a volatile mining market created a dynamic industry responsive to change and well versed in technological adaptions to either produce more for less money, or work associated minerals that could be raised and marketed at a profit. The story of Tyndrum is not a new one, but the abundance of surviving documentary evidence opens a wider window onto both the process of adaptive strategies and sub invention at a mining operation nearing the end of financially viable extraction and processing; and it captures the futility of economic resilience in working a finite resource.

Although Scotland was not a major contributor to the total national output, lead ore was mined in the majority of the Scottish shires (Wilson 1921, 2); yet research on the industry located north of the border compared to that in England and Wales has been sparse. Burt, in his study of the British lead mining industry, only makes fleeting references to Scotland (Burt 1984). Smout offers a single but detailed chapter on the economic context, and Harvey has explored aspects of the social history of the ventures at Leadhills and Wanlockhead in the Southern Uplands (Smout 1967, 103–135; Harvey 1972, 1991, 1994a, 1994b, 1999). Callender and Macaulay have focused on the metal mines of Islay (Callender & Macaulay 1984). More recently Callender, together with Reeson, has examined the Scottish gold rush at Kildonan in the 1860s, largely from an archaeological perspective (Callender & Reeson 2007). There are also several short studies on the mines of the Ochils, Tomnadashan on south Loch Tayside, and Galloway (Bainbridge 1980; Dickie & Forster 1974; Devéria 2001; Cressey *et al.* 2004; Moreton 2008). The mine site at Tyndrum has primarily attracted the interest of environmental and geo-scientists (MacKenzie & Pulford 2002; Farmer *et al.* 1997). More recently Mills, Simpson and Adderley have attempted to link current pollution levels at the site to historic mining practices (Mills *et al.* 2014). This study expands both the burgeoning Scottish narrative and the specific history of mining at Tyndrum from a technological perspective.

Tyndrum lead mine and the second Marquis of Breadalbane

The mine is located in the Loch Lomond and Trossachs National Park at the western fringes of Tyndrum (see Fig. 1), in the north-west of the historic Campbell family estate of Breadalbane in the southern Scottish highlands. It is situated south of the A82 Glasgow to Fort William road on the northern flanks of Sròn nan Colan, commonly known as Minehill. The mine was one of Scotland's largest producers of ore after Leadhills (Smout), and has a two hundred year documented history of intermittent operation (see Table 1). The lease of the mineral rights in the early eighteenth century was part of wider commercialisation of the estate following the Act of Union in 1707 (MacInnes 1998, 177–201,

Table 1   Timeline: Tyndrum mine

Year	Lease holder	Production annual average (tons)
1730	Sir Robert Clifton	424
1745	English Company of Mine Adventurers	136
1760	Rippon Company	165
1762	Paton and Richardson	157
1768	Scots Mining Company	153
1791	abandonment	0
1838	second Marquis of Breadalbane	25
1865	abandonment	0
	Tyndrum Mining Company	0
1916	Tyndrum Lead and Zinc Company	27.5
1928	abandonment	0

191). Although there is some indication that the lead had been worked in the vicinity of Tyndrum in the fifteenth century (OSA 1791–99, Parish of Glenurchy and Inishail, 35), it is Sir Robert Clifton who is credited with the discovery of the ore in 1735.

In the eighteenth and nineteenth centuries the remote and isolated location of the mine (Fig. 1) hindered the transportation of both lead (ore and bar) to market and coal (for fuel)

Fig. 1   Tyndrum location

and materials into the site. The route involved carriage by packhorse to the head of Loch Lomond, a distance of around 18 kilometres, and then by boat to the river Clyde. Not only was this expensive, but in the late 1830s it took five weeks from purchase to get material delivered from Glasgow (NRS, GD112/18/8/7/14). The final company to work the mineral lease, the Tyndrum Lead and Zinc Company (see Table 1), was the only venture to be able to take advantage of the Callender to Oban Railway for transportation, which reached Tyndrum in 1873, but by then the quality and quantity of the ore had dwindled and the company primarily re-worked the dumps. As a consequence the mine was heavily reliant on water power and the vagaries of the weather for most of its history. The water supply was either frozen in winter or in flood or dry during the remaining months. This, coupled with miners' need to cut peat for fuel, both for the mine and domestic use, together with hay for winter fodder, produced a marked seasonal pattern of working. The site of the mine also posed difficulties (Fig. 2). It was at high altitude, the entrance to the upper workings being at 500 metres above sea level, and Minehill was steep sided, averaging an incline of around 1 in 4. Mine labour was housed in cottages on the western fringe of the village of Tyndrum. These were built in the 1730s under the terms of Clifton's original lease. The miners were largely inexperienced and recruited locally from within the Breadalbane estate.

This study focuses on the period 1838 to 1865 when the landowner, John Campbell, the second Marquis of Breadalbane, essentially worked his own mineral lease primarily under the management of German engineers. The Marquis took an interest in science and technology and was a keen amateur geologist (Easson 2011, 63). He frequently roamed the hills between Taymouth Castle and Tyndrum in the company of his dogs, searching for minerals with a leather bag and a geologist's hammer (Gillies 1980, 212). His personal collection of minerals was exhibited at Crystal Palace in 1851. The Marquis also believed somewhat erroneously that the estate would produce great mineral wealth (Robertson 1992, 189–217, 192). Aside from Tyndrum mine, mineral deposits had been located at Lochearnhead and immediately south of Loch Tay at Corrie Buie, Ardtalnaig, and Tomnadashan, which was worked for copper pyrites. There were sufficient small-scale discoveries throughout the adult life of the Marquis to reinforce his belief that the Breadalbane estate would eventually yield rich deposits; examples of such discoveries were a small nugget of gold at Lochearnhead in 1855 and the small silver yield at Tyndrum (NRS, GD112/18/8/16/1; also see Table 2 below).

In spite of a nationwide advertising campaign in the early nineteenth century the Marquis failed to attract any interest in the mineral rights to the estate (NRS, GD112/18/9/8/33), and in 1838 he decided to work the lease himself. The Marquis employed George Baron to manage what was essentially an ailing venture at Tyndrum. Baron had previously worked at the Strontian lead mines and brought with him experienced miners (NRS, GD112/18/8/7/2).

The landowner employing a salaried manager, with varying degrees of autonomy, appears typical of the Scottish metal mining sector. For example, John Erskine primarily directed his silver mining venture at Alva, in Clackmannanshire, leaving his wife Catherine in charge

Fig. 2   Tyndrum mine today: the upper workings of Tyndrum showing the open cut and the remains of two dressing shelters constructed during Clifton's original lease (to left of centre)

of operations whilst he was raising guns and gold for the Jacobite cause and later in exile (Moreton 2008). In the case of Tyndrum, the Marquis vigorously directed his managers, either himself – when he was resident at Taymouth Castle at Kenmore, some 57 kilometres from Tyndrum – or via his factor, John Wyllie, whilst he was resident in London.

The Marquis demanded a detailed monthly account of his managers' activities, and in turn they requested weekly reports from the overseers, who primarily managed the Marquis' peripheral ventures. These reports together with correspondence and other documentation, such as the factor's business notes and records of the miners' bargains, have all survived and are archived at the National Records of Scotland in Edinburgh (NRS, Breadalbane Muniments, GS112/). Unfortunately the archive contains few copy letters from the Marquis and, whilst the mine managers recorded expenses, full financial details are sporadic. Nonetheless the surviving documentation, together with substantial archaeological surface remains at the site, opens a window onto Scottish metal mining history, the daily operation of the mine, social conditions, labour relations and, specifically in relation to this study, mining practice and technology.

Whilst the Marquis employed the German mining engineers specifically for their expertise, he would only heed their advice if it suited him. For example, he would often send the same mineral sample for assay several times until he got the results he wanted and between 1837 and 1856

he spent £42,457 primarily on the assaying of minerals from his estate, trials, independent surveys and continued exploratory work at Tyndrum (NRS, GD112/18/1/8/4). He eventually had a laboratory installed at Taymouth Castle to assay minerals himself (NRS, GD112/18/9/5/7). The Marquis would also interfere, either directly or via John Wyllie, with the management of the workforce. For example, Wyllie determined which tenants were employed at the mine, and the Marquis himself cut the pay of miner John Forbes for requesting a pay rise (NRS, GD112/18/9/8/37–8). The records suggest that the Marquis was not an easy man to work for.

Aside from the innate difficulties of a remote location, when the Marquis began his operation, the workings at Tyndrum had been abandoned for over thirty years and the mine was nearing exhaustion. The increasing complexity of the mineralisation made it difficult to extract the lead ore from the country rock and associated gangue ores. In particular zinc, galena and blende occurred in equal proportions, and occurred as small single crystals dispersed in quartz (Wilson 1921, 95). In addition, as Odernheimer, the first German to arrive at Tyndrum, described, the quartz was 'too hard and the ore too soft' to separate efficiently (NRS, GD112//18/8/7/25). The Scots Mining Company had astutely pulled out at the end of the eighteenth century when their lease had expired.

The Marquis began his venture by replacing the surface infrastructure at Tyndrum without first having proven the ground. He had a water powered crushing mill with adjacent sheds for bruising and washing the ore constructed at Glengarry some 1.5 kilometres east of the mine site, together with a stone lined leat to supply water from the Crom Allt, taken from just east of the mine site. He also had a new waggon way laid from the base of Minehill to Glengarry linked to the main levels at the mine site via an inclined plane (NRS, GD112/18/8/7/1). There were no arrangements for primary separation of the lead ore from waste rock or gangue metals at the mine. If the rock was of mixed mineral content it was either dumped *in situ* at the surface of the mine or carried by the waggon way to Glengarry. Plans were also drawn up to erect a smelter adjacent to the crusher. Baron certainly implied that the walls were subsequently constructed by stating that the roof would be prepared as soon as the chimney was built (NRS, GD112/18/8/7/2). In the interim ore was sent for smelting to Alloa in Clackmannanshire and also to north Wales, but primarily to Glasgow (NRS, GD112/18/8/1/6 and 10). Previously both Clifton and the Scots Mining Company had dressed their ore on Minehill and smelted around 3 kilometres downstream from the mine at the confluence of the Crom Allt and the river Cononish at Dalrigh (see Fig. 3). The ambition of the Marquis' plans is indicated by the proposals to construct a canal linking the Clyde with the southern end

of Loch Lomond and the northern end with Loch Tay, providing a through route to Kenmore at an estimated cost of between £40,000 and £50,000. The ore from Tyndrum was cited as a key source of revenue (Lindsay 1968, 183–184). Only a short section (around half a kilometre) of the canal at the northern end of Loch Lomond was built, with turning space and landing stage.

How much Baron was responsible for suggesting the introduction of the improvements at the mine is not clear from the record; neither is the total sum of the initial outlay. Robertson has estimated that just under £8,000 was spent between 1838 and 1839 (Robertson 1992, 192). This investment is significant to the story of the venture as it set the scene for the next twenty years. The Marquis placed an ever increasing emphasis on recouping the investment.

Four levels, Long, McDougall's, Bryan's and New, were allegedly being worked (NRS, GD112/18/8/7) out of a total of nine, and in January 1839 Baron assured the Marquis 'that considerable profit will arise from the mining operations of the past year' (NRS, GD112/18/8/7/3). Baron did not wait to find out. He suddenly decided to leave and take his family out of the country. Whether or not Baron foresaw the financial difficulties is not made clear in the record. There was no compensating income recorded at the mine during his period of management (Robertson 1992, 192).

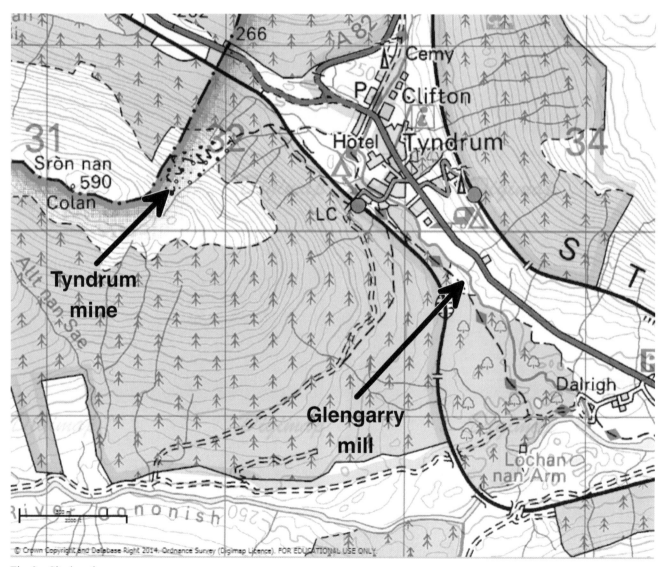

Fig. 3 Site locations

There had, however, also been problems with the Strontian miners over their bargains, which is also revealing. The men wanted payment by the fathom and not 'under any consideration' by the quality of the ore. These were experienced miners who would have had some knowledge of the viability of the operation; they were clearly not willing to share the risk (NRS, GD112/18/8/7/2).

Baron's son Edward, who was currently engaged at Leadhills, offered his services to the Marquis upon his father's departure, but he was perceived as too young to take on the responsibility of managing the operation (NRS, GD112/18/8/7/3). It is at this point in the history of Tyndrum that the German engineers, Odernheimer, Reichendorf and Thost, entered the picture.

German management at Tyndrum

Odernheimer, the first German engineer, arrived at Tyndrum shortly after Baron's departure early in 1839 and remained until 1841. Odernheimer was accompanied by a colleague named Horstmann and a 'practical miner' known as Laubach who would teach the Tyndrum men mining skills (NRS, GD112/18/8/7/10). Neither professional nor personal details are recorded for any of the three men. For example, Odernheimer's qualifications, his experience and how he was recruited are not known; neither are first names recorded. Odernheimer's salary perhaps gives an indication of his expertise. He was paid £200 in the first year; this was increased to £250 in the second year, and from year three he would receive a percentage of all profits (Bainbridge 1980, 40).

Stephen Reichendorf replaced Odernheimer in 1847. Reichendorf had studied at the University of Heidelberg, had a background in both metal and coal mining and had previously worked in Austria, India and eastern Europe. He had met the Marquis in Paris and was persuaded to take up the position at Tyndrum by the Marquis' enthusiasm for the mine's alleged mineral potential and his promises that Tyndrum was 'a very cheap place to live' (NRS, GD112/18/9/5/25). Reichendorf's stay in Scotland was short; he left for Valencia after three months.

Gustav Thost followed some two years later in 1849 and he remained until around 1859. Thost was a colleague of Odernheimer, had studied in his home town of Freiburg and had previous experience both in Saxony and Spain. He was essentially a fugitive from his homeland, having 'taken the side of the Constitution of the Parliament of Frankfurt' during the constitutional revolutions in Europe in 1848–49 (NRS, GD112/18/9/7/14). Shortly after his arrival in Scotland his property in Freiburg was confiscated and he elicited the support of Campbell in ensuring his family's safe passage to Scotland (NRS, GD112/18/8/10/8).

The Germans found highland Scotland and conditions at the mine very different from their homelands, and there are many statements that 'it is not the German way'. These appear to refer to three key elements: good diet and housing and strict discipline to maximise labour efficiency. Odernheimer described his style of management in relation to the workforce as 'an almost religious point', 'to take care of the workmen', 'to be kind to them', 'it's worthwhile', he claimed, 'they return plentifully' (NRS, GD112/18/8/7/9).

Reichendorf in particular could not bear the solitude, the weather, the conditions and what he perceived as undue interference from the Marquis' factor. He resided at the Tyndrum Inn, where he described the walls as black with wet; at one point he asked for Mr Wyllie to be removed from his post (NRS, GD112/18/9/5/1–25). Reichendorf struggled with poor industrial relations and the lack of capital investment. All three managers found the pressure exerted by the Marquis to produce and process ore at minimum costs frustrating.

The Marquis wanted a return on his initial investment and as long as production remained at a low level he was reluctant to invest any further capital, yet at the same time he was keen to keep the mine working in the hope of an eventual bonanza. All Tyndrum's mine managers were caught between a rock and a hard place and their working lives became increasingly difficult as time progressed and production continued to dwindle. Odernheimer's, Reichendorf's and Thost's responses to the Marquis' demands were two-fold: increase labour efficiency and adapt and modify existing technology to increase production. Whilst this study touches upon the management of the labour force, particularly in relation to Thost's administration, the following sections concentrate on the key technological responses, particularly at the surface of the mine; this is followed by discussion of how successful the modifications and adaptions were in terms of the economic survival of the mine.

Adaptive strategies
Odernheimer
When Odernheimer first arrived at the mine he commented that the 'last year of work', under Baron's management, 'was only to clear out old levels' and there had been little productive work. There were problems with water beneath Long Level and the 'biggest part of the vein was already worked out leaving the remaining ore in long strings of no great length or depth'. He suggested that continued work 'in all levels was worthwhile' but a 'good mining operation would not be founded on the borders of the old working'; he began trials north of the mine (NRS, GD112/18/8/7/9). Although details of its commencement are not recorded, a new level named after the 'practical miner' Laubach appears on plans drawn up in 1860 (BGS, 16592, 1860).

Odernheimer emphasised the 'disorder' at the mine which, he noted, 'could not be rectified overnight' (NRS, GD112/18/8/7/14). He damned the earlier investment in the crusher at Glengarry as 'fool hardy and premature' and despite the high cost of transporting the ore to Glasgow for smelting – estimated at 19% of the annual cost of running the entire operation in 1840 – he brought a halt to the plans for a smelter (NRS, GD112/18/9/2/3). This suggests that Baron perhaps made a wise decision in quitting his position.

By June Odernheimer was already under pressure, commenting that he would not pander to the Marquis' desire for him to promise wealth (NRS, GD112/18/8/7/12). By December he was struggling with the attitude of the workforce, the severity of the weather and economies of scale. Tyndrum mine, he grumbled, 'is to small an operation' to pay (NRS, GD112/18/8/7/17). In response to the mounting difficulties Odernheimer began by adapting and extending the existing infrastructure at the mine site to both improve the efficiency of moving the ore around the steep hillside to the waggon way and to tackle the problem of increasingly complex mineralisation (NRS, GD112/18/4/1/66–67). He had rails laid down in the main level (McDougall's) to the surface and had a primary crushing floor constructed at the adit mouth with a 'stampwork and moving hearth' to separate the lead ore from zinc blende and reduce the amount of waste rock and gangue minerals transported over the 1.5 kilometre distance to the crusher at Glengarry (NRS, GD112/18/8/7/15 and GD112/18/9/5/5–6). Shortly before his departure he also introduced washing and dressing at the entrance to New Level. It took a total of six months to process the mixed ore that had been stockpiled at the mouths of the adits, which gives an indication of the mineral wealth discarded as waste (NRS, GD112/18/8/7/20).

When Odernheimer arrived at Tyndrum there was no mechanism in place to transport the ore down the incline on the eastern flank of Minehill (marked 'Breadalbane's' on Fig. 4) to the waggon way, so to further increase transport efficiency he introduced a self-acting mechanism. This was an innovation that he takes credit for introducing into Scotland, described as 'full wagons pulling the empty ones to the top' (NRS, GD112/18/8/7/25). Ore had previously been moved around the mine site by use of wheelbarrows and ponies down a zig-zag path to the head of the waggon

way. The embanked route of the 'Breadalbane' incline and the pony path are both still visible at the site today, together with two further higher inclines (marked 'high incline' and 'middle incline' on Fig. 4; see also Figs 5 and 6) running vertically through the site to the primary dressing floor. Unfortunately, no details of these inclines are recorded in the documentary evidence. At the Glengarry crusher site Odernheimer introduced two 'German shaking herds', powered by the existing wheel, to tackle what he termed the 'tenace slimes' in an attempt to extract ever more ore from the waste rock (NRS, GD112/8/8/7/2). Every mine, he claimed, needed to find its own way of working; this sits comfortably with the notion that local conditions determine technological adaptions (Burt 1991, 254).

By June 1840 Odernheimer began to suspect his services were to be dispensed with, and hoped the Marquis would not be offended by his proposal to return to Germany in the coming year (NRS, GD112/18/4/1/166). In his request to return home, Odernheimer hoped that there would be a discovery of new ore, so that he could leave behind a 'legacy' before he left Scotland (NRS, GD112/18/4/1/166). Laubach's Level did not come to fruition. Odernheimer missed his homeland, found conditions at the mine and the

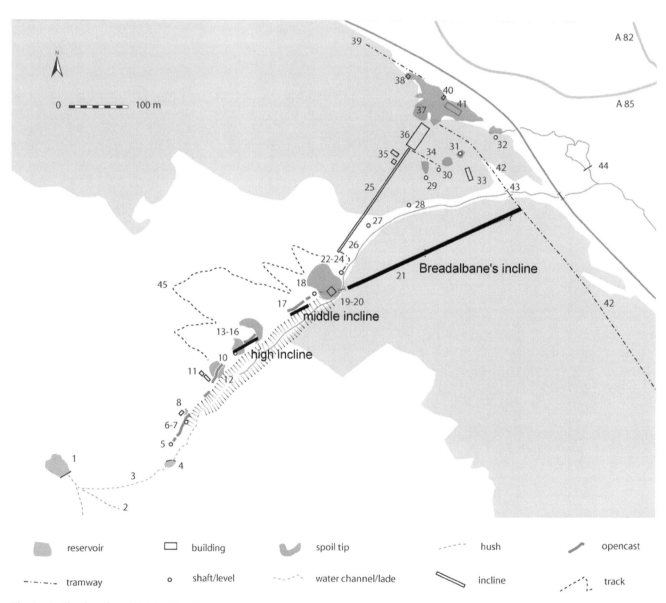

Fig. 4   Incline locations (© John Pickin)

Fig. 5   High incline (© John Pickin)

Fig. 6   Middle incline (© John Pickin)

climate dispiriting – one day of rain, he commented, 'makes the whole place swimming' (NRS, GD112/18/8/7/12) – and he was clearly not envisaging a substantial cut of the profits if he remained for a third year. He departed Scotland as planned in 1841 (NRS, GD112/8/4/1/180). During his period of management the mine made a total loss of around £4,500 (calculated from Robertson's data: Robertson 1992, 192).

Crerar and Wilson

The Marquis immediately employed James Crerar, the company storekeeper, who was originally from Strontian, to manage his venture together with the current overseer at Tyndrum, Joseph Wilson. These two continued as managers until the arrival of Stephen Reichendorf in 1847. Their joint reports across the period predictably focus on justifying the increasing cost of the bargains. Although there was

exploratory work, for example on Ben Odhar, and development work in the existing levels, particularly in Stamps Level, Crerar and Wilson were fairly gloomy in their overall outlook. The explorations were yielding very little and they grumbled that the ground was becoming increasingly hard; yet these comments were tempered by the occasional optimistic comment suggesting potential improvements in the quality of ore. But by February 1844 the crushing mill was standing idle, the rollers were worn out by the hardness of the rock, and later that year the men were back barrowing ore round the site (NRS, GD112/18/8/9/1–34).

This period of management is largely superfluous to the discussion of technological adaption: Crerar lacked practical mining experience and neither he nor Wilson held the authority to implement changes. Their role was simply to keep the mine operational. Their story, however, is important for historical continuity and for the context of Reichendorf's subsequent difficulties as mine manager. For similar reasons Robert Harrison's period of supervision is briefly discussed below in order to show what had been happening between Reichendorf's departure and the arrival of Thost.

Reichendorf

Reichendorf's initial assessment of the mineral wealth at Tyndrum was fairly bleak – 'it is not a rich field' he commented – but, as with Odernheimer, his brief was to make the mine a financial success (NRS, GD112/18/9/5/3). His key responses on arrival were again to increase production efficiency, particularly in terms of the workforce (NRS, GD112/18/9/5/9). He also attempted to tighten up the system of accounting, which was integrated with both the company store and other operations of the estate. Predictably there was tension between Reichendorf, Crerar (who was back running the store) and Wilson. Wilson, whom Odernheimer had previously described as 'more blockhead than scoundrel', was dismissed for dishonesty by Reichendorf shortly after his arrival. In response, Wilson called his fellow workers to strike and industrial relations at the mine deteriorated.

Reichendorf too was disparaging about the investment in the crusher at Glengarry – he referred to it as 'that expensive mill' – but bemoaned the fact that there was no smelter; to have constructed both, he claimed, would have made for a wiser investment (NRS, GD112/18/9/5/7). The desire to smelt on site may also reflect the fact that John Wyllie, the estate factor, controlled the sale of all processed ore, and Reichendorf found it very difficult to establish the profitability of the mine.

In terms of technological adaptions Reichendorf built on the existing transport infrastructure initiated under Odernheimer's management and introduced what he termed 'wooden canals'. From Reichendorf's descriptions these may have been ore chutes from the upper workings down to McDougall's Level so that ore could be transported by rail to the primary crushing floor (NRS, GD112/18/9/5/24). To streamline transportation further, he also proposed double track or passing places in McDougall's Level so that empty waggons could be ready and waiting to be loaded (NRS, GD112/18/9/5/18). In effect he was adapting Odernheimer's original adaptions. Reichendorf's stay in Scotland was too short for his plans to come to fruition and, reflecting the poor industrial relations, the wood from the ore chutes was repeatedly pilfered and used to construct a pig sty at the Tyndrum Inn (NRS, GD112/18/9/5/24).

Reichendorf arrived at Tyndrum in June, by July he was asking permission of the Marquis to leave, and by September he had fled to Valencia indicating that the Marquis had reneged on the terms of his contract. In a ten page letter addressed to the Marquis, Reichendorf detailed accounts of alleged mismanagement and corruption at the mine involving Crerar, Wilson and Wyllie.

According to Reichendorf the three men were operating the mine to their own advantage rather than in the financial interest of the Marquis. They turned a blind eye to the constant pilfering of material from the site, charged wood for the church to the mine accounts and, in particular, Crerar allowed the men food and whisky from the store irrespective of their ability to pay or their mounting debts, whilst at the same time he exercised very little supervision and the men rarely fulfilled their bargains (NRS, GD112/18/9/5/23).

To what extent Reichendorf's allegations were true is difficult to assess. Certainly, when Reichendorf arrived at Tyndrum and for the duration of his short stay the Marquis was in London, and Wyllie persistently denied Reichendorf any direct communication with him. He also undermined Reichendorf's authority by repeatedly removing 'a quarter' of the mining labour force to work on the construction of the canal at the north end of Loch Lomond (NRS, GD112/18/9/5/23). There is no copy letter in the archive recording the Marquis' response to Reichendorf's resignation letter. Wyllie's correspondence, in contrast, survives. On Reichendorf's sudden departure he wrote that Reichendorf was too young and 'exceedingly active'. Wyllie intimated that he was also overambitious in his aims for the mine and, perhaps somewhat hedging his bets, he described Crerar as 'addicted to drink'.

Harrison

In the two year interim period between Reichendorf's resignation and Thost's appointment the mine was managed by Robert Harrison. There is no indication in the records of where Harrison was from or his background or previous employment. His early reports support the idea that Crerar, Wyllie and Wilson had run the mine down. Harrison ordered repairs to the railway, the reservoir and the crusher. New Level had become 'impassable' and 'bad and dangerous' (NRS, GD112/18/9/6/10/15). It was cleared and retimbered. He also reported that the labour force were 'not disposed to work' and he employed 'new hands' both at the surface and underground (NRS, GD112/18/9/6/10/13). Crerar was still minding the company store and Harrison reports a disagreement over timber in November 1848 between Crerar and Griffiths Roberts, the overseer at Tomnadashan mine, the Marquis' copper venture on south Loch Tayside, but otherwise operations ran smoothly (NRS, GD112/18/9/6/10/19).

Harrison was successful in discovering promising new veins in three of the original levels at Tyndrum – Stamps, New and McDougall's – although these were not proven long term. Harrison worked with what was on site without introducing new technology and infrastructure or adapting that which already existed. Although he appears to have had more authority than Crerar and Wilson in terms of the day to day operation of the mine, the extent of his control is unclear. He made no suggestions for change, neither did

he place any significant financial demands on the Marquis other than to request copies of the *Mining Journal* (NRS, GD112/18/9/6/10/21). There were certainly opportunities to apply engineering knowledge and skill to increase productivity. For example, New Level was 100 yards below the top of the incline to the waggon way that led to the secondary crushing floor at Glengarry. In order to load ore onto the waggons it had to be barrowed up a steep slope with a gradient of around 1 in 6 (NRS, GD112/18/9/7/12).

Nevertheless, Harrison oversaw a successful period at the mine with the discovery of new ore, despite the 'great gloom than hung over the lead market' (NRS, GD112/18/9/6/13) and this meant he would have been under less pressure to increase efficiency. When Thost was engaged Harrison remained employed at Tyndrum, but as the overseer, and he was clearly subordinate to Thost. For example, at one point he was tasked with locating a bed and fresh linen for Thost (NRS, GD112/18/9/7/24).

Thost

Thost had been engaged originally to report on the copper mine at Tomnadashan. He had responded to an advertisement placed in the *Mining Journal* by the Marquis (NRS, GD112/18/9/7/14). How and why the transition occurred from writing a one off commissioned report to managing the Marquis' entire mining operations is not recorded. Of the three Germans it was Thost who remained in post for the longest period but, given his fugitive status, he may have perceived that he had little choice. He had struggled to find work in England and had hoped to go to America (NRS, GD112/18/9/7/14).

Thost arrived in Scotland with very limited skills in written or spoken English but was fluent within a few months and, once he was reunited with his family, he settled comfortably into highland life. Although Thost, like his predecessors, never gained autonomy over the finances or the shipment and sale of ore, of the three Germans, he sustained working within the convoluted chain of command and was not averse to manipulations himself. He would often be late when he returned from leave or holiday and in one instance he managed to negotiate a pay rise with Wyllie while the Marquis was away in London (NRS, GD112/18/8/14/22 and GD112/18/8/16/32).

Much of Thost's activity was focused on the Marquis' peripheral mining ventures: the operations at Tomnadashan, proving the recent discovery of a vein of lead ore at Ardtalnaig on south Loch Tayside, and the discovery of a small nugget of native gold at Lochearnhead (NRS, GD112/18/8/16/1). His initial thoughts on Tyndrum concerned establishing 'profitable methods of working', getting 'the minerals from every place' and 'preparation with water powered machinery' (NRS, GD112/18/9/7/19). Like his predecessors, Thost focused upon improving efficiency in the dressing process and in the movement of the ore around the site at Tyndrum, and upon increasing labour efficiency. In contrast to Reichendorf and Odernheimer, Thost also emphasised safety as well as the wider wellbeing of the workforce to improve productivity. He used technological adaption to achieve this and, predictably, industrial relations under his management were generally good.

A prime example of this is his response to the operation of the 'Breadalbane' incline, originally modified during

Odernheimer's period of management. By 1854 Thost was expressing concern that it was too long for 'waggoning', particularly using hemp rope, and he was concerned that there would be an accident on which he comments, this '[I] dare not pass over with silence' (NRS, GD112/18/8/14/21). Although it was a somewhat backward step, throughout 1855 ore was once again being transported from the upper workings on Minehill to the head of the waggon way by pack ponies (NRS, GD112/18/8/16/9). By 1858, Thost had solved this particular problem with the use of angular piping or troughs filled with water running down the incline. He claimed that 12½ cubic feet of water was sufficient to carry a total of 4 tons 4 cwt 32 lb of lead ore in 2 inch pieces down the incline. Angular troughs, he claimed, can carry anything from 2½ inches down to a fine powder at a 'trifling inclination'. Although Thost refers to the angular troughs as an 'invention' it is likely this was an adaption of Reichendorf's earlier introduction of wooden canals. Nonetheless, Thost presented his 'invention' at the Royal Scottish Society of the Arts, where he also advocated its use by road trustees both for conveying road metal from quarry to depot and for street sewers to prevent clogging in the drains (*Caledonian Mercury*, 26 July 1858; also see Easson 2011, 61).

Thost also discovered poor underground conditions, described as 'wretched and dangerous', due to lack of timbering and attempts to save money on the use of wood (NRS, GD112/18/4/1/65). Poor ventilation had also been problematic throughout the mine's history and was hindering development work (NRS, GD112/18/9/5/10). New communications were cut between levels and Thost also erected a 'wind engine' in May 1857 to improve the quality of the air via a system of pipes and 'fanners' (NRS, GD112/18/9/5/10). There are no descriptions of the machine, its location or its style of construction other than that it was probably hand powered. Thost described how 'three little boys are able to satisfy by dividing 16 hours between them' (NRS, GD112/18/9/1/38).

All three Germans preferred a day labour rate to the bargain system, but it was Thost who initiated changes to encourage work discipline, remove the need for an overseer thereby saving more expense, and to help tackle the problem of debt that had remained since Crerar's period of management and which, according to Thost, reduced the incentive to work. The miners' wages were eventually calculated by waggon load of ore and a system of rules with fines was introduced (NRS, GD112/18/9/27).

Another key example of Thost combining the wider well-being of the workforce and technological adaption to improve productivity was his addressing the problem of water supply at the mine site. The primary dressing floor, originally introduced by Odernheimer, was constantly out of sequence with the crushing mill at Glengarry. This resulted in unprocessed ore stockpiled at the mine and the surface workers were laid off at both dressing floors with no pay. Thost simply repaired the dam and reconstructed a disused leat from the western side of Minehill that was built during the Scots Mining Company lease (NRS, GD112/18/8/15/4). Much of the revetment and stonewalling of the leat is clearly visible at the site today (Figs. 7 and 8).

Thost also persuaded the Marquis to fund his new design for ore dressing at the Glengarry mill site. It permitted the self-acting reduction of 2½ inch pieces of ore to a fine powder using a series of stepped grates reducing in size, again utilising Thost's right-angled inclined troughs together with a corresponding right-angled hoe. He published details of his 'New Arrangements for Cleansing, Sizing, Trunking and Buddling Ores at the Tyndrum Mines' in the *Mining Journal* (copy article with plates at NRS, GD112/18/8/9/4; also see Fig. 9 below, based upon Thost's drawings) and wrote to Breadalbane to request that he personally inspect the apparatus and support its patent (NRS, GD112/18/8/16/13). On a less grandiose scale, to address the constant repairs to the crushing rollers Thost had these cast to a new design so that one guided the other and reduced the potential for accidental damage (NRS, GD112/18/8/14/27; also see Fig. 10, based on Thost's drawing).

In July 1860 Thost wrote to the Marquis and made reference to his 'particular circumstances', which prevented him from obtaining a passport from 'any country'; he requested that the Marquis support his application to travel to France and Switzerland with his wife and two daughters. Interestingly, Thost was then signing his letter Charles Henry Gustav Thost (NRS, GD112/18/1/5/11 and 17). What is not clear in the record is whether this trip to the continent was permanent, or whether Thost's services were simply being dispensed with, and why. The Marquis had entered into negotiations with George Henwood early in 1860 for a survey of all mines, including Tyndrum, and Thost disap-

Fig. 7   Route of leat

Fig. 8   Leat wall

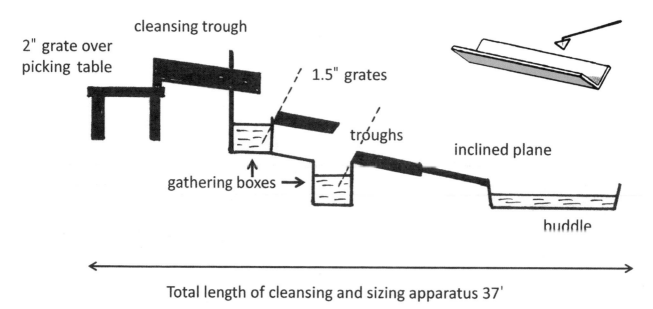

Fig. 9 Cleansing and sizing apparatus: sketch of Thost's original plates. (NRS, GD112/18/8/9/4). Detail, top right, is a conjectural reconstruction, based on Thost 1860, of the right-angled inclined trough and triangular hoe, used in the apparatus.

Fig. 10 Crushing rollers: sketch of Thorst's original drawing (NRS GD112/18/8/14/27)

pears from the record in 1860. There is no trace of him or his family in the 1861 Census.

Economic resilience

To what extent did the managers' technological adaptions of the existing infrastructure and machinery increase efficiency and prolong the working life of the mine? Production figures, although sparse, indicate that the amount of ore extracted and metal produced increased during Thost's period of management. Production rose from 60 tons of ore and 43.8 tons of metal in 1850 to 130 tons and 94 tons respectively in 1856 (Burt, Waite & Atkinson 1981, 156). In terms of increased output Thost's adaptions were a success, albeit a short-lived one. However, if the price of Tyndrum ore sold at Holywell is considered, it reveals a very different picture: the ore only ever received the lowest amount, which prompted Thost to consider stockpiling the poor quality ore and selling only the richer stuff to ensure a better price (Easson 2011, 61 and NRS, GD112/18/9/8/11). Income during the period 1850 to 1856 was roughly £2,500, which was a marked improvement on the zero amounts

recorded during the preceding four years, but expenditure for the same period amounted to just under £11,000 (Robertson 1992, 189–217, 192). Given the financial losses under Odernheimer's management, his decision not to wait for a share in the profits that were due for his third year of employment was arguably prudent. Production began an overall slow trend of decline from 1856 onwards (see Table 2) but mining did not cease until 1865, some three years after the death of the Marquis and the Breadalbane estate executors called a halt to all mining activity (Wilson 1921, 95).

Although what was an ailing and exhausted mine from the outset of the Marquis' tenure continued to work for almost thirty years, technological adaption had not extended its economic viability and substantial amounts of money were wasted in what Firsoff described as a 'brave attempt to carry on [mining] at a loss' (Firsoff 1954, 133).

The mine essentially operated to bolster the over-optimistic ideas of the Marquis and to keep the estate tenants in employment. Reichendorf noted at the end of his resignation letter that the Marquis kept 'an emu and deer and pheasants

Table 2 Production

Year	Lead ore (tons)	Metal (tons)	Silver (ounces)
1857	61	42.5	93
1858	54	37	160
1859	69	40	160
1860	80	57.2	229
1861	60	43	172
1862	67	47.5	120
1863	46	32	64
1864		no data	
1865	49	35	0

(Data from Mineral Statistics, cited in Burt, Waite & Atkinson 1981, 156)

and a museum and other remarkable things' for his pleasure and 'not for any use'. Reichendorf went on to state that he was of the opinion that, in the same way, the Marquis had 'a mining officer, miners, a mine, a railway, a crushing mill all in the greater glory of the Lord', suggesting the mine was little more than a 'show piece' as opposed to a viable economic operation. His comments, however, do not accord with Thost's succeeding management of the venture from 1849 onwards and his optimistic outlook when he claimed to have taken 'the mine onto a new and better road' and wrote that he was hopeful of 'carrying on continuous economical and reasonable mining' (NRS, GD112/18/8/9/44). George Henwood commented that the mine was run for 'the employment of the poor of Clifton village' (Henwood 1860, 715), Clifton, now subsumed into Tyndrum, having been the name given to the original row of miners' cottages built in the 1730s. Henwood too had a somewhat difficult relationship with the Marquis. For example, he became increasingly frustrated with the lack of response to his letters and the Marquis' failure to confirm the terms of his employment. He did, however, eventually survey the mineral workings within the Breadalbane estate (NRS, GD112/18/8/15/30 and 35; GD112/18/1/5/5).

The difficult and often complex relationships that all the external managers had with the Marquis make assessment of the validity of their comments difficult. Reichendorf had essentially reneged on his contract of employment and was unlikely to portray the mine in a good light. It is unclear whether Odernheimer and Thost colluded with the over-optimistic ideas of the Marquis. Thost certainly had a vested interest in pandering to his hopes and dreams; he was a refugee in Scotland and reliant on the favours of his employer.

Although there is no direct evidence in the record to suggest that estate employment was a primary aim of the Marquis, he never wavered in his belief in the great mineral wealth of his land. There is, however, the question of paternalistic relationships and public duty; whether by default or design, the mine did support local employment. This is clearly seen in the case of the Strontian men brought in by Baron. The strategy engineered between Wyllie and the Marquis was to ensure that the mine would become independent of outside labour: the Strontian miners would be used to train the young men of Tyndrum and the surrounding settlements in mining skills and then they would be removed (NRS, GD112/18/8/7/2). A local workforce was eventually achieved. For example, throughout the 1850s, excepting a handful of men at Tomnadashan and James Crerar, the lists of miners employed all reveal local estate names (see, for example, NRS, GD112/18/9/8/15).

What is quite interesting is the Germans' failure to explore the potential for adapting processing technology to work the zinc blende and the other gangue ores which could potentially have prolonged the economic viability of the venture. Shortly before his departure Thost began to sort and stockpile blende rather than dumping it as waste (NRS, GD112/18/8/15/). Yet even the Tyndrum Lead and Zinc Company, who worked the mineral lease from 1916, failed to realise a profit from both zinc and lead ores. This was despite the introduction of modern crushing and separation technology. It prompted old Tyndrum miner John Macfarlene to comment that the Company had made so much money abroad that they would not mind operating at a

loss (Firsoff 1954, 133). Neither small adaptions of existing technology nor the introduction of new technology could overcome the poor and declining quality of the lead ore.

Conclusion

The majority of the studies in this volume examine key developments in mineral extraction and exploration, such as mechanical cutting, drainage and boring. In contrast, this study has explored technological change on a much smaller scale: the adaption and modification of existing infrastructure and technology and its role in increasing productivity and sustaining the economic viability of extracting a finite resource.

The survival of substantial documentary evidence for the surface operations at Tyndrum mine permitted a focused case study approach. The study reveals an intriguing history of mismanagement, personality clashes and potential corruption; in many ways the story was ideal for an assessment of the efficacy of adaptive technological strategies. The nineteenth century history of the enterprise is one of hasty and ill-considered extensive capital investment in a mine with complex mineralisation that was nearing exhaustion, based on the landowner's grandiose belief in the mineral wealth of both the operation and his landed estate. Reichendorf cut his losses and reneged on his contract of employment, but Odernheimer and Thost both had a vested interest in realising a profit: Odernheimer in terms of salary, although he cut his losses, and Thost in terms of his refugee status. All three Germans tackled the movement of ore around the site and the dual problem of a dwindling supply of quality ore and complex mineralisation by making small adaptions and modifications to the existing arrangements. Henwood suggests that there was no continuity between managers but he was referring specifically to underground development work at Tyndrum; at the surface each engineer expanded and developed the work of his predecessor. In theory their modifications should have reduced operating costs and increased the opportunity to achieve the ideal concentration of ore for smelting, at roughly 60–70%; they should ultimately have increased the profitability of the operation (Burt 1983, 1–10). Only Thost managed to increase the production of dressed ore, albeit very briefly, but the poor quality of the ore was reflected in the price. Even in a good year expenditure always exceeded income. It was the Campbell family fortune and the Marquis' faith and conviction, rather than technology, that allowed the venture to continue operating. Although it was not what the Marquis desired, or perhaps even perceived, nonetheless the end result was, as Henwood suggested, a charitable public works.

What the study does highlight is the success of technological adaption in meeting local conditions. The German engineers were responding to a very specific set of circumstances, both geological and practical, and also the unique situation created by their employer's desire for rich mineral deposits and great mineral wealth. They were essentially caught in a cleft stick so they simply applied their cumulative knowledge and experience of the mining arts to overcome the practical difficulties while neither challenging nor supporting the erroneous beliefs of the Marquis. This application of practical skill supports Burt's original argument, discussed in the opening section, that technological change occurs where necessary and without formal diffusion mechanisms (Burt 1991, 249–271, 254). Ultimately, for the German engineers, the difficulties at Tyndrum mine could not be solved. The venture was exhausted of viable lead ore and worked beyond its economic viability.

Acknowledgements

The author would like to thank the Carnegie Trust for the Universities of Scotland for generously funding the historical research.

Abbreviations

BGS   British Geological Survey
NRS   National Records of Scotland
NLS   National Library of Scotland
OSA   Old Statistical Account of Scotland
       http://stat-acc-scot.edina.ac.uk.

Bibliography

Bainbridge, J., 1980. 'Lord Breadalbane's mines', *Scots Magazine* 114, 1 (1980), pp. 38–45

Burt, R., 1983. *A Short History of British Ore Preparation Techniques in the Eighteenth and Nineteenth Centuries* (Netherlands: De Archaeologische Pers)

Burt, R., 1984. *The British Lead Mining Industry* (Redruth: Dyllansow Truran)

Burt, R., 1991. 'The international diffusion of technology in the early modern period: the case of the British non-ferrous mining industry', *Economic History Review* XLIV, 2 (1991), pp. 249–271

Burt, R., Waite, P., & Atkinson, M., 1981. 'Scottish metalliferous mining 1845 to 1913: detailed returns from the Mineral Statistics, Part II', *Industrial Archaeology* 16, 2 (1981), pp. 140–157

Callender, R., & Macaulay, J., 1984. 'The ancient metal mines of the Isle of Islay, Argyll', *British Mining* 24 (1984), pp. 1–46

Callender, R., & Reeson, P., 2007. *The Scottish Gold Rush of 1869*, British Mining 84, pp. 1–164

Cressey, M., Pickin, J., & Hicks, K., 2004. 'The Silver Rig, Pibble and Woodhead metal mines, Galloway, Scotland', *Mining History* 15, 6 (2004), pp. 49–62

Devéria, R., 2001. 'Tomnadashan: a re-examination of a 19th-century copper mining and smelting operation in Perthshire, Scotland', *Historical Metallurgy* 35, 2 (2001), pp. 87–98

Dickie, D.M., & Forster, C.W., 1974. *Mines and Minerals of the Ochils* (Stirling: Clackmannanshire Field Studies Society)

Easson, M., 2011. 'Environmental Degradation and the Lead Industry at Tyndrum Scotland 1730–1930', unpublished M.Res. University of Stirling

Farmer, J.G., MacKenzie, A.B., Eades, L.J., Kirika, A., & Bailey-Watts, A.E., 1997. 'Influences on the extent and record of heavy metal pollution in sediment cores from Loch Tay in a mineralised area of Scotland', *Journal of Geochemical Exploration* 58 (1997), pp. 195–202

Firsoff, V.A., 1954. *In the Hills of Breadlabane* (London: Hale)

Gillies, W.A., 1980. *In Famed Breadalbane: the story of the antiquities, lands and people of a Highland district* (Strathtay: Clunie)

Harvey, W.S., 1972. 'The rules of the Leadhills Mining Company', *British Mining* 2 (1972), pp. 60–66

Harvey, W.S., 1991. 'Miners or crofters?', *British Mining* 43 (1991), pp. 82–95

Harvey, W.S., 1994a. 'Pollution at Leadhills: reponses to domestic and industrial pollution in a mining community', *Local Historian* 24, 3 (1994)

Harvey, W.S., 1994b. 'The restless years: Leadhills Company Ltd., and the labour disputes at its mines, 1903–1929', *British Mining* 50 (1994) pp. 41–66

Harvey, W.S., 1999. 'Lead and labour: the miners of Leadhills, a social history', unpublished manuscript, copy held at NLS, HP4.203.0481

Henwood, G., 1860. 'Mining in Scotland', *Mining Journal*, 20 October

MacInnes, A.I., 1998. 'Highland society in the era of improvement', in A. Cooke, I. Donnachie, A. Macsween and C. Whatley (eds), *Modern Scottish History 1707 to the Present: Volume I* (Dundee: Tuckwell)

MacKenzie, A.B., & Pulford, I.D., 2002. 'Investigation of contaminant metal dispersal from a disused mine site at Tyndrum, Scotland, using concentration gradients and stable Pb isotope ratios', *Applied Geochemistry* 17, 8 (2002), pp. 1093–1103

Mills, C.J., Simpson, I., & Adderley, W.P., 2014. 'The lead legacy: the relationship between historical mining, pollution and the post-mining landscape', *Landscape History* 35, 1 (2014), pp. 47–72

Moreton, S., 2008. *Bonanzas and Jacobites: the story of the Silver Glen* (Edinburgh: National Museum of Scotland)

NRS, Breadalbane Muniments, GD112/

Robertson, C.J.A., 1992. 'Railway mania in the Highlands: the Marquis of Breadalbane and the Scottish Grand Junction Railway', in R. Mason and N. Macdougall, *People and Power in Scotland: essays in honour of T.C. Smout* (Edinburgh: John Donald), pp. 189–217

Schmookler, J., 1966. *Invention and Economic Growth* (Cambridge, Massachusetts: Harvard University Press)

Smout, T.C., 1967. 'Lead-mining in Scotland, 1650–1850', in P.L. Payne (ed.), *Studies in Scottish Business History* (London: Cass), pp. 103–135

Wilson, G.V., 1921. *The Lead, Zinc, Copper and Nickel Ores of Scotland*, Memoirs of the Geological Survey: Special Reports on the Mineral Resources of Great Britain 17 (Edinburgh: HMSO)

Boreholes: a Brief History of an Essential Mineral Exploration Technique

Rob Vernon

Abstract: In the last 250 years boreholes have been an essential exploration method in the UK for establishing the presence of mineral reserves. As the technique improved it became possible, for example, to bore a large diameter shaft or turn a borehole through 90 degrees. Consequently, the number of uses for boreholes has increased and they now can be used for extracting gas from shale, which even 30 years ago may have been considered inconceivable.

The paper briefly describes the various drilling techniques employed and shows how the technology evolved, drawing on examples from Britain and elsewhere. It includes exploration for coal, particularly the search for concealed coalfields, as well as the use of boreholes for proving other mineral deposits, including examples from North Wales.

Introduction

This brief history of boreholes, an essential mineral exploration technique, will cover some of the significant technological changes required for drilling a borehole, and show how important boreholes are for the discovery of minerals and their development.

In addition to the development of mechanised drilling, the need to drill deeper brought about major changes with drilling rig design; for example, drilling rigs became more robust and the derricks or masts taller. The developments referred to will mainly be British, with some European and American, which in the late nineteenth and early twentieth centuries were centred on the search for coal and water, and in America oil. Fig. 1 shows a typical coal exploration drilling rig of that period. Where appropriate, significant developments achieved in the USA in the search for oil will also be included, as inevitably these innovations were introduced to Britain.

Boreholes are drilled for a variety of reasons. The majority of those drilled today are less than 10 m deep and are for site investigation purposes, usually to determine soil properties prior to building. However, until about 1920 most boreholes in the UK were for finding water, salt, coal or ironstone. Boreholes for oil, gas and base metals can now be added to that list. Rarely, boreholes are drilled for academic purposes to determine the sequence of strata, usually for the British Geological Survey. The Mochras Farm borehole (Allen and Jackson 1985, 88), for example, sited on the western edge of the Harlech Dome, drilled between 1967 and 1969, was for this purpose. It reached a depth of 1983.83 m and is probably the deepest (and possibly the most expensive) single onshore borehole drilled in Wales. Elsewhere, deep boreholes have been used to evaluate the properties of rock for the generation of geothermal energy.

An examination of boreholes sited in the surrounding area of the Conference venue (Bangor University, North Wales), on the British Geological Survey internet site (onshore borehole database – http://www.bgs.ac.uk/data/boreholescans) shows that the majority of holes were drilled for site investigation purposes. The records show them grouped on building sites, or in lines along the routes of major roads, or pipelines. There are only two holes shown deeper than

Fig. 1 The Barlow No.1 Borehole site near Selby, North Yorkshire. Drilled 1904–06 to a depth of 2371 ft (722.6 m). It is typical of a number of boreholes that explored the concealed extension of the Yorkshire-Nottingham Coalfield. (St. John Durnford 1908, 436)

30 m. The first, on Anglesey, was drilled by the Marquis of Anglesey in 1917 and reached a depth of 74 m, and the second, for Bangor Laundry, drilled in 1942, reached a depth of 57 m. Both holes were drilled for fresh water extraction.

Boreholes can be drilled using various techniques:

a. Augering is by far the simplest method, and involves rotating a helical shaft (like a very large cork screw) into generally soft ground. Rotation is stopped and the helical shaft is pulled out of the ground, together with a sample of the ground it passed through. This method is generally used in shallow unconsolidated deposits, but has in the past been used for proving coal seams.

b. Percussive drilling involves dropping a weighted cutting head, attached to a rope or steel cable, up and down continuously on the rock being penetrated. Broken rock is usually removed by removing the cutting tool and inserting a bailer, a hollow tube with a simple valve arrangement that opens as it is being dropped into the borehole, and closes when motion ceases, thereby trapping any broken rock in the hollow tube, which is then removed from the borehole and emptied. This was the earliest method for drilling deep boreholes.

c. The majority of boreholes are now rotary drilled. A cutting head, either a type of drill bit, or a diamond core barrel, is rotated on a string of steel drill rods. Rock cuttings are transported out of the borehole in the annulus between the rods and the side of the borehole by fluid (water or drilling mud) or air, introduced down the drill rods. There are many variations to this method. For example, a down-hole motor operated by the pressure of the drilling fluid can be used to turn the drilling bit. This is commonly used for directional or deviated drilling, where the borehole is accurately steered in a planned direction.

This paper is not intended to be a definitive history of drilling, but rather to highlight some of the main developments in the evolution of drilling techniques for mineral exploration, and to demonstrate, where appropriate, how mineral exploration in Wales may be part of this history.

Earliest boring methods

Evidence would suggest that the ancient Egyptians were the first to develop a drilling method. Cores of igneous rock from tubular drill holes have been found in the Gizeh area that can be dated to the Fourth Dynasty (about 2500 BC). It is thought that a bronze tube was rotated using a bow. (This is similar to the method of generating fire by rotating a wooden stick with a bow on a block of wood.) The tube was placed in contact with the material to be cut. Dry sand, placed at the contact point, was probably used as the abrasive, certainly for cutting soft material. Flinders Petrie (1883, 175) suggests that precious stones of suitable hardness, for example sapphires, diamonds etc., may have been used to drill harder rocks. The resulting shallow circular hole is thought to have been used for a simple door hinge mechanism. This Egyptian method demonstrates the four basic requirements for engineering a borehole: a means to rotate; cut rock; lift the cutting head; and remove rock waste.

Whilst this Egyptian method of drilling is partly based on speculation, it is known from documented evidence that by 250 BC the Chinese had perfected a method for sinking wells into a brine aquifer (Kuhn 2008). By

1 BC in the Sichuan district this had been developed into percussive drilling (anon. n.d.(b)). The method involved dropping bamboo drill pipes, with a triangular iron drill bit attached to the end, up and down to form the borehole. By 300 AD depths of 140 m were being achieved. Around 1050 AD the bamboo pipe was replaced by rope, which reduced the weight of the drill string. Derricks to hold and locate the drill assembly over the borehole were constructed from bound bamboo sheaves, and were known as a 'churn' (Kopey 2007). The drilling rope could be lowered or raised with a manual or oxen-operated windlass. The percussive action was generated by teams of men pulling on, and then releasing, the rope. To achieve a straight borehole, bamboo flights were attached to the bamboo drill rod on which the chisel bit was fastened. There are various illustrations of the method (see Fig. 2), and examples of the equipment used can be seen on the Zigong Salt Museum website (http://www.chinamuseums.com/zigong_Salt.htm). By the 1700s Sichuan salt wells were typically between 300 and 400 m deep, whilst in 1835 the Shenghai well became the first in the world to exceed a depth of 1000 m (Kuhn 2008; Norman 1901, 686).

In Europe, Kopey (2007) indicates that Leonardo da Vinci (1452–1519) designed a rotative drill bit with worm drive but, as with many of Da Vinci's proposals, it is not known whether he actually constructed one.

The development of drilling in Great Britain (seventeenth to early nineteenth century)

The first known reference to boreholes drilled in England dates from the seventeenth century (Lister 1699). It confirms that

> Thomas Waike bored for Coal at Mauston [sic – probably Marston] near Leeds, in the Grounds hereafter named, May the 20th, 1639. In the Rye-Close, or upper Pig hill, on the east of the way, 38 Yards, from the North East Hedge. (Lister 1699)

Fig. 2   Ancient Chinese percussive drilling. 'Churn' type rig constructed from bamboo together with a bullock powered windlass. (anon. n.d.(b))

We will probably never know the exact site of this borehole, but we learn from the account that it reached a depth of 21 fm (38.4 m) and cost £9 5s to drill. Drilled several centuries before the science of geology came fully into fruition, the borehole log records that one of the horizons it has drilled through was 'a Cowshot coloured stone with Catheads in it 1 yard.' Other Coal Measure strata are described as metal, slate, ramel and whinstone, terminology still in mining usage into the first half of the twentieth century (MIME 1927, 18–19). In 1670 boreholes for coal were also being drilled at Northwich, Cheshire, but instead of coal they discovered salt (Nicholson 1809, 'Salt').

By the eighteenth century it was becoming common practice to patent inventions. The 1857 *Subject Matter Index of Patents of Invention* (Woodcroft 1857, 80) shows that between 1711 and 1851 there were 11 patents taken out for 'Boring, Drilling, Punching earth, stone etc.', as well as various types of auger.

On 31 May 1728 Bryan Moore patented

an Engine for boring stone (Patent No: 498) in either a straight, square or circular direction or form, for pipes, pumps, and other uses (Woodcroft 1857, 80)

It is unclear whether this patent could be applied to mineral exploration, as apparently no fuller description, or illustrations, have survived. However, by the end of that century, exploration boring was becoming commonplace. An illustration dated 1794 shows two men boring for coal, manually turning what was probably a large type of auger (Fig. 3). Practical experience would suggest that some type of derrick arrangement may also have been required with this method: it can sometimes be very difficult to manually pull a standard auger from the ground, even from relatively shallow depths.

Drilling equipment had to be manufactured. In 1808, for example, Boulton and Watt of Birmingham advised that they could supply coal-boring tools and apparatus (City of Birmingham Central Library, Boulton and Watt Collection, MS 3147/1463).

Probably the first known illustration of a set of drilling tools (Fig. 4) can be found with John Ryan's patent (patent 2882) dated 12 February 1805 (anon. 1805, 324–329). Ryan was Irish and an 'Engineer to the Undertakers of the Grand Canal'. The well illustrated patent and description show that the equipment was clearly used for mineral exploration,

with many of the items intended for taking samples. The patent is described as:

For sundry tools, implements, or apparatus for boring the earth for Coal, and all kinds of minerals and subterraneous substances, by which the different strata may be cut out in a cheap and expeditious manner, in cores or cylinders, from 1 inch to twenty inches and upwards in length, and from two inches to twenty inches and upwards in diameter, so as to be taken up entire at any depth that has hitherto been bored; by which, not only the quality of such minerals and substances, can be ascertained beyond a possible mistake; and which tools, implements or apparatus, are also advantageously applicable to the purpose of sinking for wells, and giving vent to subterraneous water in bogs, and draining mines and grounds, and ventilating pits, and other beneficial purposes.

John Goode, a well sinker from Tottenham, Middlesex, had a patent granted 20 August 1823, for improvements in machinery, tools, or apparatus for boring the earth, for the purpose of obtaining and raising water (anon. 1825, 113–116). The illustration accompanying the patent shows a variety of down-hole tools, perhaps not as elaborate as Ryan's, above. Ironically, in 1854 Goode was killed when

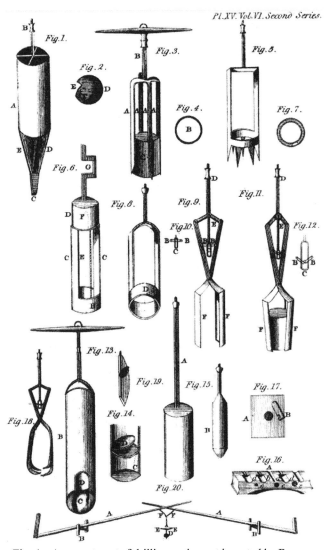

Fig. 4   An assortment of drilling equipment invented by Ryan. Items include tools for manually making an auger type borehole; cutting, and then extracting a sample of strata. (anon. 1805, Plate 15 facing 328)

Fig. 3   Exploration for coal with a hand turned auger type drill. (Taylor 1832, facing 105)

he fell down a well he was lining with steel casing (anon. 1854).

Drilling rigs at this time were also becoming more elaborate. A type of derrick or mast structure over the borehole, with a windlass for raising and lowering the drill string and bit, was now standard. The need to mechanise the rotation of the drill string was becoming a necessity even for percussive boring, as it was by this means that the chisel-type drilling bits could be re-orientated at the bottom of the borehole. Where the drill string was composed of steel rods, it was possible to rotate them by passing the rods through a manually turned capstan. The windlass was used to control the progress of the drill string down the borehole. Suggestions were also being promoted to turn the drill string by other means. In 1829 Dixon Vallance of Libberton in Lanarkshire submitted a design to rotate the drill rods using wind-power (Fig. 5), but apparently it was never patented, or constructed.

The mechanisation of drilling (nineteenth century)

The first reliable information on the time taken to drill a borehole comes from France. In the early nineteenth century Paris was growing and so was the drive for good public sanitation. It was known that the city was located on top of a major Cretaceous aquifer so it was decided to drill a borehole at Grenelle, south-west Paris, to tap it. The borehole would take about eight years to complete. There are various accounts of the borehole that provide great detail about the progress of the borehole and the drilling equipment (Azias 1845), and some are illustrated (Appleton 1873;

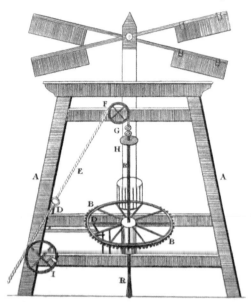

Fig. 5   Wind powered drilling rig suggested by Dixon Vallance, Lanarkshire. The horizontally mounted sails turned gears to rotate the drill rods. (anon. 1829, plate facing 44)

anon. 1841). The following is a simplified account of the operation taken from anon. 1841. The constructed derrick was 29 ft 6 in tall, and rotational power was produced by a geared horse-whim located adjacent to the derrick (Fig. 6). The initial augered borehole was commenced in 1833 and was 12 inches in diameter. At 500 ft and 1100 ft the diameter was reduced to 9 inches and 7½ inches, respectively.

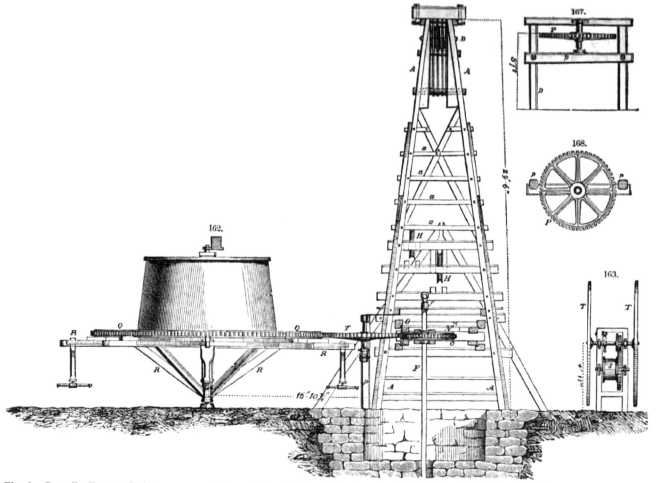

Fig. 6   Grenelle, France: the horse-powered rotary drilling rig. The illustration also includes a manually operated winch. However, a separate horse-powered windlass was located at the other side for raising and lowering the drill string. (Appleton 1873, 61)

It had taken over three years to reach this depth. However, during May 1837 at 1254 ft, the drill rods broke and 270 ft of drilling equipment dropped to the bottom of the borehole. Fortunately, by August 1838 all this equipment had been recovered. At 1300 ft the diameter was reduced again to 6 inches. In April 1840 there was another mishap. The chisel cutting tool dropped off the drill rods and took two months to recover. Finally, on 26 February 1841, at a depth of 1800 ft, the borehole penetrated the Upper Greensand aquifer. The hydrostatic head was powerful enough to force all the drill rods out of the borehole. It is presumed that much of the Grenelle borehole was drilled through a competent rock: chalk, which would present few major drilling problems. Most of the problems during the drilling operations appear to have been caused by failures of the drilling equipment. Fig. 7 is an external view of the drilling site.

The 1844 patent by Robert Beart, Godmanchester, titled 'Improvement in Apparatus for boring in Earth and in Stone' brought in the concept of circulating a fluid down the drill string. A Frenchman, Fauvelle, is also credited with the idea (Fauvelle 1847). This innovation may also be partly based on an idea patented in 1810 by William Murdock (anon. 1812), who devised a method for drilling stone slabs whereby cuttings were removed by the hydrostatic pressure in the drilling pipe. Circulation is very important for all rotary drilling as the circulating fluid (i) lubricates the cutting bit, (ii) cools the cutting bit, contributing to less wear and breakage of the cutting teeth, and (iii) removes rock cuttings without having to remove the drill rods from the borehole. The circulating fluid is pumped under pressure down the drill string, and returns to the surface (usually into a settling pit) via the annulus between the drill string and the strata.

Boreholes were frequently commenced from the bottom of a wide shallow well (Fig. 8). Although elaborate

and costly, this method had a double advantage. Firstly, any unconsolidated material at the surface that would be difficult to drill through was retained by walling. Secondly, it removed the need to construct a high derrick as drill pipes could be stacked vertically in the well. However, this was also a confined working space and gas could be encountered by the borehole.

Methane gas was frequently encountered when drilling through Coal Measures. In 1861 a borehole at Featherstone, West Yorkshire, struck gas at a depth of 420 ft.

> On Saturday, April 13th, while the borers were at work, a strong smell of gas was perceived, and suddenly an eruption took place, which threw the muddy water from the borehole about 30 feet into the air. This continued, and put an end to the boring. [Someone later ignited the gas] which formed a fiery pillar of considerable height. (anon. 1861)

But, thankfully, no one was injured on this occasion.

In 1893 on the Isle of Wight four drillers were not as lucky.

> Three men employed in boring for water for the Shanklin Local Board being missing at midnight, the contractor

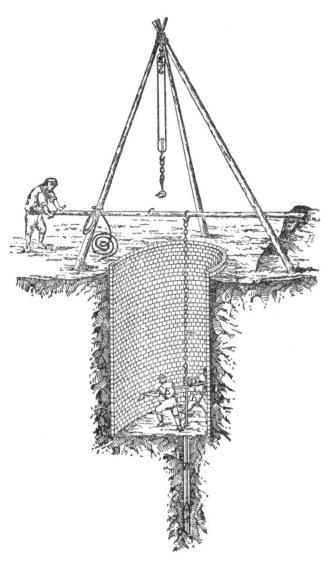

Fig. 7   Grenelle, France: sketch of the drilling derrick. A fountain of water issues from the top of the pipes. (anon. 1841, 441)

Fig. 8   Borehole drilled from the base of a well. The well was usually 20 to 30 ft deep but had the advantage of holding back unconsolidated ground, and eliminating the need for a high derrick. The man on the surface is generating a percussive action whilst the two men in the well rotate the rods. (Isler 1921, 55)

for the work descended the well on which they were employed to search for them. Missing his footing he fell into the water and was drowned. The lifeless bodies of four men, including the contractor and his son, were afterwards found in the well.

It is thought that all of them were overcome by noxious gases suddenly escaping from the boring tube, which it had pierced at depth of two hundred feet. (anon. 1893)

The author recollects reading about a similar incident in Sicily, where drillers exploring the sulphur deposits were suffocated when the borehole struck a pocket of sulphur dioxide. In fact poisonous 'sour gas', as it became known, was frequently encountered in oil prospection.

By the mid-nineteenth century drilling tools were becoming standardised, mainly for rotary-percussive drilling. Drilling bits were generally chisel shaped with a variety of cutting edges, pointed, flat or crossed. Other types took the form of short tubes with a circular cutting edge for taking a core sample, or some were just an auger-type helix. To

remove cuttings a type of bailer (as described under percussive drilling) would be lowered into the borehole. Gard's patent of 1847 (Robertson 1848), combined the cutting tool with the bailer to remove the 'bored-out material … out of the way of the cutting edges'. Kind's method (Blackwell 1854) allowed the percussive bit to fall freely to the bottom of the borehole. The bit was then picked up by a grapple mechanism dropped into the borehole on the end of the drill-string or rope. Once grappled, the bit was raised a little way up the borehole and then released again.

Other types of down-hole tools included a side chisel that could be used to shave the side of a borehole. This was usually employed to widen a borehole at points where the side was squeezing into the hole. Drill rods were also becoming uniform. They were sometimes made from wood with metal screw joints at each end, and were lighter than the iron rods, which were often the preferred option, as they were stronger. Similarly, a variety of metal down-hole tools were designed to 'fish' for any detached equipment in the borehole.

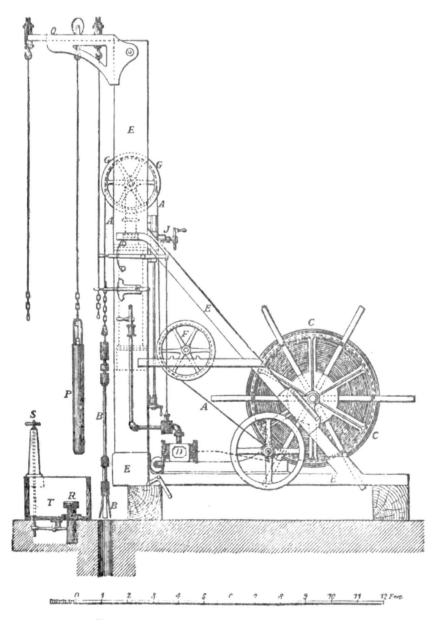

FIG. 53.—MATHER & PLATT BORING PLANT.

Fig. 9   Mather & Platt rotary percussive drilling rig (Isler 1921, 118)

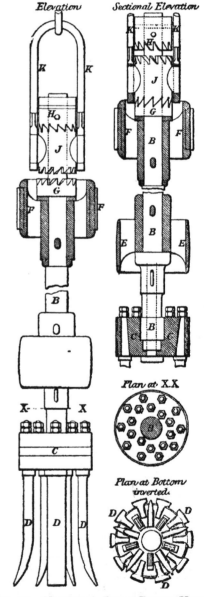

FIG. 57.—MATHER & PLATT BORING-HEAD.

Fig. 10   Mather & Platt boring head showing bit and turning mechanism (Isler 1921, 125)

The rotary-percussive method devised and patented in 1855 by the Manchester engineers Mather and Platt (Marley 1864) incorporated all the best points from previous methods, and was widely used for coal exploration. The windlass and short derrick with jib were mounted on the same frame, and a mechanism on the frame produced and controlled the continuous percussive action (Fig. 9). The drilling bit was quite elaborate and consisted of a gear arrangement that gave the cutting head a short turn each time the equipment was raised for the next percussive fall (Fig. 10). The drilling bit was also of a completely new design consisting of a series of long curved teeth bolted to a circular disc (Fig. 10). However, rock cuttings still had to be removed by a bailer.

By the late 1870s borings for water in the Paris Basin were exceeding depths of 3000 ft (Dru 1867). Still being drilled by percussive methods, the percussive motion was now being produced by a small steam engine, rocking the beam onto which the drill rods were attached. Immediately below the beam there was a manually turned screw mechanism, later referred to as a temper screw (Blake 1871, 65–66), that could be used to lengthen the drill string as the borehole got deeper. Fig. 11 shows exactly the same mechanism as the one described by Dru (1867).

Advances were also being made with rotary drilling. Fig. 12 shows a manually operated rotary drilling rig used at Hilton, County Durham, where two men turned gearing to rotate the drill rods. In the USA rotary drilling equipment had become fully mechanised. Fig. 13 shows a rotary steam-powered drilling rig manufactured by the New York

Fig. 12   Mineral borers, Hilton, County Durham. Obviously for shallow boring operations, there is a mechanism on top of the drill rods, turned by two men, to rotate the rods. A third man, to the rear of the rig, manually operated a circulation pump. (Postcard dated 1908, author's collection)

Fig. 11   Steam-powered percussive drilling, France (Simonin 1869, facing 76)

Fig. 13   A portable steam-powered prospecting rig manufactured by Severance and Holt, New York, USA (anon. 1870, 328)

engineering company of Severance and Holt. Eventually this technology would evolve into an engine turning a rotary table sited immediately on top of the borehole. The drill rods down the borehole were attached to a rod with a square cross-section that ran through the centre of the table, known as the 'kelly rod'.

The advent of diamond drilling (1862 to 1872)

It was an observation made by a Swiss horologist, Georges Auguste Leschot (1800–1884), that would ultimately revolutionise drilling technology. Like many major discoveries, the idea was simple; it just needed someone to devise an application. Leschot realised that the deep fine lines on an ancient Egyptian porphyry plate could only have been etched by a diamond, and therefore diamonds could be used to cut hard rock (Day & McNeil 2005, 734).

In 1862 Leschot patented a diamond drilling technique. The cutting head was composed of eight relatively cheap black diamonds set in the circumference of a mild steel tube (Day & McNeil 2005, 734). His first experiments involved drilling into granite, and he succeeded in boring a 5 cm diameter borehole to a depth of 37 cm in 1 hour and 20 minutes, which at this time was a phenomenal rate of drilling (anon. 1884). Leschot's patent was adapted further by his son Rudolph, an engineer, and later used on the Alpine Mont Cenis railway tunnel (Day & McNeil 2005, 734). The Mont Cenis tunnel seems to have been a test-bed for new tunnelling innovations and many papers were written at the time about the tunnel. One was written by Thomas Sopwith junior but unfortunately he visited the tunnel just before Leschot's invention was put into use (Sopwith 1864). Later work confirmed the success of Leschot's invention. Rudolph's diamond drilling machine could be

driven by steam or compressed air. A small jet of water passed through the drill rods to lubricate the bit and remove debris. The equipment produced a rock core. Fig. 14 is a representation of the equipment together with the diamond crown. Unlike conventional drilling techniques, Leschot's method was only cutting the circumference of the borehole and therefore cutting considerably less surface area (anon. n.d.(a), 116–117).

Leschot's invention was soon taken up by others. These included Captain Frederick Edward Blackett Beaumont (1833–1899) of the Royal Engineers and MP for South Durham (1868–1880) (http://en.wikipedia.org/wiki/Frederick_Beaumont). He was also a member of a family with long associations with North Pennine lead mining so mining may not have been unfamiliar to him. On 21 May 1868 Beaumont, together with Charles James Appleby, an engineer, took out a patent (No. 1682) for 'Improvements in apparatus for drilling rock and stone for blasting and other purposes' (Woodcroft 1869, 117). In order to accrue capital to apply the patent, Beaumont floated the Machine Tunnelling Company Ltd. (Kew, National Archives, BT31/1537/4884) to develop the technology further. In subsequent years Beaumont became involved with the Channel Tunnel Company Ltd., and patented a tunnel boring machine, as well as refining his original patent for the drilling apparatus in 1873 and 1874. The first prospecting machines were manufactured by Messrs. Appleby of London (Beaumont 1875, 96).

One of the first applications for the Beaumont-Appleby drilling machine was in 1870 when the Machine Tunnelling Company was awarded a contract by the Croesor United Slate Company, North Wales, to drive an inclined tunnel (dipping at 40 degrees from the horizontal, see Fig. 15) to intersect a major slate vein (Haw & Dredge 1870, 405). A shareholders' meeting was imminent and, although the tunnel had been driven 633 ft, the slate vein had not been encountered and there was an urgency that the information should be presented at the meeting. So the Machine Tunnelling Company, using ¾ inch diameter gas piping and experimental drilling equipment operating at 250 rpm, cored one of the shot holes a further 84 ft and retrieved cores of the hard chert band known to exist above the slate

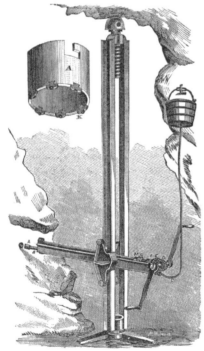

Fig. 14 A representation of the diamond drilling rigs used for tunnelling that were later adapted for the Mont Cenis Tunnel. An insert shows the diamond crown, which has six diamonds (most descriptions refer to eight diamonds). The crown had a bayonet fitting to attach it to the drill rods. A head of water arrangement is shown feeding water through the drill rods. (Silversmith 1867, 228)

Fig. 15 The Machine Tunnelling Company's equipment driving the inclined tunnel at the Croesor United Slate Company's quarries (Haw & Dredge 1870, 405)

vein. The cored hole was drilled 84 ft in 36 hours (2.3 ft per hour) in relatively hard ground, undoubtedly a record at this time. This accomplishment was reported by H.N. McKie, the manager of the Croesor United slate quarries, in a profound letter that he sent to *The Engineer* (McKie 1870, 171). He concluded:

> The above having been actually obtained, I ask you to give it publicity, as I consider it is the forerunner of a change in the system of boring, the importance of which may be difficult to estimate.

He would never really know just how right he was.

This accolade was reinforced the following year when the Machine Tunnelling Company drilled a further borehole in North Wales for the Ffestiniog Slate Quarry Company. James Tuxford, in an open letter to the Machine Tunnelling Company (anon. 1872), declared:

> Before making any statement, I should premise that, being the first of its kind constructed for deep boring, it may be fairly called an experimental machine, that the men engaged were unaccustomed to its use; and that, as the hole progressed, many unexpected, and consequently unprepared for, difficulties were encountered, and had to be overcome.
>
> In face of these disadvantages a hole 318 feet in depth has been put down in 74 working days, of which upwards of 3¼ were wasted in recovering broken bars, and from other causes readily remediable with proper appliances to hand. Of this depth more than 33 per cent. Consisted of Gwynithian, chert, greenstone, and quartz (materials as hard as anything to be met with in boring operations), which was passed through at an average rate of 4.92 feet per day (nearly 5 feet), while in softer strata more than 20 feet have been gone through in a days work.
>
> Before entering into your contract we had employed a gang of experienced mineral borers, who, working in the ordinary methods, in 69 days attained a depth of 74 feet, the rate of progress through the harder strata as above (though reaching 12 to 14 inches when near the surface), at a depth of 70 feet, in no case exceeded four inches per day, and in 35 days only average 2 per day.
>
> The contrast between this and your last days work, passing through 8 feet, of which 59.52 per cent. Consisted of very similar hards, needs little comment.
>
> A further valuable feature of your machine is the production of a cylindrical core of the rock passed through, and which in the present case has reached 26 per cent. of the whole. With the experience you have gained, I believe this percentage will be largely increased, and that the new machine you are now constructing, with certain modifications and improvements, will be found to give more valuable general results.
>
> In conclusion, I think it is right to say, that this hole was stopped on account of our having attained the information we sought to acquire, and that I see nothing to prevent a depth being reached double, or even treble, that above named.'

The Machine Tunnelling Company went on to have further successes. Later in 1871 it drilled a cored borehole for the Stanghow Ironworks Company to prove the Cleveland ironstone (anon. 1872). The borehole commenced on 7 October 1871 and was completed on 14 December 1871, a total of 69 days of short-daylight. Some time was lost due

to adverse weather, with pumps freezing up, but nevertheless it was cored to a total depth of 689 ft 4 in., and averaged a drilling rate of 9.9 ft of core per day.

In 1872 Beaumont with others, having now perfected the drilling equipment for drilling exploratory boreholes (see Fig. 16), formed the Diamond Rock Boring Company Ltd. (National Archives, BT31/1790/6795) to take over the Machine Tunnelling Company. This was a relatively short-lived affair and in 1879, the Diamond Rock Boring Company was dissolved and reformed as the Aqueous Works and Diamond Rock-Boring Company Ltd. (National Archives, London BT31/2501/12890), which survived several re-organisations until it was wound up in 1922.

Fig. 16   The diamond rock-boring machine. Power was provided from a belt off a portable steam engine. The lower gearing transmitted the power to a shaft that ran up the sloped rear of the frame. Further gearing then transmitted the power off the shaft to rotate the drill rods. Other manually controlled gearing controlled drill speed and rate of penetration. (Routledge 1881, 259)

In its first year of operation (1872/73), the Diamond Rock Boring Company drilled eight boreholes (Beaumont 1873). Three were drilled to prove the Cleveland ironstone, where average drill rates of 10.7 to 16.7 ft per day were achieved. The remaining holes were to prove coal. The deepest, at Beeston, near Leeds, reached a depth of 1008 ft in 146 days, a drill rate of 6.9 ft per day. The records indicate that lower drill rates were attained when drilling in Coal Measures, which may suggest that perhaps adverse geological conditions were having some effect on the drilling operation. For example, faulted ground conditions, massive hard sandstone, or even the friable nature of coal seams, could all cause drilling difficulties. Nevertheless, for the next 120 years in Great Britain, by far the greatest number of mineral exploration boreholes would be drilled for coal.

The search for concealed coalfields (1872 to 1920)

It was a paper given in 1855 by Godwin-Austin to the Geological Society of London, titled, 'On the Possible extension of the Coal-Measures beneath the South-Eastern part of England', that traditionally created the impetus to search for concealed coalfields (Godwin-Austin 1855). In his paper Godwin-Austin postulated that the Nord Pas-de-Calais Coalfield of northern France extended westward under the English Channel and would be geologically similar to the Bristol, Somerset and South Wales coalfields, suggesting that a concealed coalfield existed under southern England, certainly under the county of Kent.

The first serious attempt to find coal in southern England was initiated at a meeting of the British Association for the Advancement of Science held at Brighton in 1872. At that meeting the Sub-Wealden Exploration Committee was formed and was subscribed to by many famous geologists of the day (Willett 1878, 2–3). Eventually, two boreholes were drilled by the Diamond Rock Boring Company at Netherfield, near Battle, Sussex. There were drilling difficulties and eventually the first borehole was abandoned and a second one drilled. Boreholes 1 (1017 ft (309.9 m) deep) and 2 (1906 ft (580.9 m)) were stopped in Kimmeridge Clay and Oxford Clay, respectively. Both clays are sub-divisions of the Jurassic. The Committee was dissolved in 1878 because of lack of funds. It concluded that, if they were present, the Coal Measures would be too deep for economic exploitation. In addition, the boreholes were becoming technically difficult to drill (Beaumont 1878).

Meanwhile, on the southern flanks of the Cotswolds at Burford Signet, just to the south of Burford, an independent attempt was being made to discover coal. One borehole drilled by the Diamond Rock Boring Company between 1875 and 1877 did prove Coal Measures at a relatively shallow depth of 1184 ft. The borehole was abandoned at a depth of 1409 ft and was still in Coal Measures, with evidence for at least one coal seam (De Rance 1878, 437–439).

The breakthrough came in 1890 when a borehole sited on Shakespeare Cliff, Dover, proved a sequence of Coal Measures. The discovery was announced in the *Pall Mall Gazette* (anon. 1890, 4).

Sir Edward Watkins Again in Luck

Discovery of a Coal Field in Kent.

For the past two or three years Sir Edward Watkin, the chairman of the South Eastern Railways and Channel Tunnel Companies, has been directing his attention to a search for coal at a point on the South Eastern railways adjoining the experimental heading for the tunnel. The discovery of a bed of coal is announced in the following report from Mr. Francis Brady, C.E. the engineer-in-chief of the South Eastern and Tunnel Companies, under whose directions the operations have been conducted:-

17th Feb 1890

I have pleasure in reporting that coal was reached on Saturday last, the 15th inst., at 1180 feet below the surface. It came up mixed with clay and reduced almost to a powder by the boring tools. A small quantity of clean bright coal found in the clay was tested by burning, and proved to be of good bituminous character. The seam was struck after passing through twenty feet of clay, grits, and blackish shales belonging to the coal meas-

ures, which at this point lie close under the lias, there being only a few intervening beds of sand, limestone, and black clay separating them. The correspondence of the deposits with those found in the Somersetshire coalfield is thus pretty close, the difference consisting in the absence of new red marl at the Shakespeare boring. The lines of bedding in the shale are distinctly horizontal. This is an indication that the coal measures will probably be found at a reasonable depth along the South Eastern Railway to the westward. I beg to hand you herewith two specimens of the clay containing coal, one taken at 1,180 feet and the other at 1,182 feet. I also enclose a specimen of clean coal taken today at 1,183 feet 6 inches from the surface.

To Sir Edward W. Watkin, Bart, M.P. (Signed) F. Brady

The description of the strata samples confirms that the main problem encountered by all the early coal exploration borehole drilling was virtually non-existent, or very poor, core recovery when drilling through a coal seam. Bright bituminous coal by its nature is usually well-cleated (jointed) and can fragment readily. Quite often the presence of a coal seam would be determined by a faster rate of drill penetration combined with traces of coal in the rock samples.

Nevertheless, between 1886 and 1916 a total of 42 boreholes, with a combined total length of 94,945 ft, had been drilled to prove the extent of the Kent Coalfield (Ritchie 1919, 301). The evidence from the borings indicated that the Coal Measures incropped against younger strata just to the east of Canterbury as well as to the north and south – essentially the Kent Coalfield was a concealed coal basin. The original borehole at Shakespeare Cliff took four years to drill (1886 to1890) and reached a total depth of 2300 ft. Later, boreholes sometimes exceeded depths of 3000 ft and were taking about one year to complete.

After the discovery of the Kent Coalfield attempts were made to seek a westward extension, but all proved abortive. The Coal Search Syndicate Ltd. (National Archives, BT31/5193/35145), for example, was formed in 1891 to search for coal in the south-eastern counties of England, but by 1898 had been dissolved. On the north side of the Thames estuary the Eastern Counties Coal Boring and Development Association Ltd. (National Archives, BT31/5560/38682), formed in 1893, petitioned a number of local councils to raise money for exploration. They did succeed in drilling two boreholes, but the discovery of coal proved fickle, and both holes encountered older rocks normally found beneath the Coal Measures.

Elsewhere, in the north Midlands several attempts were made in the early 1800s to sink shafts for coal: at Northampton and in the Evesham area, perhaps looking for concealed extensions to the South Warwickshire Coalfield. As far as it is known, they never encountered Coal Measures. Success was achieved, however, with a borehole drilled for the Batsford and Todenham Coal Syndicate Ltd. (National Archives, BT 31/9741/72564). This borehole was drilled in 1902 just to the north of Moreton-in-Marsh, and was supervised by Professor Lapworth, a geologist from Birmingham University. At a depth of 1022½ ft the borehole entered a 367½ ft thick sequence of Coal Measure strata lying unconformably on older rocks. In the ensuing years several boreholes were drilled between Moreton-in-Marsh and London, notably by the Guildhall Syndicate Ltd. at Calvert Station, north Buckinghamshire, in 1911 (Davies and Pringle 1913), and at Great Missenden prior to 1915, but neither attempt was successful in finding coal (Whittaker 1921, 150).

There was a long-held view that there was a concealed extension of the Somerset Coalfield on the south side of the Mendip Hills (Ussher 1890). Bridgwater Collieries Company Ltd. (National Archives, BT31/12851/104036) was formed in 1909 to examine this possibility. The Company drilled one borehole to a depth of 2148 ft but was still in Triassic sandstones at this point. It was realised that the Coal Measures, if they did exist, would be too deep, and drilling was stopped. The borehole did, however, prove a number of salt horizons between 646 and 719 ft, so the Company established a salt works instead of a colliery (McMurtrie 1911). Surface evidence for these boreholes could certainly still be seen in 1991 (Farrer & Murless 1997).

In total contrast to the Bridgwater Collieries Company, it is unclear what went through the minds of the promoters of the Radnor Coal Syndicate Ltd. (National Archives, BT 31/21301/127749), who drilled the aptly named Folly Farm borehole in 1913 at Presteigne on the Welsh Borders (Fig. 17). Despite the borehole proving a sequence of Silurian rocks lying on Precambrian strata, adjacent to a fault, the company decided to sink a drift mine for coal, which was clearly not the right decision (Cantrill 1917; Parker 1983).

Fig. 17   Drilling the Folly Farm coal exploration borehole at Presteigne, Radnorshire (photograph courtesy of Keith Parker, Presteigne)

However, other attempts to drill for coal on the Welsh borders were more successful, although the proven coal seams were not exploited. In 1890 the Sealand Exploring Company Ltd. (National Archives, BT31/4931/32870) examined the Sealand area on the eastern side of the Flintshire Coalfield just to the north-west of Chester. Three boreholes were drilled through a sequence of superficial and glacial deposits and all proved Coal Measures. The third borehole was the deepest, 1637 ft.

Perhaps the most enigmatic of all the Welsh coalfields is that on Anglesey. Lying approximately 11 km due west of Bangor, it occupies much of the area beneath the Malltraeth Marsh. In essence, the coalfield consists of a narrow block of Carboniferous strata downthrown against Precambrian rock by the Berw Fault. It is partly concealed both by Triassic

sandstones and superficial deposits. The collieries were last worked extensively in the 1870s (Bassett & James 1969). Neither the geological structure nor the actual sequence of coal has ever been accurately determined. This is understandable, as the ground is heavily faulted, and all mining activity had ceased long before techniques to correlate coal seams accurately had been discovered. The Menai Colliery Company Ltd. (National Archives, BT31/13889/121899), formed in 1912, drilled three boreholes at the south-western end of the coalfield. All proved coal seams, the deepest borehole being 1283 ft deep. However, the Company was wound up 1915 without exploiting the coal.

Numerous deep boreholes were also drilled on the east side of England to prove concealed extensions to the large Yorkshire-Nottingham Coalfield, which resulted in new collieries being opened: for example, Thorne Colliery. One limitation to these ventures was the presence of significant water-bearing strata above the Coal Measures. At Thorne Colliery the aquifer was grouted prior to sinking. Wilson (1926) provides some details for these boreholes.

Many of these early coal exploration boreholes were drilled by just three or four boring companies. Vivian's Boring and Exploration Company Ltd. (National Archives, BT31/31156/28663) was probably the largest and most prolific. It was formed in 1889 by John Vivian, who had previously been a superintendent with the Diamond Rock Boring Company. The Vivian Company finished trading in 1904 but, amazingly, carried on drilling boreholes whilst in the hands of the receiver, until 1934.

Early twentieth-century developments in drilling technology

Prior to 1900 the tube that received the core during drilling had not undergone many changes. Diamond-studded coring bits were predominantly used for cutting though hard rock, whilst most bits for cutting through softer rock were toothed, and usually manufactured from hard steel. In addition, despite several attempts to patent the idea, there was no specific means to retain the core in the tube. In most cases the core was usually wedged in the barrel by rock cutting that had become trapped in the annulus between the core and the inner surface of the tube. Eventually the core tube became known as the core-barrel. In 1898 Francis Harley Davis filed a patent application in the USA (Patent 642587 dated 6 February 1900, Apparatus for Boring) for a method that retained the core in the tube, referring to it as a core gripper. Combined with a modified drilling bit, the technique became known as the Calyx drilling method (Davis 1898).

Two years later Davis was granted a patent for a further modification where the diamond bit was replaced by a small section of slotted tube (USA Patent 694535 dated 4 March 1902, Apparatus for boring holes in rock or similar material in the Earth's strata). Chilled steel shot, introduced with the circulating water down the drill string, then escaped through the slot and rolled under the cutting edge of the barrel. It was the rolling action of the chilled shot that cut the rock. The chilled shot method was promoted as a cheaper alternative to using diamonds for drilling. Davis formed several drilling companies that would utilise his patented techniques. The Davis Calyx Patent Drill Manufacturing and Contract Company Ltd. was formed in 1898, but in

1899 the name was changed to the Calyx Drill and Boring Company Ltd. (National Archives, BT31/7929/56873). This company was wound up in 1901 and reformed as the New Calyx Drill and Boring Company Ltd. (National Archives, BT31/16645/70236), which operated until 1923.

It was probably Michael Ahearn, from Denver, Colorado, who made the next major modification to the core-barrel. In 1910 he filed a patent for a 'new and useful double-tube core-barrel'. The object of the invention was to provide 'a core-barrel in which two tubes are employed, means being employed for rotating the outer tube, while the inner tube is held stationary'. The USA patent (patent 982456) for a Double Tube Core Barrel was registered on 24 January 1911 (see Fig. 18). Ahearn used water pressure to keep the inner tube stationary but later this was improved upon with the addition of a thrust-bearing at the top of the inner tube assembly. The idea was simple. The rotating outer tube and drilling bit would do the cutting, with circulated fluids passing between the two tubes. The inner tube would stay stationary as the cut core passed into it. A further modification, a core catcher spring at the base of the inner barrel, ensured that the core did not drop out when the barrel was raised up the borehole. To extract the core, the barrel was dismantled and water pressure was applied at the top end to force the core out. Later modifications included an inner core barrel that could be split in two, or in which a plastic liner was placed

to hold the core together. Later triple core-barrels were also developed. This was an innovation that produced 100% core recovery, and certainly revolutionised coal exploration. Boreholes drilled by this method provided reliable information about coal thickness, and complete recovery of a coal seam that could be physically and chemically analysed.

The drilling bit design also significantly changed at the beginning of the twentieth century. Drilling bits for open holing, as opposed to coring, were usually based on some form of chisel design. In 1908 Howard Hughes senior filed a patent application in the USA (Patent 930759) for a 'drill', which was granted on the 10 August 1909 (see Fig. 18). What made the design different from previous bits was that it consisted of two serrated conical rollers that rotated and turned. The bit cut by rolling the teeth over the rock. This design evolved into the tri-cone toothed roller bit, which has now become the principal method of open-holing a borehole. For really hard ground, roller cones embedded with tungsten buttons can be used. The author remembers the introduction of the tungsten button bit in the early 1970s, when it was most effective for open-holing through the hard South Staffordshire Bunter Pebble Beds, essentially a conglomerate composed of large pebbles of very hard quartzite. Prior to the introduction of this type of bit boreholes through the Pebble Beds were drilled by a percussion drilling rig, a much slower method.

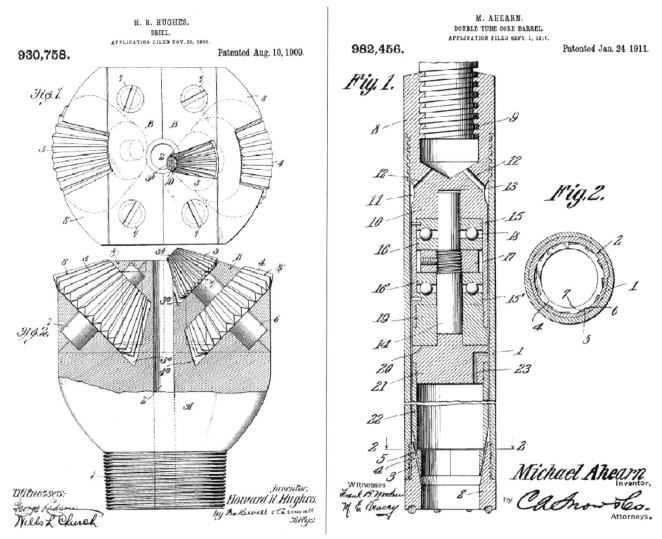

Fig. 18   Two patents that significantly changed the concept of drilling. Left: the di-cone drill bit patented by Howard Hughes senior in 1909, which evolved into the standard tri-cone bit. Right: the double-tubed core barrel patented by Ahearn in 1911. (US Patent Office)

By the 1920s specific drilling equipment manufacturers had become well established in Britain. The English Steel Corporation was an example. Their catalogue, shown in Fig. 19, offered a complete range of equipment for the various drilling companies that by now were advertising their services in appropriate technical periodicals.

It was also about this time that the first onshore boreholes for oil were being drilled. Although some abortive attempts had been made in 1902, at Heathfield, Sussex, initiated by the discovery of natural gas in 1898 (Hewitt 1898), it was not until 1918 that serious oil exploration commenced. Between 1918 and 1921 Messrs S. Pearson and Sons Ltd. drilled 11 boreholes (7 in Derbyshire, 2 in Staffordshire and 2 in Scotland) under a British Government contract. Eventually oil was struck at Hardstoft, Derbyshire, and the first oil well in Britain went into production in June 1919 (Lees & Cox 1937, 157).

However, the two prime reasons for drilling a deep borehole were still to search for a suitable water supply or for coal. After 1947 exploration for coal would escalate.

The National Coal Board (British Coal Corporation after 1987) (1947 to 1994)

The nationalisation of the British coal industry in 1947, with the formation of the National Coal Board, meant that, for the first time, all coal mines and future development would become part of a national plan. There was a period of mine closure, but also one of replacement. A 'Plan For Coal' emerged. Part of that plan was to assess the future potential of all the coalfields by exploration and, where appropriate, to establish new collieries.

North Wales was no exception. Six coal pits were in production. They were, from north to south, Point of Ayr, Llay Main, Bersham, Gresford, Hafod and Ifton. Six boreholes were drilled between 1947 and 1955 (Foster 1947). Two boreholes examined the coal reserves to the east of Gresford Colliery; one borehole was drilled to the east of the closed Wynnstay Colliery; and three boreholes were drilled in the Dudleston area to the east of Ifton Colliery. A combined total of 18,355 ft of hole was drilled. The highest drill rate achieved was about 42 ft per 24 hour day. The boreholes at Dudleston took the longest to drill, varying from 213 days to drill 2444 ft to 606 days to drill two boreholes, the first one being abandoned. From the borehole records it would appear that there were severe drilling problems to the east of Ifton, brought upon by heavily faulted ground, with the consequence that Ifton Colliery was one of the first in the group to be closed. Fig. 20 shows the rig mounted on a lorry that was used to drill some of the boreholes in 1947. Foster (1947) gives a detailed account of the equipment.

However, new collieries were also being established elsewhere in Britain, and involved drilling numerous boreholes to prove the coal reserves. One example was Lea Hall Colliery, south Staffordshire, classed as a 'Superpit' and projected to produce 2 million tonnes of coal per annum. Lea Hall was sited on the eastern side of the Eastern Boundary Fault, which forms the eastern edge of the South Staffordshire Coalfield, to the south of the market town of Rugeley (Hoare & Mitchell 1955). The Coal Measures were concealed by Triassic sandstone, a major aquifer. By

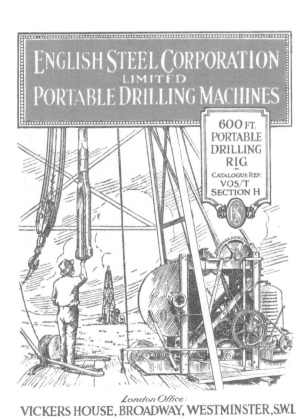

Fig. 19 The cover of the English Steel Corporation's catalogue of drilling equipment c. 1920s. Many of their products were marketed under the 'Vickers' brand. (Author's collection)

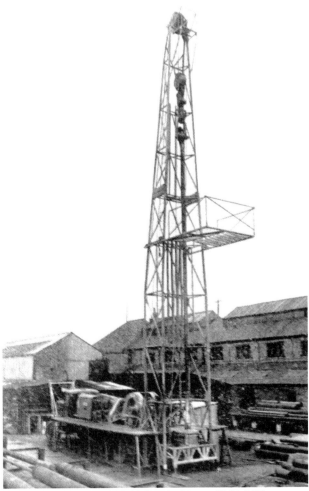

Fig. 20 A lorry-mounted drilling rig (Foster 1947, 259)

the mid-1950s more than 20 boreholes had been drilled to the east of the boundary fault and proved that economically workable reserves were available in at least six coal seams, which justified the sinking of a new pit. Boreholes were drilled for ground freezing purposes prior to sinking the new shafts through the aquifer. This pattern was repeated elsewhere in Britain with the sinking of Daw Mill (south Midlands), Bevercotes (Nottinghamshire) and Kellingley (Yorkshire), to give just a few examples. As these collieries developed, further exploration was conducted to determine safe-cover between the workings and aquifers, as well as to prove extensions for known reserves, and also to help to evaluate the geological structure.

One interesting development occurred in Scotland. A new colliery was proposed at Kirkcaldy, Fife, to be called Seafield. Coal reserves were known to extend under the Firth of Forth, so two boreholes were drilled offshore to prove coal reserves and identify targets for the proposed underground spine roads. The set-up was unique and was devised some twenty years before the offshore exploration for North Sea oil became common practice. Using the company that had manufactured towers for offshore forts in World War II, a drilling platform was constructed (Fig. 21). The upper platform housed the crew's living quarters and the drilling rig. The latter was provided by Foraky, a major boring company, who would drill numerous boreholes for the National Coal Board in the ensuing years (anon. 1955). The two boreholes were successfully completed to depths of 963 m and 549 m and Seafield Colliery started production in 1960. As far as the author is aware, future reserves at Seafield were proved by underground drilling.

The second National Coal Board 'Plan For Coal', in 1974,

produced a flurry of exploration. Five deep boreholes had already been drilled in the Selby area, Yorkshire, between 1964 and 1967 by Foraky, with a high-derrick constructed drilling rig (Goossens 1973). The holes had been drilled to prove the concealed north-eastward extension of the Yorkshire Coalfield under the Vale of York, and to improve upon suspect information produced by nineteenth-century boreholes. So, after an extensive drilling programme, the Selby Coalfield was conceived and planning permission was gained to work the thick Barnsley seam. Five pairs of shafts were ultimately sunk, all through water-bearing ground, and connected to a pair of underground tunnels, partly excavated by full-face tunnelling machines, that surfaced on the west side of the coalfield at Gascoigne Wood. Elsewhere, in the Vale of Belvoir, at the south-eastward end of the Nottinghamshire Coalfield, exploration was also being vigorously conducted. However, after a drawn-out planning enquiry, permission was given for only one pair of shafts at Asfordby. At existing collieries numerous minor mining schemes were approved to access new reserves, all involving site-investigation and exploration boreholes. Fig. 22 shows the interior of a typical core shed where the core was logged. Rock types and coal seams were identified, depths logged, and the coal cores boxed prior to transportation to the laboratory for physical and chemical analysis. Samples of the rocks would also be taken to determine their geotechnical properties. Strata adjacent to coal seams were particularly important, as rocks with a high quartz content could be a sparking risk when struck by the steel picks of mining machinery.

One objective of the 'Plan For Coal' was to identify the coal reserves of Great Britain fully and more accurately. Much of the required exploration work was removed from

Fig. 21   Seafield Colliery: the offshore drilling platform under construction (anon. 1955, 739)

Fig. 22   National Coal Board: inside a typical core shed. The author examines the core whilst Sam Cochrane looks on. (Author's collection)

the working coalfield areas and put under the jurisdiction of a National Exploration Unit with its own team of geologists and a drilling engineer. It was also considered at the time that there was insufficient capacity in UK-based drilling companies to complete the planned extensive programme of exploration work. Consequently, offers were placed with two Canadian companies, Thomson Drilling and Kenting Drilling, and the German company Thyssens to drill a set number of boreholes. Their equipment utilised some of the latest drilling technology. Such was the efficiency of these drilling operations that eventually boreholes over 2500 ft deep could be completed in less than a fortnight. Core-barrel length had increased as well, to 60 ft.

In addition to proving concealed extensions to the known reserves of the Yorkshire-Nottingham Coalfield (Allen 1995), exploration was extended well to the south of the Warwickshire Coalfield. In Oxfordshire three bore-holes (Steeple Aston [1960–61], Apley Barn [1971–72] and Withycombe Farm [1971–7?]) drilled by the British Geological Survey, have proved up to eight seams of coal over 2 ft thick (Dunham & Poole 1974). This exploration work was extended during 'Plan For Coal' and the latest revision of the British Carboniferous shows an Oxfordshire-Berkshire coalfield, although the workability of the coal seams has yet to be determined (Waters *et al.* 2011, chapter 7). Exploration ceased when the coal industry was privatised in 1994. Fig. 23 shows the last deep borehole drilled for the British Coal Corporation (Deep Mines). It was drilled in 1994 at Osgodby, North Yorkshire, to prove the thickness of the Barnsley coal seam for the Riccall Mine, Selby Coalfield. Rigs of this type were very much the standard for drilling boreholes over 2000 ft deep.

The boreholes drilled by the National Coal Board Opencast Executive should also be mentioned. Prior to an opencast coal mine being worked a very tight grid of rela-

tively shallow boreholes would be drilled over the area of the proposed opencast site to prove the reserves and evaluate the geo-technical properties of the surrounding strata. The total footage of boreholes drilled nationally by the Opencast Executive almost certainly exceeded that of those drilled by the National Coal Board (Deep Mines).

The 47 years leading up to the demise of the British coal industry represent a period when major advances were made in obtaining reliable geological information by borehole. Perhaps one day it will be determined just how many kilometres of borehole were drilled by the National Coal Board. To date, it undoubtedly represents the highest amount of exploration drilling activity ever conducted in Great Britain for one specific purpose: to prove coal reserves.

An interesting application for boring arose during the 1984–85 miners' strike, at Fryston Colliery, West Yorkshire. An underground fire had started in the Beeston seam waste in an area accessed by two underground drifts (inclined cross-measure roadways). The worked seam rose away from the base of the drifts so it formed a potential sump. A borehole was drilled into this area from the surface and water was introduced down it to flood the sump area, thereby isolating the fire from the rest of the colliery. To put out the fire, a second borehole was drilled closer to the perceived seat of the fire, nitrogen gas was pumped down the borehole and

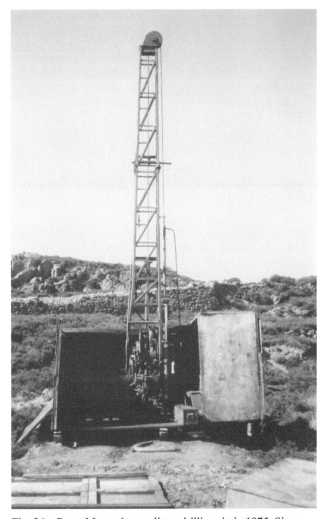

Fig. 24   Parys Mountain: a solitary drilling rig in 1975. Since Anglesey Mining commenced exploration in 1985, there has been a significant increase in the number of exploratory boreholes drilled, both on the surface and from their underground development at Morris Shaft. (Author's collection)

Fig. 23   The last borehole drilled for the British Coal Corporation, at Osgodby, Selby, in 1994 (author's collection)

the fire was extinguished. The intention was to work the face after the strike, so simply flooding the coal face area would have required a large amount of water and ultimately would have damaged the equipment.

Boreholes for proving mineral veins (post 1945)

Borehole exploration for base metals has never been well recorded. Such boreholes often have a high degree of confidentiality attached to them, which ensures that the information does not get into the public domain. There is little doubt that such boreholes have been drilled, though predominantly after the Second World War. In most cases the boreholes were inclined to intersect the near-vertical mineral veins. In the early days of drilling this would have presented a major technical problem. Consequently, it probably was not until the drilling unit could be angled that the first boreholes for base metals were made. In North Wales both Trecastell and Parc mines, on the west side of the Conwy valley, were explored by inclined boreholes prior to being reopened in the 1950s. Some of the problems encountered with this method of prospection are detailed in Dennison and Varvill's (1952) classic paper on the subject. Boreholes have also been drilled to evaluate the Drws-y-Coed copper deposit in the Nantlle valley. Elsewhere, on Parys Mountain, Anglesey, for example, the absence of a drilling rig would seem out of place. Fig. 24 shows a small rig on Parys Mountain in 1975. The Dolgellau gold belt also received similar attention when, in the early 1970s, Rio Tinto Zinc drilled inclined boreholes to evaluate the Turf Mine deposit.

Since the 1960s wire-line drilling has commonly been used for base-metal prospection. A double core-barrel is still used, but the inner tube of the barrel, which contains the core, is detached from the core barrel assembly when it is full. A wire with a latch or 'overshot assembly' on the end is dropped down the string of drill rods. The latch snaps onto the top of, and detaches, the inner tube of the barrel which is then hoisted rapidly within the string of drill rods to the surface. Thus, the core is retrieved without having to pull all of the rods out of the borehole. A second inner core barrel is introduced into the drill string, so that drilling can continue whilst the core is being retrieved from the full inner barrel.

Conclusions

This paper is not a definitive history of drilling, nor of drilling techniques. There are many aspects not included, for example down-hole motors, directional drilling, diverting a borehole, borehole surveying, mud technology, lining boreholes, blow-out prevention, to list but a few. But it is hoped that the paper has given a flavour of the difficult journey that has been undertaken by many to bring us to the level of drilling technology that we see today.

I have so far not mentioned the 'f' word, 'fracking' or, to give the technique its proper title, hydro-fracturing. If 'fracking' is permitted it will undoubtedly bring new advances in drilling technology, especially in directional drilling, and will probably become one of the most heavily regulated and monitored industries in Britain. But if it is a success, and gains public acceptance, perhaps one day the kilometres of borehole needed to release shale gas in economical quantities may even surpass those drilled by the National Coal Board.

Acknowledgements

I would like to acknowledge the help given by the librarians at the National Coal Mining Museum for England, and the staff at the National Archives, Kew, for access to papers and company information, respectively. In addition, I would like to thank David Leigh for reminding me of several facts.

I would also like to thank Geoff Fitton, for information about the Bridgwater Collieries Company, and Keith Parker, Presteigne, for permission to copy the photograph relating to the Radnor Coal Syndicate borehole.

Lastly, and as always, I would like to thank my wife, Margaret (Boo), for proof reading this paper.

Dedication

I would like to dedicate this paper to the memory of Simon 'Sam' Cochrane, who for twenty years served as a geologist in the National Coal Board (Deep Mines), Yorkshire. His untimely death on 21 August 2014, occurred when I was completing this paper and brought back many memories of shared experiences on borehole sites. In their own poignant way, those memories made a contribution to this paper.

References

anon., 1805. *The Repertory of Arts, Manufactures, and Agriculture: Vol. VI – Second Series* (London: Repertory Office)

anon., 1812. *Retrospect of Philosophical, Mechanical, Chemical, and Agricultural Discoveries, VII* (London: John Wyatt), pp. 109–111

anon., 1825. *Register of the Arts and Sciences, II* (London: G. Herbert)

anon., 1829. *Arcana of Science and Annual Register of the Useful Arts* (London: John Limbird)

anon., 1841. 'The artesian well at Grenelle, Paris', *The Penny Magazine of the Society for the Diffusion of Useful Knowledge*, pp. 441–442

anon., 1845. *The Repertory of patent Inventions and other Discoveries and Improvements in Arts, Manufactures, and Agriculture: Enlarged Series – Vol. V (January to June)* (London: Alexander Macintosh), pp. 239–241

anon., 1854. 'Fatal accident', The Essex Standard, and General Advertiser for the Eastern Counties (7 April), p. 2

anon., 1861. 'Singular phenomena near Pontefract', *York Herald*, 4 May, p. 11

anon., 1870. 'Portable steam prospecting drill', *Engineering* (4 Nov.), p. 328

anon., 1872. 'Prospectus for the Diamond Rock-Boring Company Ltd.', *The Times* (7 Dec.), p. 13

anon., 1884. Obituary: Georges Auguste Leschot, *The Times* (16 April), p. 10

anon., 1890. 'Sir Edward Watkins again in luck: discovery of a coal field in Kent', *The Pall Mall Gazette* (20 Feb.), p. 4

anon., 1893. 'Four men drowned in a well', *The Morning Post* (14 July), p. 3

anon., 1955. 'Off-shore coal boring tower', *The Engineer* (27 May), p. 739

anon., n.d.(a). 'Wonders of engineering: the Mont Cenis tunnel', *The World of Wonder: a record of things wonderful in nature, science and art* (London: Cassell, Petter & Galpin)

anon., n.d.(b). 'The Annals of Salt Law of Sichuan Province', in Song Yingxing. *Tiangong Kaiwu* (The Exploitation of the Works of Nature) (1637): see World Digital Library http://www.wdl.org/en/item/3021 (accessed April 2015)

Allen, M.J., 1995. 'Exploration and exploitation of the East Pennine Coalfield', in *European Coal Geology*, ed. M.K.G. Whateley and D.A. Spears, Geological Society Special Publication 82 (London), pp. 207–214

Allen, P.M., & Jackson, A.A., 1985. *Geology of the Country around Harlech: Memoir for 1:50 000 geological sheet 135 with part of sheet 149* (British Geological Survey)

Appleton, D., 1873. *Appleton's Dictionary of Machines, Mechanics, Engine-Work, and Engineering, 1* (New York: D. Appleton and Company), pp. 58–63

Azias, M., 1845. *Explanation and History of the Artesian Well of Grenelle* (Boston: J.N. Bang)

Bassett, T.M., & James, G., 1969. 'Coalmining on Anglesey', *Transactions of the Anglesey Antiquarian Society and Field Club*, pp. 137–163

Beaumont, Major, 1873. 'On the Diamond-Rock Drill', *The Engineer* (5 Sept.), p. 197

Beaumont, Major, 1875. 'On rock boring by the diamond drill and recent applications of the process', *Proceedings of the Institution of Mechanical Engineers*, pp. 92–125

Beaumont, Major, 1878. 'The Search for Coal', *The Standard* (11 March), p. 5

Blackwell, S.H., 1854. 'On Kind's improved method of boring', *Proceedings of the Institution of Mechanical Engineers*, pp. 87–96

Blake, W.P., 1871. *Notices of Mining Machinery and Various Mechanical Appliances in use chiefly in the Pacific States and Territories for Mining, Raising, and Working Ores* (Connecticut, USA)

Cantrill, T.C., 1917. 'On a boring for coal at Presteigne', *Geological Magazine* 6:4, pp. 481–492

Davies, A.M., & Pringle, J., 1913. 'On two deep borings at Calvert Station (north Buckinghamshire) and on the Palaeozoic Floor north of the Thames', *Quarterly Journal of the Geological Society* 69, pp. 308–342

Davis, F.H., 1898. 'Davis Calyx-Drill', *Transactions of the Federated Institution of Mining Engineers* 15, pp. 363–377

Day, L., & McNeil, I. (eds), 2005. *Biographical Dictionary of the History of Technology* (London: Routledge)

Dennison, J.R., & Varvill, W.W., 1952. 'Prospecting with the diamond drill for lead-zinc ores in the British Isles', *Transactions of the Institution of Mining and Metallurgy* 62, pp. 1–21

De Rance, C.E., 1878. 'On the Palaeozoic and Secondary rocks of England, as a source of water-supply, for towns and districts', *Transactions of the Manchester Geological Society* 14, pp. 437–439

Dru, M., 1867. 'On the machinery for boring artesian wells', *Proceedings of the Institution of Mechanical Engineers*, pp. 174–191

Dunham, K.G., & Poole, E.G., 1974. 'The Oxfordshire Coalfield', *Journal of the Geological Society* 130, pp. 387–391

Farrer, J.S., & Murless, B.J., 1997. 'Dunball Salt Works', *Bulletin of the Somerset Industrial Archaeological Society* 74 (April), pp. 16–27

Fauvelle, M., 1847. 'On a new method of boring for arte-sian springs', *Report of the Sixteenth Meeting of the British Association for the Advancement of Science held at Southampton in September 1846*, Reports Section, pp. 105–106

Flinders Petrie, W.M., 1883. *The Pyramids and Temples of Gizeh* (London: Field and Tuer)

Foster, R., 1947. 'North Wales Coalfield, exploration by rapid boring', *Transactions of the Institution of Mining Engineers* 107, pp. 257–272

Godwin-Austin, R., 1855. 'On the possible extension of the Coal-Measures beneath the south-eastern part of England', *Quarterly Journal of the Geological Society* 11, pp. 533–536

Goossens, R.F., 1973. 'Coal reserves in the Selby area', *Transactions of the Institution of Mining Engineers* 132, pp. 237–246

Haw, H.W., & Dredge, J. (eds), 1870. 'Diamond rock-boring machine at Croesor slate quarries', *Engineering: An Illustrated Weekly Journal* IX (10 June), pp. 405–406

Hewitt, J.T., 1898. 'Note on natural gas at Heathfield Station (Sussex)', *Quarterly Journal of the Geological Society* 54, pp. 572–574

Hoare, R.H., & Mitchell, G.H., 1955. 'The geology of the Lea Hall Colliery area, Rugeley, Staffordshire', *Bulletin of the Geological Survey of Great Britain* 7, pp. 13–37

Isler, C., 1921. *Well Boring for Water, Brine and Oil* (London: E. & F.N. Spon)

Kopey, B., 2007. 'Development of drilling techniques from ancient ages to modern times', *Proceedings of the 12th World Congress of the International Federation for the Promotion of Mechanism and Machine Science* (Besançon, France)

Kuhn, O., 2008. *Ancient Chinese Drilling*. http://www.epmag.com/item/print/Ancient-Chinese-drilling_4266 Divestco Inc.

Lees, G.M., & Cox, P.T., 1937. 'The geological basis of the present search for oil in Great Britain by the D'Arcy Exploration Company, Ltd.', *Quarterly Journal of the Geological Society* 93, pp. 156–194

Lister, M., 1699. 'Of Coal Borings, Communicated by Dr. Martin Lister, Fell. Coll. Phys. et R. S which Role or Record He Had from Mr. Maleverer, of Arncliffe in Yorkshire', *Philosophical Transactions* 21, pp. 73–78

Marley, J., 1864. 'On the discovery of rock salt in the New Red Sandstone at Middlesborough', *Transactions of the North of England Institute of Mining Engineers* XIII, pp. 17–24

McKie, H.N., 1870. 'Rapid boring', letter to *The Engineer* (9 Sept.), p. 171

McMurtrie, J., 1911. 'On a boring at Puriton, near Bridgwater, in search of coal south of the Mendip Hills, *Proceedings of the Somersetshire Archaeological and Natural History Society* Third Series 18:2, pp. 25–53

MIME (Midland Institute of Mining Engineers), 1927. *Sections of Strata of the Coal Measures of Yorkshire* (Wakefield)

Nicholson, W., 1809. *The British Encyclopedia; or, Dictionary of Arts and Sciences, VI, S–Z* (London: Longman, Hurst, Rees and Orme)

Norman, F.J., 1901. 'Boring in Japan', *Transactions of the Institute of Mining Engineers* 23, pp. 685–698

Parker, W.K., 1983. 'The Presteigne coal venture, 1912–15',

The Radnorshire Society Transactions 53, pp. 10–27

Ritchie, A.E., 1919. *The Kent Coalfield: its evolution and development* (London: Iron and Coal Trades Review)

Robertson, J.C. (ed.), 1848. 'Gard's Patent Boring and Sinking Machinery', *Mechanics Magazine, Museum, Register, Journal and Gazette* 1291 (6 May), pp. 433–435

Routledge, R., 1881. *Discoveries and Inventions of the Nineteenth Century* (London: George Routledge & Sons)

St. John Durnford, H., 1908. 'Deep boring at Barlow, near Selby', *Transactions of the Institution of Mining Engineers* 34, pp. 426–448

Silversmith, J., 1867. *A Practical Handbook for Mines, Metallurgists, and Assayer* (New York: American Mining Index)

Simonin, L., 1869. *Underground Life: or Mines and Miners*, trans. H.W. Bristow (London: Chapman and Hall), pp. 69–93

Sopwith, T., jun., 1864. 'The actual state of the works on the Mount Cenis tunnel, and description of the machinery employed', *Minutes of the Proceedings of the Institution of Civil Engineers* 23, pp. 258–319

Taylor, I., 1832. *The Mine*, 4th ed. (London: John Harris)

Ussher, W.A.E., 1890. 'On the probable nature and distribution of the Palaeozoic strata beneath the Secondary, etc., rocks of southern counties, with special reference to the prospects of obtaining coal by boring south of the Mendips', *Proceedings of the Somersetshire Archaeological and Natural History Society* 16:2, pp. 88–136

Waters, C.N., *et al.*, 2011. *A Revised Correlation of Carboniferous Rocks in the British Isles*, Geological Society of London Special Report 26 (Bath: Geological Society)

Whittaker, W., 1921. *The Water Supply of Buckinghamshire and Hertfordshire from Underground Sources*, Memoirs of the Geological Survey (HMSO)

Willett, H. (ed.), 1878. *The Record of the Sub-Wealden Exploration* (Brighton: W.J. Smith)

Wilson, G.V., 1926. *The Concealed Coalfield of Yorkshire and Nottinghamshire*, 2nd ed., Memoirs of the Geological Survey England and Wales (HMSO)

Woodcroft, B., 1857. *Subject Matter Index of Patents of Invention, Part 1 (A to M)* (Great Seal Patent Office, Holborn, London)

Woodcroft, B., 1869. *Chronological Index of Patentees and Applicants for Patents of Invention for the Year 1868* (Office of the Commissioners of Patents for Inventions, Holborn, London)

Mine Drainage at Mynydd Parys:
an Intriguing History and Recent Problems

David Jenkins

Abstract: Parys Mountain provides a useful illustration of drainage problems in abandoned mine sites. Its history poses interesting questions as archival information is incomplete, early historical evidence is obscured by a deep blanket of spoil and crucial underground access is limited. Water was important to mining in the processing of ore and also in an efficient system developed for the recovery of dissolved copper by precipitation. Mine shafts were pumped up to the 45 fm level but, on cessation of working, the main drainage adit was dammed and workings flooded to the 25 fm level in the last century. This raised the possibility of serious flooding in nearby Amlwch town by very acidic water. The immediate answer was the de-watering of the mountain down to 45 fm by the pumping of 250,000 m³ containing some 50 tonnes of copper and other contaminants, and discharging to the Irish Sea. Problems nevertheless remain should future underground collapses occur.

Introduction

Abandoned mines can cause problems for the drainage of their area in terms of both water flow and of pollution, as illustrated by the event at Wheal Jane mine in Cornwall (Banks *et al.* 1997) and reviewed generally by Younger *et al.* (2002). This paper focuses on the problems of water flow, as illustrated by the historic mines at Parys Mountain in Anglesey, North Wales. Although heavy metals and acidity are major pollution factors at these mines, it is intended that they will be described in a separate paper.

A mine, or group of mines jointly, was generally served by a deep drainage level which was sited so as to provide the lowest practical outlet of water that the local landscape and finances would allow, and this is illustrated by the '45 fm drainage level' and its adit at Dyffryn Adda on Parys Mountain. Unfortunately, for many abandoned mines there are no maps available detailing drainage management and the relevant history of the workings. Their deep drainage levels may also have become blocked or their location lost.

In terms of mining history, drainage is an important and intriguing feature in its own right, and this is illustrated here by the workings on Parys Mountain. A brief history of the mines will first be given with observations on the water drainage from records and from what can be seen at the present day, to supplement the general accounts of the surface workings on the mountain (Harris 1964; Cockshutt 1965; Rowlands 1966; Hope 1994) and more detailed accounts of the underground workings (Manning 1959; Jenkins in press). This will then lead to the recent recognition of potential drainage problems, to their solution and finally to their aftermath (Jenkins 2004).

Mines on Parys Mountain – general context

The orefield at Parys Mountain (Fig. 1) comprises beds of shales and tuffs enriched in places with copper-iron sulphide (chalcopyrite) and also zinc sulphide (sphalerite) and some lead sulphide (galena). These ores formed as 'smoker' debris on the submarine flanks of volcanoes some 436 million years ago in the early Silurian period. The beds were strongly folded in the following Caledonian orogeny and,

as a result, they now outcrop as the ESE–WNW strata of a tight syncline tilted over to the south which dips at 30–50° to the north (Pointon & Ixer 1980); being on the upper limb of this syncline the succession of these beds in the mines is inverted.

Mining of the ores on Parys Mountain has a long history that has been dated back to the Early Bronze Age, with underground dates recorded of ca. 3900 years BP (Jenkins 1995 and in preparation). There are few records of significant mining subsequently although later activity in the form of a hearth with lead fragments (ingots?), together with surface investigations in earlier centuries, were noted by Pennant (1883). No further mining is recorded until the mid eighteenth century when, after prospection and the 'Great Discovery', exploitation began (traditionally on 2 March 1768) of the copper ore found at a shallow depth, and thereafter extraction on an industrial scale took place.

As the ore-bearing land was divided in ownership, two separate mines of comparable size developed (Fig. 1). Mona mine to the east was owned by Nicholas Bayly (whose descendants were to take the title of Marquess of Anglesey) and Parys mine to the west, owned jointly by the Reverend Hughes and Bayly (Rowlands 1981). Mining was to be on a large scale; a copy of a map of 1786 records over 140 shallow shafts at the larger Mona mine alone (Bangor University Archives, MSS:31603). However, when Bayly's lease to Charles Roe of Macclesfield approached expiry in 1785, there was a removal of the supporting underground portions that were rich in ore. This led to further collapse of ground, already evident in the map of 1786, and it was then decided to work the mines as the two opencasts that are such a striking feature of the mountain surface today.

Both mines, separately, had by then come under the control of a local lawyer, Thomas Williams ('Twm chwarae teg' – 'Tom fair play'), and under his successful management of their development they were soon to underprice other major copper mines in Britain (e.g. in Cornwall) and Europe. Williams by this stage was also marketing Cornwall's copper and effectively had a monopoly of copper and controlled its world prices. Pennant (1810) records that 1500

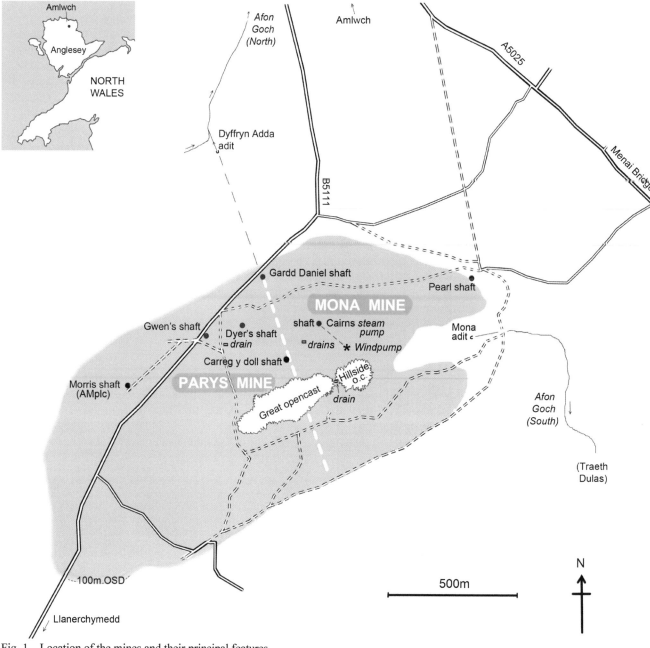

Fig. 1　Location of the mines and their principal features

workers were employed in the mines at their height, which by then dominated world copper. The orefield became known as the 'Copper Mountain' (Rowlands 1964), and Williams was referred to by his contemporary Matthew Boulton as the 'Copper King' (Harris 1964). After Williams died in 1802 he was replaced as manager of Mona mine by the Cornishman Thomas Treweek, who brought the mine back from a period of decline into one of expansion in the 1830s, Parys mine following a similar progression. This involved sinking shafts deeper than the 45 fm level (Parys mine) and extracting ore to greater depths, reaching 156 fm at Gwen's shaft, Parys mine, in the 1870s (Jenkins in press). Deep mining effectively ceased in the 1880s as much larger mines had already been developed overseas, in places such as Chile and Cuba, producing cheaper ore (Rowlands 1984). Since then there have been phases of further assessment and minor production, for example by John Taylor & Sons in the early twentieth century.

More recently, in 1988, Anglesey Mining plc began sinking the 300 m Morris shaft to the north-west of the old mines (Fig. 1), from which they have driven 900 m of exploratory workings. They also extended the number of exploratory diamond cores on the mountain and increased their combined length to a total of over 20 km. By these means they have established the existence of workable reserves of zinc, copper and lead, supplemented by small but financially significant amounts of silver and gold, and plan to restart mining if the economic climate were to justify it. (AMplc 2013)

Early drainage of the mines
The mountain is an area with a modest rainfall of around 850 mm per annum and, as a consequence, the problems this caused were relatively minor and manageable in the working of the mines. The Early Bronze Age mining may have involved some control of surface water, but no evidence for drainage has been found, nor for such activity in following periods from the Roman up to the Middle Ages. There are suggestions of possible Bronze Age drainage management, however, in the mines in mid Wales in the surface 'hushing' of veins (Timberlake 2003). On Parys Mountain the evidence for early eighteenth-century mining drainage is fragmentary,

Fig. 2   Features of mine drainage in the mines: (a) buried stone-walled and capped drainage channel, Mona footway (b) cylinder and piston of wooden drainage pump in Carreg y Doll chamber (c) pump rod in Cairns shaft

any features having been obscured by the later industrial mining and by deposition of its extensive spoil in particular. But it is interesting to read that in 1762 Alexander Fraser discovered ore on the mountain but 'before any quantity could be gotten, the mines were overpowered with water' (Pennant 1810).

Fascinating glimpses can, however, be seen of a possible early system of drains of similar design – entrenched, stone-lined, slab-covered and ca. 0.5 m wide, 0.3 m deep – that occasionally emerge from beneath the later spoil (Figs 1 and 2a). One was encountered in the recent construction of a walkway across a ridge between the Great and Hillside opencasts, which it clearly predated, disappearing into mid-air at one end above the Great Opencast. Two in parallel have been identified in excavations at the Mona footway, buried under a metre of later spoil, and one has been identified beneath the spoil in the northern tips south-east of the road entry to the mines. As such evidence accumulates it may be possible to understand the early drainage system(s) that existed at the beginning of industrial mining on the mountain and, for example, could have serviced the industrial recovery of copper in solution by precipitation ?(e.g. Davidson, this volume).

As the separate Mona and Parys mines developed, they contributed to a 'joint drainage level' at a depth of 45 fm, the only point at which the two mines are joined. This was driven at the beginning of the nineteenth century, and is evidenced by air-shafts on a copy of a map of 1815 (Bangor University Archives, MSS:31602), although a more precise date has yet to be found. This adit is ca. 450 m long and issues on the north side of the mountain at Dyffryn Adda (Fig. 1).

As the mining progressed to greater depths pumping engines were installed at several shafts to raise water to the 45 fm level. The problems for such schemes were discussed at length in correspondence between Boulton & Watt and Mona mine in 1819 in relation to the pumping of the 187 m Pearl shaft at the east end of the mountain. In particular they considered the difficulties arising from the highly corrosive nature of the acid water (pH <3) in the mine that restricted

the use of iron in machinery. Remains of more recent wooden pumps have been found at the 45 fm level in the Parys mines with plungers of ca. 10 cm diameter and, in one case, with remains of its leather clack valve (Fig. 2b). These too would have been used to raise water from lower levels up to the 45 fm drainage level. At Cairns shaft, steam power was supplemented in 1879 by wind power from the summit windmill ('windpump'), transmitted some 100 m by flat-rods and thence, via an angle-bob, down to the 45 fm level where the remains of the pump rod are still present underground in the shaft (Fig. 2c). The use of wind power appears to have lasted only a few years as the base of the windmill is now covered by cinders, presumably from the adjacent steam pump it was supposed to supplement.

Recent history
When deep mining ceased in the late nineteenth century, a concrete dam was installed in the Joint Drainage level, fitted with metal outlet valves, superseding earlier wooden and brick versions (see below). These, when closed over a period of several months, allowed water to build up some 40 m in the mine workings behind the dam to the '25 fm' (as measured in Parys mine) level. On the surface, this was manifested as a perched lake in the bottom of the Great Opencast, tinged brown by the oxidation of the iron dissolved from pyrite. The level then stabilised as water passed through Mona mine and out to the surface from the Mona adit (Fig. 1) from which it drained for some 8 km southwards and inland into Anglesey before turning back northwards to the sea at Traeth Dulas. Underground, the impounded highly acidic water dissolved residual copper from the workings and this was then released from the Dyffryn Adda adit into a series of carefully built ponds ?(Davidson, this volume) and the copper precipitated with remarkable efficiency by the addition of iron plates and scrap iron. This procedure decreased the copper in solution from around 70 ppm to 15 ppm to produce over 30 tons of copper annually (as recorded by Ivor Brown). As in the earlier history of the mines, the dissolved iron was itself subse-

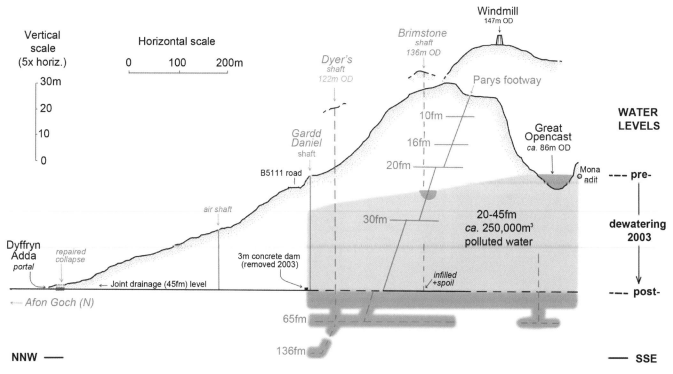

Fig. 3 Vertical section through the mountain along the deep (45 fm) drainage level showing water levels pre- and post de-watering

quently reprecipitated as 'ochre' by aeration (oxidation) in further ponds. This was then recovered and dried to provide another valuable by-product from the underground mining.

This procedure ceased in 1964 (Ivor Brown) but without a management plan as would be required today. The dam itself, 450 m up the Dyffryn Adda adit, was not re-accessed until 2000, when PUG (the Parys Underground Group) repaired a dangerous collapse in the adit entry (Fig. 3) and then excavated through the considerable deposits of orange ochre which then blocked the passage: when the dam was reached the three (Saunders) valves in it proved to be inoperative. It was then realised that a potentially dangerous situation would arise should this concrete dam fail under the acidic mine conditions. This would release a volume of polluted water that was calculated from passage length on archive maps (and using an estimated 'fudge' factor to account for the extensive stopes not shown on the maps) to be of the order of 50,000 m³ with a 40 m initial head, as depicted in the vertical section of the mine (Fig. 3). Any water so released would flood down the adit into the Afon Goch North and thence through the town of Amlwch to the sea.

This situation was reported to the then Countryside Council for Wales (CCW), the County Council, the Environment Agency, the Marquess of Anglesey (landowner) and Anglesey Mining, who held the mining rights to the mountain. As a result an advisory committee was set up to resolve this problem under the chairmanship of Michael Barton (Isle of Anglesey County Council) and under the guidance of Professor Paul Younger of Newcastle University. This concluded with the recommendation that the mountain should be de-watered down to the deep drainage 45 fm (Parys mine) level, a decision accelerated by

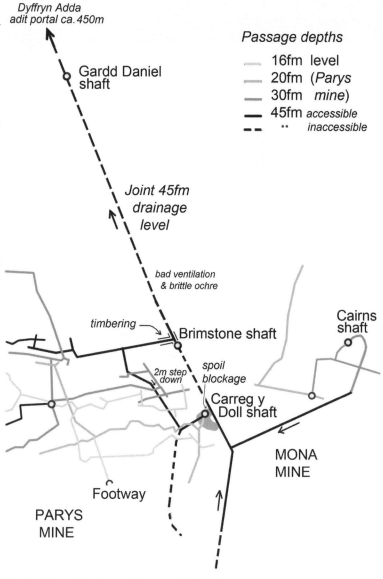

Fig. 4 Map of blockage at Carreg y Doll shaft

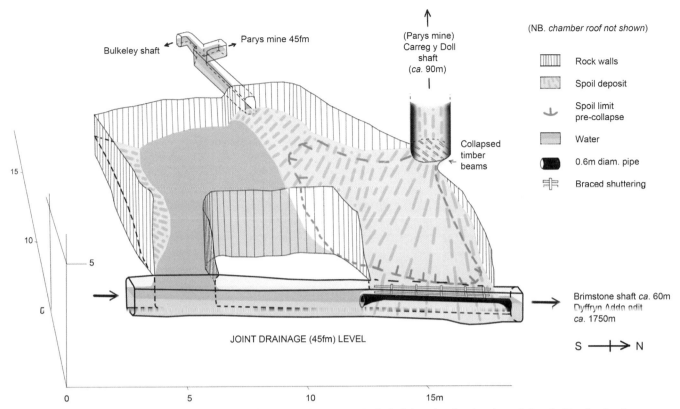

Fig. 5   Block diagram showing the collapsed spoil from (Parys) Carreg y Doll shaft into the chamber, bounded to the East by the deep drainage level

the loss of the Longannet deep coal mine system in Scotland due to flooding, possibly by the failure of a concrete dam under similar circumstances (HMIM-HSE 2002).

De-watering of the mountain

The proposed scheme to de-water the mountain was adopted and an emergency grant was obtained from the Welsh Assembly for its realisation. To implement the scheme it was first necessary to identify a shaft 'upstream' of the dam that was connected to workings throughout the two mines. This was achieved by the trial pumping of 30 m³ into water wagons from a possible shaft when its suitability, in terms of underground drainage connections, would be indicated by a minimal drop in the water level; by this criterion Gardd Daniel shaft (Figs 1 and 3) was identified. Ironically, the water was then returned from the wagons back into the shaft to avoid the otherwise very expensive procedure of transporting 'a polluted material, mine water', to the Midlands for official disposal.

Over 250,000 m³ of water were removed from the mines and allowed to flow down Afon Goch North and directly into the Irish Sea over a period of 3 months in 2003. This was five times the estimated volume and allowed a more relevant 'fudge' factor to be calculated for overall volume of passages and work chambers in both mines, as described above. When removed, the dam was found to be around 3 m thick, with evidence for an earlier brick dam just beyond with a wooden water valve/shutter system operated from the surface at Gardd Daniel shaft during the early operation of the precipitation process.

De-watering subsequently allowed workings in the Parys mine to be explored successively down to the 30 fm and then to the 45 fm level. Here the Joint Drainage level was entered, which gave access 'upstream' to a link to the Mona mine

(Fig. 4) that could then be followed upwards through successive levels towards the surface. Later, in July 2009, PUG excavated an entry to Mona mine from the surface via its collapsed 'footway', so providing a second safe access into this mine to supplement the wet 'through route' between the two mines. Overall the danger of possible flooding of Amlwch had been averted, and the length of passages becoming accessible for on-going exploration, recording and conservation, increased to some 10 km, of which 65% has now been entered. However, the successful de-watering was to have unpredicted consequences.

Subsequent consequences and remedies

One inevitable consequence of de-watering was a decreased stability of vulnerable flooded structures. This was dramatically illustrated by the collapse of accumulated spoil trapped in the Carreg y Doll shaft, whose entry into the roof of Carreg y Doll chamber had been boarded up (Fig. 5). The weighting on this submerged boarding had been increased by the loss of up-thrust from the displaced water, and the shaft delivered its spoil content as an expanded cone of sediment into the Carreg y Doll chamber in Parys mine. Unfortunately this nearly blocked the Joint Drainage level that ran along the east side of the chamber, as shown in Fig. 5; any further spoil would have sealed the drainage tunnel completely and caused the water level to rise back up to the 20 fathom level. Consequently a dangerous situation would then have arisen since the blockage at this point in the drainage tunnel would have quickly submerged the chamber and approach passages. The blockage would therefore have become inaccessible from downstream within the mines and also from upstream due to a 2 m step-up in the connecting passage to Brimstone shaft by-passing the blockage (Fig. 3), which would quickly have been flooded. The very low permeability observed in

Fig. 6   Drainage in Carreg y Doll chamber, 45 fm level, Parys mine: (a) the conical spoil deposit impeding water flow in the drainage level (b) emplacement of the drainage tube to ensure unimpeded drainage

the country rock, as evident in the initial differing water levels in Dyers shaft and small adjacent stopes after de-watering (Figs 1 and 3), might have equalised water levels in the long term but this would not alter accessibility. This low permeability was also evident in the gradient of the perched water table (Fig. 3) observed before de-watering occurred.

An emergency scheme was therefore carried out by PUG to ensure unimpeded flow of the drainage across the east side of Carreg y Doll chamber. This involved digging a trench in the newly expanded spoil cone down to the water level, stabilising it with shuttering, and then emplacing a 0.6 m diameter polyethylene pipe which linked the tunnels at the two sides of the spoil heap (Fig. 5). The pipe was carried down from the surface to the chamber in Parys mine in three 2 m sections, which required the temporary removal of supporting stemples in some passages *en route*. The sections were then butt-jointed, covered and sealed in with spoil (Fig. 6), and by this means the problem was successfully solved.

However, further potentially serious complications could still arise. As can be seen from the section and map (Figs 3 and 4), a 250 m length of the Joint Drainage level downstream from the Carreg y Doll chamber has not yet been entered from either end because of poor air quality and underwater obstructions. It has therefore not been possible to assess whether it could be subject to further blockages through a future collapse. Such a blockage would rapidly become inaccessible and be sealed off as the water level rose back to its pre-de-watering 25 fm level. As a contingency measure, the dam in the Dyffryn Adda level could be replaced and fitted with valves that could be adjusted under such conditions. The mine drainage would then revert to that prior to de-watering in 2003, but under controlled conditions. Another contingency measure would be to continuously monitor water level in a nearby shaft, such as Dyer's (Figs 1 and 3).

There was a further unforeseen consequence of the de-watering. The outflow from Mona adit was greatly reduced after the diversion of the drainage to the Afon Goch North

via Dyffryn Adda adit. A positive result was the removal of pollution in the Afon Goch South such that its ecology has recovered with the return of a fish population and of kingfishers. On the negative side, the reduction in outflow resulted in the drying out of the extensive precipitation ponds that Mona adit originally fed. This in turn caused the wind-blow of dust from their surfaces to nearby houses at Henwaith, a dust composed of iron ochre that concentrates low levels of arsenic. These levels were found to be marginally above those permitted on health grounds and necessitated an expensive remediation process of stabilising some surfaces by revegetation with heather and others by keeping them wet with water circulated by a solar-powered pump.

Conclusions

The events described illustrate the problems that can arise in the management of drainage in abandoned mines and in schemes such as de-watering. As at many other mines in the UK, all entries to those on Parys Mountain were fully capped with concrete for safety and insurance reasons in 1980, a common practice in the last century. Underground access through the capping, for heritage and research purposes, was only regained by PUG in 1996 through the kind permission of the late Marquess of Anglesey and, for reasons of insurance, access is now controlled by PUG. In the course of subsequent exploration and recording PUG became incidentally aware of the potential problems concerning drainage. Although these and subsequent difficulties have been resolved successfully for the moment, future management will require continued surveillance and proposals for contingency planning by the appropriate authorities.

This particular case history is presented to illustrate the need, where possible, for continued access to abandoned mines. Experienced groups with appropriate insurance can monitor conditions and recognise in advance potential problems. They could then recommend possible solutions, validated through a qualified mining engineer, to appropriate authorities. When problems do arise in mine drainage systems an immediate response is often necessary to either remedy the problem fully or to prevent it becoming worse pending a satisfactory solution being agreed and implemented. If possible, contingency funding and arrangements should therefore be considered in advance of the occurrence of an emergency.

Acknowledgements

In writing this paper the help and comments, particularly of Oliver Burrows, and of colleagues Lionel Joynson (PUG) and Ian Cuthbertson (Anglesey Mining plc), are gratefully acknowledged. Simon Lowe kindly allowed his photograph of Cairns shaft (Fig. 2c) to be used.

References

AMplc, 2013. Annual Report (and previous reports)

Banks, D., Younger, P.L., Arnesen, R.T., Iversen, E.R. & Banks, S.B., 1997. 'Mine-water chemistry: the good, the bad and the ugly', *Environmental Geology* 32, pp. 157–174

Cockshutt, E., 1965. 'The Parys Mountain copper mine in the Isle of Anglesey', *Archaeologia Cambrensis* 114, pp. 87–111

Harris, J.R., 1964. *Copper King*, Liverpool

HMIM-HSE, 2002. 'Report on the Circumstances Surrounding the Flooding of the Longannet Mine, Fife, Scotland', HM Inspectorate of Mines, Health and Safety Executive (42pp)

Hope, B.H., 1994. *A Curious Place: the industrial history of Amlwch (1550–1950)* (Wrexham: Bridge Books)

Jenkins, D.A., 1995. 'Mynydd Parys copper mines', *Archaeology in Wales* 35, pp. 35–37

Jenkins, D.A., 2004. 'Mynydd Parys', in *Urban Geology in Wales*, ed. D. Nichol, M.G. Bassett and V.K. Deisler, National Museums & Galleries of Wales: Geological Series no. 23 (Cardiff), pp. 144–151 (Mine water in Wales)

Jenkins, D.A., in press. 'Management of the mining heritage on Mynydd Parys', in *Mining Legacies* (Bulletin of the Peak District Mines Historical Society)

Jenkins, D.A., in preparation. 'Mining for copper in the Early Bronze Age: Parys Mountain, Anglesey'

Manning, W., 1959. 'The Parys and Mona mines in Anglesey', in *The Future of Non-Ferrous Mining in GB and Ireland* (London: Institution of Mining and Metallurgy), pp. 313–328

Pennant, T., 1810. *Tours in Wales*, vol. 3 (London), pp. 53–67

Pointon, C.R., & Ixer, R.A., 1980. 'Parys Mountain mineral deposit, Anglesey, Wales: geology and ore mineralogy',. *Trans. Institution of Mining and Metallurgy* (Section B: applied earth science) 89, pp. B143–155

Rowlands, J., 1981. *Copper Mountain*, 2nd ed. (Llangefni)

Timberlake, S., 2003. *Excavations on Copa Hill, Cwmystwyth (1986–1999): an Early Bronze Age copper mine within the uplands of Central Wales*, BAR British Series 348 (Archaeopress/British Archaeological Reports)

Younger, P.L., Banwart, S.A., & Hedin, R.S., 2002. *Mine Water: hydrology, pollution, remediation* (Kluwer Academic Publishers)

Copper Precipitation at Parys Mountain, Anglesey

Andrew Davidson and David Gwyn

Abstract: This paper focuses on the extraction of copper by precipitation as carried out at Parys Mountain, Amlwch, Anglesey. The historical origins of the process in eastern Europe are examined, followed by a discussion of its introduction into Britain and Wales. Descriptions by visitors to the mines when the pits were in operation are examined and their descriptions compared to the present archaeological remains. The results of the comparison suggest a development from smaller, often square, pits to large rectangular pits separated by low wide walls and interconnected by sluices.

Introduction

Archaeological remains at the former copper mines of Parys Mountain, Anglesey, contain the best known examples of structures associated with copper precipitation in the United Kingdom, and possibly in Europe. These take the form of extensive chequer-board patterns of shallow tanks or pits, often in conjunction with larger and deeper lakes for the extraction of ochre, and fragmentary remains of associated furnaces. Recent surveys of several of these structures by Gwynedd Archaeological Trust have contributed to a better understanding of how they worked, and their development. The results of these surveys are discussed below, but prefaced by a discussion of the origins of the method in central and eastern Europe as described in texts of the seventeenth and eighteenth centuries, and the subsequent dissemination of the technique into Britain and Ireland.

The precipitation process

This process, also called cementation, relies on the presence of copper ions in solution, that is, copper rich waters either obtained directly from the mines through drainage or pumping, or enhanced by steeping the water in pools into which were placed low grade ores. The copper is precipitated out of the solution by the addition of iron. Greenly (1919) gives the formula $CuSo_4 + Fe > Cu+FeSo_4$ for the process, that is, copper sulphate in solution plus solid iron gives solid copper plus iron sulphate in solution. The process as carried out at Parys Mountain is further described below but essentially the copper solution was collected in large ponds, allowed to settle, and then run into rectangular tanks, into which iron objects were placed for precipitation to take place. The resulting copper, in the form of a sludge, was removed from the tanks and dried before smelting.

The origins of precipitation as a means of production

The precipitation of copper in water was practised at a number of mine sites throughout Europe, though none on such an enormous scale as Mynydd Parys. It is not entirely clear how knowledge of the possibilities of copper precipitation might have spread, or whether separate discoveries took place. However, from the sixteenth century onwards, the most advanced and the most influential mining-fields in terms of technology transfer were those of the German-speaking world, which in practice also meant Hungary and Russia, whither many German miners went. A few made

their way westwards – the Hochstetters to the Mines Royal in England in the 1560s, German labourers to Talybont in Cardiganshire in the 1660s – and they were enough to bring the use of railways, flat rods and explosives with them to the British Isles (Rees 1968, 440–442). However, there is no evidence that they brought with them knowledge of precipitation, and the practice is mentioned in neither Biringuccio's *Pirotechnia* (1540) nor Agricola's *De Re Metallica* (1556).

As well as the movement of personnel, written sources can be instrumental in technology transfer. For many years a state of warfare or at best armed truce between Christendom and Islam into the eighteenth century made it difficult to learn much about what was happening in those mines which lay near the border between the Hapsburgs and the Ottomans. Even so, there is evidence for the visits made to mining areas by interested observers from elsewhere in Europe, who often wrote up an account of their travels. The digitisation of this historic source-material online has made it possible to trace both the evolution of precipitation as a technology and dissemination of knowledge.

Thomas Pennant's (1783, 270) account of precipitation at Parys, published not long after the mine had broken through to the low-grade but easily accessible copper ore in 1768, mentions that precipitation was:

> … far from new; it has been practised long in the Wicklow mines in Ireland, and above a century in those of Hern-grundt in Hungary, where it is called Ziment Copper.

The mine at Herren grund[1] (Hungarian: Úrvölgy) and the principal nearby mining town of Neusohl (Hungarian: Besztercebánya) now go under their Slovak names, Banská Bystrica and Spania-Dolina respectively.

Pennant continues:

> The waters of the Hungarian mines are much more strongly impregnated with copper than those of Parys mountain. The first effects its operations in about twelve or twenty days; the last requires two months.

He footnotes two sources, one of which is 'Brown's travels', the other of which is 'Keysler's travels'. The first of these was from the pen of Dr Edward Brown, son of Sir Thomas Browne of Urn Burial fame, who embarked on a

---

1 Variously Herrngrund, Herren grund or Herren grundt.

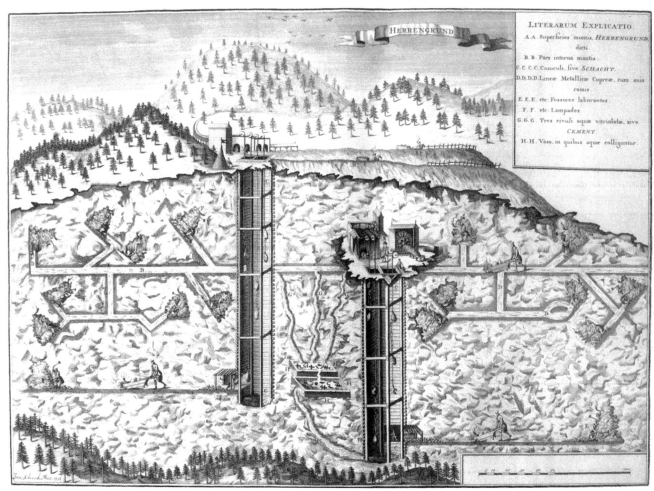

Fig. 1   The mines at Herrengrund in 1726, showing two pits fed by three streams where precipitation is being undertaken (Marsigli 1726)

Fig. 2   A map of 1784–86 (NMR C8235) which shows a set of early precipitation pits, now buried beneath spoil. The small block of 10 pits to the east is the precursor of the Hillside system. (Crown Copyright: RCAHMW)

journey through central Europe in 1668 which took in the mines of Hungary (*Biographia Britannica*, 1000).

There are also two Springs of a Vitriolat water which turn Iron into Copper, called the old and the new Ziment; these springs lye very deep in the Mine, and the Iron is ordinarily left in the water fourteen days. These waters are very profitable, seeing that the worst sort of Iron, and useless old Iron is hereby turned into the purest sort of Copper, which hath this commendation above other Copper to be more ductile, malleable, and easily melted; and I have melted it without the addition of any other substance, without difficulty ... Some will not have this to be a Transmutation of one Metal into another, but that this Water of the Ziment being saturated with a Vitroleum Veneris, and meeting with such a body so ready to receive it as Mars, it deposeth Venus, who immediately insinuateth herself so far into Mars, that she doeth dividere & imperare, and at last she substitutes her own body, and precipitates that of Mars. (Brown 1673, 109)

The second source is John George Keysler, *Travels Through Germany: Hungary, Bohemia, Switzerland, Italy, and Lorrain*, which does not appear to have been digitised but is a translation of Johann Georg Keysler, *Neueste Reisen durch Deutschland, Böhmen, Ungarn, die Schweiz, Italien und Lothringen* (Hanover, 1751). The relevant passage reads in modern translation:

Herrengrund, a mile from Neusohl, is also famous on account of the spring which under normal conditions changes iron into copper.

In these circumstances, the water, wherein the iron is placed, is nothing more than a solution of copper in which the iron is dissolved, leaving copper particles.

This occurs over two or three weeks; if the iron remains too long in the ore-rich water (*camentwasser*) it disintegrates into a copper powder. One can also carry out the same experiment with ordinary water in which a strong solution of Hungarian or Cypriot vitriol has been dissolved. (Other types of vitriol are not suitable because they draw out the iron).

Where the water flows away from the above-mentioned Herrengrund spring, a lot of Berggrun (?verdigris), Borax or Chrysocolla, nothing more than a coating/layer of *uberreife* (?over-ripe/over saturated) copper, is washed out and is green in colour. Blue, green red and white vitriol are found in Herrengrund.

An earlier and more detailed account of the mine which Pennant does not seem to have seen is Luigi Ferdinando Marsigli's *Danubius-Pannonico-Mysicus*, volume 3 of 1726. The text and the accompanying drawing (Fig. 1) make clear that copper-rich water flowing in three streams was collected in wooden tanks where the copper was precipitated. The drawing implies a fairly small system, and it seems to be intended as an accurate depiction of the mine rather than as reflection of the ideal qualities of such an undertaking.

The Reverend Dr William Henry of Dublin in 1751 described an apparently accidental discovery 'which happen'd not long ago', when a miner at Cronebane mine in County Wicklow left an iron shovel in the stream issuing from the mine, which became encrusted with copper. On this basis pits 10 feet by 4 feet in plan were built, with

stone and lime sides and flag floors, perhaps from the small nearby slate workings, in which iron bars were laid (Henry 1751, 500–503). Yet both Brown and Marsigli are referenced by Dr Henry, which leaves open the possibility that both happenstance and published sources played a part in the general transfer of this technology.

Eight years later, an account was published by the naturalist Emanuel Mendes da Costa in *The Critical Review* under Tobias Smollett's editorship. Mendes da Costa observes that water was precipitated from copper in mines in Cornwall, Yorkshire, Cumberland and Derbyshire, and that 'some quantity of this ochre has lately been found in the copper-mines of Wicklow county in Ireland' (but does not mention Parys). He states that this method was to be found in Saxony, Bohemia, Poland and Sweden, but the greatest quantity, and of the finest sort, in the kingdom of Hungary. He translates directly from the mineralogist Franz Ernst Brückmann (1697–1753), who states that at:

Neusohl, in the mountainous territory called Herrengrund, in Hungary ... the waters of those mines abound with this substance; the miners, to collect it, turn and carry off these waters by numbers of wooden pipes, to great square wooden reservoirs, made of large planks, wherein the water deposits this green substance; when they have thus obtained a large quantity of the ochre, and that the reservoirs are incrusted with it to a good thickness, the water being turned off, they scrape off the chrysocolla, or green ochre from these vessels , then dry it and divide it into three sorts; the first sort, which is the worst or common kind, is that taken out of the first or upper reservoir, wherein the water first falls; the second or middle sort, is in like manner collected from the second reservoir; and the third sort, which is the finest and most valuable, they collect from the lower reservoir, or wherein the water flows out last of all: These reservoirs are placed above each other, but communicate by means of inclining wooden pipes, so that the first is placed higher than the second, and the second higher than third, and the water gradually flows from the uppermost to the lowest reservoir.

These ochres, thus collected, are afterwards exposed to a clear summer sunshine to dry, and are then put up for sale; the first, or worst sort, is impure, or gritty, and of a dusky green colour; the second sort is somewhat purer, of a middling colour, between the dark green of the first sort, and the bright green of the third or best sort; and the third sort is entirely fine, pure, and of a most beautiful bright green colour, and suffers no depurations or washings before it is used, as the other two sorts, which are again washed to free them from their heterogeneous parts.

At Richtergrund, about a mile from Neusohl, this ochre is also collected in the same manner; but not in so great quantities as at Neusohl.

The Encyclopaedia Britannica; Or, A Dictionary of Arts, Sciences, and Miscellaneous Literature, Volume 2 (1797), the *New Encyclopaedia* (1807) and the *Encyclopaedia Perthensis; or, Universal dictionary of Knowledge* (1816) all quote and acknowledge Pennant word-for-word.

Kauffman in 1803 observes:

Copper dissolved by the vitriolic acid. At Hern-grundt near Newsol in Upper Hungary, there are two springs, called the Old and New Ziment, so richly impregnated with Copper dissolved by the vitriolic acid, that iron thrown into them is dissolved by the latter, and the Copper precipitated in its metallic form, in the place of the iron. Some pits made purposely for this operation, are filled with the water of the springs, and old iron is thrown in, which in twelve to twenty days is taken out, and the Copper scraped off. The metal thus procured, differs little from native Copper. One hundred tons of iron by this method yield eighty-four to ninety tons of Copper. By the like process, such quantities of copper have of late years been obtained, from some spring issuing from the celebrated Copper mines at Arklow, in the county of Wicklow, in Ireland, that these springs are now of as much consequence as the mines themselves. One ton of iron there, produces sixteen cwt of fine Copper, selling for ten pounds sterling a ton more, than the Copper fluxed from the ore.

The evidence of Mendes da Costa suggests that precipitation was introduced at Parys after 1759, and that it was already a well known technology. It is unlikely that it was introduced directly to Parys by experts from central Europe, even though there was clearly interest in the practice. It is more likely that it had been introduced to the British Isles and Ireland earlier on.

The date for the introduction of precipitation to Mynydd Parys remains uncertain, though it was clearly in use by 1771 (Smith 2005, 340; Bangor University, Kinmel 1807), when 60 tons of iron was placed in pits. The mines were under the management of Charles Roe & Co, and it is probable they were responsible for the introduction of the process. Extensive pits on the south side of the mountain and in Dyffryn Coch, the valley to the south, are marked on both mines on a map of 1784–86 (NMR (National Monuments Record of Wales) C8235, Fig. 2). By 1815 the joint level was in operation. This fed precipitation pits at Dyffryn Adda, to the north of the mountain, where a furnace to dry the precipitate had been constructed (NMR C8236). By 1824, if not before, the extensive systems on the east of the mountain, known as the Hillside precipitation pits were in existence (British Library Maps 6135(1)).

Contemporary descriptions of the precipitation process at Parys Mountain

There are numerous descriptions of the precipitation process as it was undertaken at Parys Mountain, and this evidence can be supplemented from detailed maps. There are no known contemporary depictions of the precipitation pits until we get photographs of the early twentieth century. Painters sought out the sublime views of the great opencast, and were less interested in the more mundane views provided by the precipitation process (Lord 1998, 22–25).

Of the contemporary writers Pennant is the earliest, and often subsequently quoted, but other well known descriptions are given by Aikin (1797), Bingley (1800), Evans (1812), Faraday (Tomos 1972) and Lentin (Rothwell 2007), and further information is readily available in the *Mining Journal*. All carry similar descriptions of the process, though with a few minor variations. A description given in the *Mining Journal* is perhaps one of the clearest and most detailed.

The water is raised by means of wooden pumps, and stored in reservoirs specially prepared for its reception. Here it deposits any clay and grit contained, and when clear it is tapped off as required into their precipitation tanks. These tanks are filled with old iron, and the cupreous water is allowed to flow first into the head 'pit,' and from it continuously flows through a series which is lengthened or shortened as found necessary with the varying strengths of the water passing through. Four times a year the precipitate thus obtained is thus collected. The water is first drawn off, all the iron is then placed upon the "backs" of the wavy bottom, and the copper attached to it is washed away by throwing violently against it by means of scoops the water still remaining in the hollows. This process accomplished, the precipitate is allowed to subside, and the clear water is drawn off by taking out the plugs placed in the middle of each trough. The precipitate is then carried in casks to a pit, where it gradually acquires the consistency of soft mud, and is then taken to a reverberatory furnace where it is dried and made ready for smelting. The water afterwards flows into large reservoirs, some of several acres extent, and there by a natural process deposits a sediment of subpersulphate of iron, or precipitated yellow ochre. Some thousands of tons of this article are annually sold; it is used largely as a gas-purifying material, and considerable quantities are calcined for the production of the various iron oxide paints and Venetian red. These mineral waters must have issued from the ground for a very long period, for south of the mountain there is an extensive peaty tract, portions of which are cupreous, while others contain so much ochre as to produce an excellent gas purifying material. When the price of copper was so high the cupreous peat was largely burned, and the ashes thus obtained, containing from 2 to 4 per cent of metallic copper, were smelted with other ores of the mine. The streams of water proceeding from the mine are of a deep port wine colour when first pumped out, they gradually become lighter in colour as they deposit the ochre; when they enter the sea they impart to it a yellow tinge, which sometimes stretches out a mile or more into the channel. (*Mining Journal* 1878, 943)

Lentin records the steeping of water in pits filled with low grade ore for 12 to 16 hours; the ore is then taken for processing, and the water fed into the precipitation pit. Lentin also mentions agitation of the iron with a rake so that pieces of iron rub against each other and scrape off the copper, and also the scraping of iron plates with a 4 foot wide copper scraper fitted with a wooden handle. Pennant also mentions the use of new iron plates to supplement old iron. The plates were held in place by combs along the side of the pits, and could not therefore be agitated in the same way as iron objects, hence the need to scrape them. Cockshutt (1965) mentions sparging of tips to further enrich the water in the mine before it was pumped up.

Sequences of pits were laid at a slight slope, so that the solution could be moved sequentially through purpose built sluices into pits lower down the sequence (Lentin mentions a series of three pits). The copper-rich water was left approximately eight days in each pit before being drawn off to a lower set of tanks, and then eventually into the ochre ponds below. The richer ore was therefore always in the uppermost tanks, whilst lower down it became subsequently poorer. The tanks were emptied of copper sludge approximately four times a year. This was achieved by draining off the water through the sluice gates. The resulting sludge was cut into pieces the size of bricks before being dried in the air, and then subsequently in a furnace.

The process as recorded by contemporary writers is shown in Fig. 3.

There is some discrepancy in the size of the precipitation pits as recorded by visitors of the late eighteenth and early nineteenth centuries. These suggest both a mixture of sizes and, combined with other evidence, an increase in size during the nineteenth century. None of the writers specify which pits they are referring to, but Faraday, in 1819, gives measurements of 12 feet long, 8 feet wide by 18 inches deep, which is far smaller than any of the surviving pits (Tomos 1972). His measurements differ significantly from those of Pennant, who in 1783 recorded dimensions of 36 feet long, 12–15 feet wide and 20 inches deep (Pennant 1783). These dimensions are similar to those of the older Dyffryn Coch pits. For comparison, the surviving Hillside pits are some 76 feet long by 35 feet wide, and the Henwaith pits up to 130 feet long.

Maps up to 1824 tend to confirm the small size of the pits as described by Lentin and Pennant. The map evidence, as shown on the OS 25 inch maps, suggests that between 1824 and the late nineteenth century layout was regularised, and the pits made considerably larger. This is evident at the central Hillside pits and the Henwaith pits. Smaller pits can still be found on the mountain, particularly those on the north side of the Dyffryn Coch valley, now largely buried in heather, whilst the pits at Dyffryn Adda do not seem to have changed from their original construction c. 1815.

References to precipitation elsewhere in north Wales are scarce, and at present confined to the copper mines at Llanberis. The Reverend John Evans in 1798 recorded that 'Some of the ore has lately been roasted here, and a few pits formed for making ziment copper, like those already described in the vicinity of Parys Mountain' (Evans 1812, 423). The introduction of precipitation at Llanberis is later credited to Charles Roe and Co, who are likely to have been responsible for introducing the method to Parys Mountain (Smith 2005, 514–515). More widely, modern descriptions are provided for nineteenth-century and early twentieth-century precipitation of copper at the Avoca mines in Ireland and Rio Tinto mines in Spain (Schwartz and Critchley 2011, 53; Willies 1989, 72–73). At the former a slightly different process had developed from that used at Parys Mountain, and by the mid-nineteenth century mine water was 'led through a series of wooden launders inclined at angles of 10 degrees or 12 degrees interrupted at intervals by a hutch' (Schwartz and Critchley 2011, 53, where further details of the process are given, quoting from Argall 1906).

Archaeological remains of the precipitation process at Parys Mountain

Four systems of precipitation pits survive on the mountain (Fig. 4): (i) a system on the north-west side of the mountain south of Gwen's shaft; (ii) the Dyffryn Coch system which is made up of three separate systems in-line with one another, as well as a fourth group on the hillside north of the first system, and an unusual fifth series of pits at the far west end of the valley; (iii) the Hillside (or Central) system; (iv) the Henwaith system at the east end of the mountain, again made up of several conjoined systems of pits, the eastern group of which is now buried in deep heather. The Henwaith system has recently been subject to a programme of decontamination in which some of the pits have been

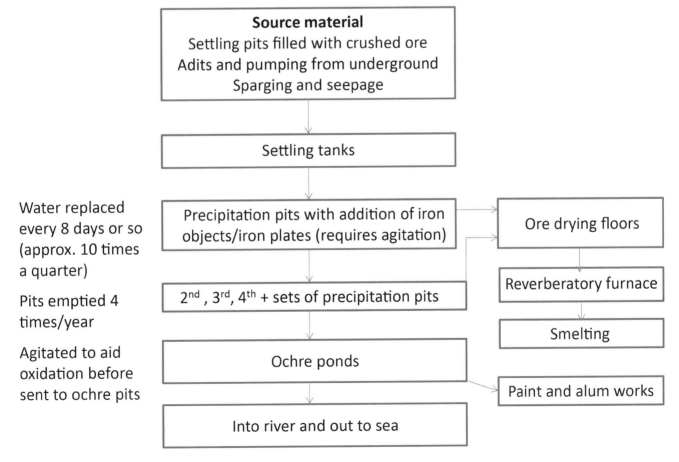

Fig. 3   The precipitation process as described by eighteenth-century and early nineteenth-century visitors to the mines

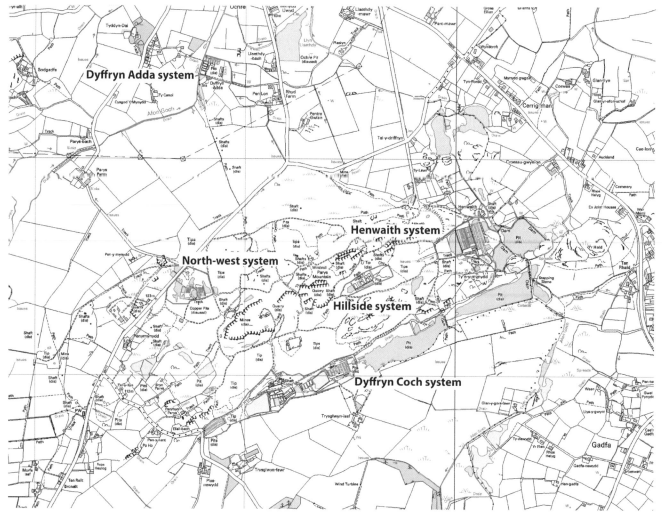

Fig. 4   Locations of the precipitation pit systems at Parys Mountain (grid lines at 1 km intervals) (© Crown Copyright and database right 2012, Ordnance Survey 100021874, Welsh Government)

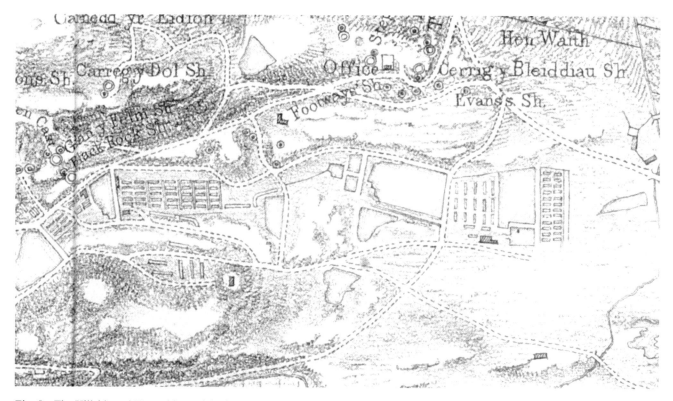

Fig. 5   The Hillside and Henwaith precipitation systems in 1824 (© The British Library Board, Maps 6135.(1.))

flooded and others planted with vegetation (GAT Report 914, 2011). A fifth system, that at Dyffryn Adda, lies north of the mountain, where the joint adit emerged.

The system of pits on the north-west side of the mountain, close to Gwen's shaft, has not been surveyed in detail and will not be described further, though the pits are clearly marked on a map of 1815 (NMR C8236) and appear to be little changed since then.

The Hillside precipitation system

The Hillside, or Central, precipitation system (Plate 1) is an extensive sequence of pits occupying a natural gulley between tips. The system is aligned south-west to north-east, the ground sloping down to the ochre ponds at the north-east end. At the south-west end, encroached on by tips, are two reservoirs, bounded by stone-built dams to the west and east. Outside the west dam is likely to have once been a further reservoir, but this is now filled in. A culvert through the centre of the dam took the water pumped up from the mines into the reservoirs. Further water was fed in via a small stone-built culvert on the north, whilst north again a rough row of launder pillars suggest yet another source. Water was fed from the reservoirs through a large partly brick-built culvert in the centre of the eastern dam (Plate 2) into the precipitation pits. A sluice gate is still in position at the western side of the culvert.

Comparison of the 1824 map (Fig. 5) with the surviving layout (Fig. 6) would suggest the pond shown at the west end in 1824 is now buried, and that the two storage ponds (3 and 4 on Fig. 6) occupy the area of the original westernmost pits. These western pits may also be shown on the map of 1784–86 (Fig. 2). The 1824 map shows seven rows of five pits. This layout may be partly preserved, if the pits shown in 1824 reflect the 'furrows' or corrugations visible today. The system visible today shows six rows (10–15 on Fig. 6), the western two slightly shorter, with a very narrow row (16 on Fig. 6) at the east end. The floors of each of the six rows are divided by wide corrugations into four or five divisions. Each row is separated from its neighbour by a low stone dam which provided walking access along each of the ponds. Sluices, positioned at the low point of each corrugation, run through the dams, connecting each series of pits. Some of the pits (e.g. 12, 14 and 15) are further divided by a south-west to north-east narrow dam, which does not appear to have sluice gates linking the pits either side. The lower courses of the dams are of brick, and the upper layers of stone. The dams stand to a maximum height of 0.6 m. The sluices narrow at the eastern end, possibly to help agitate the water as it flowed through. The narrow pit (16) at the east end of the system does not have floor corrugations. A separate water supply flowed in through a culvert from the north (30), and at the south end is the exit point leading to the large ochre pond to the east. This pit is unlikely to have been used for precipitation, but was more likely a holding pit for the spent water, whilst the additional water supply on the north may have provided additional agitation to aid oxidation or flushing out into the ochre ponds. To the north and south of the precipitation pits lie long pits at a higher level. These are also carefully floored, though with no corrugations. These are interpreted as drying pits for the copper sludge. On the north side are the remains of a stone-built structure (50). The south front has collapsed, but this building may have housed one or more reverberatory furnaces for final drying of the copper ore before being removed for smelting. An engineered track (40), though now partly damaged, leads down to this building from the east. Neither the drying pits nor furnace building are marked on the 1824 map. (Plates 3, 4, 5, 6)

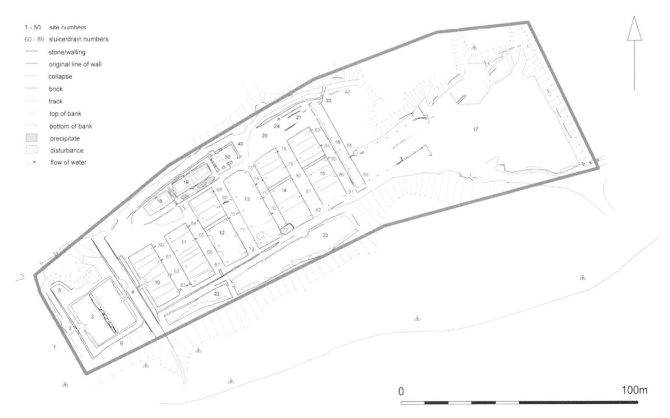

Fig. 6   A survey of the Hillside precipitation pits (Copyright Gwynedd Archaeological Trust)

Fig. 7   A survey of the Henwaith precipitation pits (Copyright Gwynedd Archaeological Trust)

The Henwaith precipitation system
The Henwaith system (Fig. 7) lies within the Mona mine on the east side of the mountain. No pits are indicated at this location on the map of 1784–86 (Fig. 2), but they are clearly shown on the map of 1824 (Fig. 5). By 1889, the date of the first 25 inch OS map, the system had been extended to the east and earlier pits re-aligned. These pits took their copper-rich water from the main adit of the Mona mine. Like the Hillside pits, they drained from west to east. The western group of pits, west of the reservoir, must have gone out of use whilst the rest of the system was still operating, as they are now heather covered and difficult to find. The OS map of 1889 shows five long pits aligned north–south, some divided into two with an east–west division. The fifth, easternmost, pit, as in the Hillside system, is much narrower, and is unlikely to have been used for precipitation. These pits originally drained into a large holding pond, but two new drains were built to run directly into the pond, one to the south of the earlier pits, and through their centre. The pits east of the pond appear to form at least two and probably three separate systems. The first system consisted of pits 3–11 on Fig. 7, the second system pits 12–19 and the third system pits 20–25. Only pits 3–8 had corrugated bases similar to the Hillside pits. Drying pits lay to the south, but on the north was a further series of small ponds of unknown function. Possible furnaces were housed in structures 28 and 39. Large ochre ponds lie to the east of the pits.

In 2010 advantage was taken during decontamination works to examine a number of features in greater detail. Particularly impressive were the stone-lined drains which lay north and west of the pits. That to the west took the water passing through the central and southern dam culverts, so that the new supply of copper-rich water was not drained straight into the pits but rather into the long north–south drain, which could then be further directed into the furrows of pits 3 and 4. It did not link up to a similar east–west drain which ran along the north side of the pits (142). This drain was fed from the north corner of the holding pond. Another drain further to the west (148) could not be followed to its origin but was fed in part by culverts emerging from the base of the adjoining tips. This drain discharged into the main holding pond (1). (Plates 7, 8, 9, 10)

The Dyffryn Coch precipitation system
This system consists of five individual groups of pits, of which three have been surveyed in detail (GAT Report 193, 1995) (Figs 8, 9). Discussion will be limited to these three, though it has already been noted that the group on the north side of the valley were early, and generally smaller and less regular in layout. The supply of copper-rich water for these groups came from the Great Opencast, and through the Dyffryn Coch adit. This adit was reopened in 2002 by the Parys Underground Group, following which it was concluded that it corresponds to the 'deep level' shown on the map of 1784–86 (Fig. 2), and therefore represents one of the earliest phases of mining, predating the development of the Great Opencast (Jenkins 2006). It was the construction of this level, or adit, which made it possible to develop the precipitation pits in the valley where it emerged. The western-most group of pits, system 1, consists of pits of irregular size, a characteristic of the earlier groups of pits on the mountain, as confirmed by the pits shown on the map of 1784–86. Of comparable type, and thought to be of similar date, are the pits now buried in heather north of system 1. Several of the pits have corrugated bases as seen elsewhere. A strong stone-built dam separates the pits from a pond to the west.

System 2 is small and more regular in layout. It is difficult to pick out the associated features seen elsewhere, such

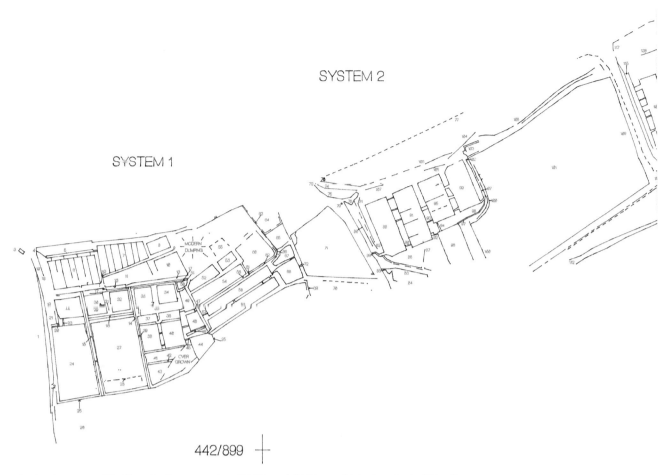

Fig. 8   A survey of Dyffryn Coch systems 1 and 2 (Copyright Gwynedd Archaeological Trust)

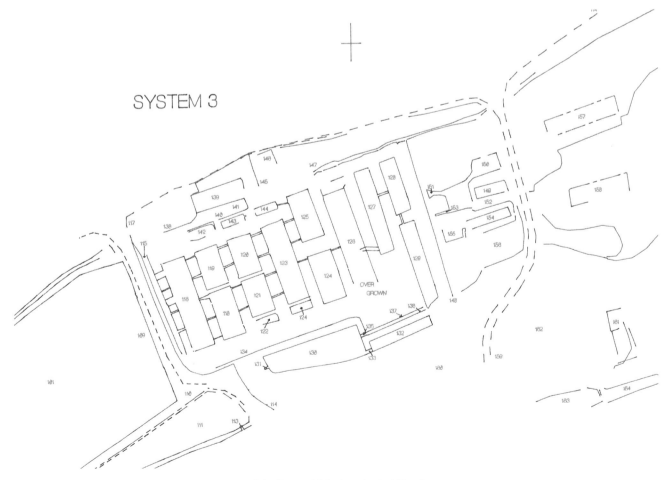

Fig. 9   A survey of Dyffryn Coch system 3 (Copyright Gwynedd Archaeological Trust)

as the drying pits and furnace house. A large ochre pond lies on the east side, followed by the system 3. This is very regular in layout, with a system of ponds able to feed water from west to east, ending in another large ochre pond. To the south of this system lay a vitriol works which made use of the output from the ochre ponds.

Conclusions

The precipitation pits at Parys undoubtedly form an extensive archaeological resource, and appear to be the most extensive remains of such a system anywhere in the world. However, it is not clear whether and to what extent they represent indigenous development, or technology transfer within an industry characterised by the movement of individuals and methods. This paper has gone some way to identifying other locations where precipitation was practised even if it cannot answer the fundamental question of the inspiration for these features in Anglesey.

The survey results indicate development from relatively small pits with a less formalised layout to larger regular systems typified by long rectangular tanks separated by wide dams which were used as access walkways. This development appears to have taken place within the mid-nineteenth century, though it is interesting that the precipitation pits which continued longest in use, those at Dyffryn Adda, remained unaltered from their construction early in the nineteenth century.

Bibliography

Unpublished sources

Bangor University Archives Collections, Kinmel Manuscripts 1807

Gwynedd Archaeological Trust, 1995, 'Mynydd Parys Dyffryn Coch Precipitation Pits Survey and Recording', Report 193

Gwynedd Archaeological Trust, 1998, 'Mynydd Parys Copper Mine: Archaeological Assessment', Report 292

Gwynedd Archaeological Trust, 2009, 'Industrial Recording 2008–9 Parys Mountain', Report 788

Gwynedd Archaeological Trust, 2010, 'Industrial Recording 2009–10 Parys Mountain', Report 859

Gwynedd Archaeological Trust, 2011, 'Henwaith Precipitation Pits, Mynydd Parys', Report 914

Gwynedd Archaeological Trust, 2014, 'Archaeological Survey of Scheduled Ancient Monuments', Report 1198

Jenkins, D.A., 2006, 'Excavation of the Dyffryn Coch Adit: Great Opencast, Mynydd Parys, Amlwch' (Parys Underground Group)

Published sources

Aikin, A., 1797. *A Journal of a Tour through North Wales*

Agricola, G., 1556. *De Re Metallica*, Libri XII (Basle: Cum Privilegio Imperatoris); trans. Herbert Clark Hoover and Lou Henry Hoover (New York, 1950)

Bingley, Rev. William, 1800. *A Tour Round North Wales performed during the summer of 1798* (London)

Biographia Britannica: or Lives of the Most eminent Persons who have flourished in Great Britain and Ireland, vol. 2 (London, 1748)

Biringuccio, V., 1540. *De la Pirotechnia* (Venice: Con Privilegio Apostolico); trans. Cyril Stanley Smith and Martha Teach Gnudi (New York: Dover, 1990)

Brown, Edward, 1673. *A Brief Account of Some Travels in Hungaria, Servia, Bulgaria* (London, 1673)

Cockshutt, E., 1965. 'The Parys Mountain copper mines in the island of Anglesey', *Archaeologia Cambrensis* 114, pp. 87–111

Crew, P., 1976. 'The copper mines of Llanberis and Clogwyn Goch', *Caernarvonshire Historical Society Transactions* 37, pp. 58–79

Evans, J., 1812. *The Beauties of England and Wales: North Wales* (London)

Greenly, H., 1919. *Memoir on the Geology of Anglesey*, 2 vols (HMSO)

Henry, W., 1751. 'A Letter from the Rev. William Henry, D.D. to the Right Honourable the Lord Cadogan, F.R.S. concerning the Copper-Springs in the County of Wicklow in Ireland', *Philosophical Transactions of the Royal Society* 84 (1751), pp. 500–503

Kauffman, C.H., 1803. *The Dictionary of Merchandize and Nomenclature in All languages*

Keysler, Johann Georg, 1758. *Travels through Germany, Hungary, Bohemia, Switzerland, Italy, and Lorrain. Containing an accurate description of the present state and curiosities of those countries. ... To which is prefixed, the life of the author, by Mr. Godfrey Schutze, trans. from the Hanover edition of the German*

Lord, P., 1998. *The Visual Culture of Wales: Industrial Society* (Cardiff: University of Wales Press)

Marsigli, Luigi Ferdinando, 1726. *Danubius-Pannonico-Mysicus*, vol. 3

Mendes da Costa, Emanuel, 1789. in *The Critical Review*, ed. Tobias Smollett

Pennant, T., 1783. *A Tour in Wales*, vol. 2 (London: Henry Hughes)

Pennant, T., 1883. *A Tour in Wales*, ed. Sir John Rhys, Caernarvon, vol. 3, pp. 55–64, pp. 395–400+plate

Rees, W., 1968. *Industry before the Industrial Revolution* (Cardiff)

Rothwell, N. (trans. and ed.), 2007. *Parys Mountain and the Lentin Letters* (Amlwch Industrial Heritage Trust)

Smith, D. Bentley, 2005. *A Georgian Gent & Co: the life and times of Charles Roe* (Ashbourne: Landmark Publishing)

Schwartz, S.P., & Critchley, M.F., 2011. 'Philip Henry Argall (1854–1922): the remarkable life and career of a Cornish-Irish mining manager, engineeer and metallurgist', *Journal of the Mining Heritage Trust of Ireland* 11, pp. 47–64

Tomos, D. (ed.), 1972. *Michael Faraday in Wales* (Gwasg Gee)

Willies, Lynn, 1989. 'The industrial landscape of Rio Tinto, Huelva, Spain', *Industrial Archaelology Review* 12:1

Plate 1   The Hillside precipitation pit system from the south-west

Plate 2   The central culvert, with sluice gate, in the western dam of the Hillside precipitation system

Plate 3   Example of sluice between pits in the Hillside system

Plate 4   The drying pits of the Hillside system from the south-west

Plate 5   The stone building (location 50 on Fig. 6) which may have housed a reverberatory furnace, with one of the corrugated precipitation pits in the foreground

Plate 6   Pit 4, Hillside system, showing corrugations in the floor

Plate 7   The large rectangular pits of the Henwaith system from the south

Plate 8   The primary east–west drain of the Henwaith system running down the north end of the pits

Plate 9   The floor of the drying pits on the south side of the Henwaith system

Plate 10   The remains of a building at the east end of the Henwaith system which probably housed a reverberatory furnace

Plate 11   Dyffryn Coch system 1 from the north

Metalliferous Mineral Exploration in North Wales since 1964

Tim Colman

Abstract: North Wales has had an extensive history of metalliferous mineral exploitation of Parys Mountain in Anglesey and numerous sites in Snowdonia. This activity has been well documented in numerous publications. However, recent exploration since the revival of work at Parys Mountain in the 1950s has received much less attention. The controversial investigations by Rio Tinto Zinc at Coed y Brenin did make headlines but much other work has been carried out with less publicity. Exploration has been more or less continuous at Parys Mountain under several companies with several attempts to restart mining there. The Government's Mineral Incentive Scheme from 1971 to 1984 encouraged a number of companies to look at various areas of Snowdonia and Anglesey for copper, gold, lead, zinc and nickel. The British Geological Survey's Mineral Reconnaissance Programme also examined much of Anglesey and some other areas of North Wales from the mid 1970s to the last decade to provide background geological, geochemical and geophysical information of use for commercial mineral exploration.

This paper reviews this activity and describes the various metalliferous targets sought by companies and the BGS.

Introduction

Metalliferous minerals have been sought and extracted from North Wales since Bronze Age times. Parys Mountain, Great Orme and Drws y Coed copper mines and Halkyn-Minera lead mines, amongst others in the region, have long and well documented histories. However, the more recent history of mineral exploration and development has been less well recorded. 'Modern' mineral exploration can be regarded as starting with the deliberate application of geological, geochemical, geophysical and drilling techniques for the discovery of concealed mineralisation. These gradually built up from the early parts of the twentieth century but accelerated from the 1960s onwards with the discoveries of major porphyry copper deposits in the circum-Pacific region, such as Bougainville by CRA in 1963; the Kidd Creek copper-lead-zinc volcanogenic deposit at Timmins, Ontario, by Texas Gulf Sulfur also in 1963 and the Kambalda copper-nickel discoveries by Western Mining in 1966. The last two are still in active production. These discoveries led to a worldwide exploration boom, ripples of which spread to North Wales.

Metalliferous mineral exploration in Britain has to cope with a number of unusual features, compared to many other parts of the world. Firstly mineral rights, apart from gold and silver which are generally owned by the Crown Estate, are privately and not state owned and there is no register of their owners making it very difficult (or impossible) to find the legal owner. Many landholdings (and their accompanying mineral rights) have been sub-divided, leading to some very complex mineral rights situations as shown in the Minera area by Fig. 7. This led to many companies preferring to deal with single, large landowners whose estate agents were used to negotiating access arrangements and which tended to have retained their mineral rights.

Secondly there is no recent history of mineral exploration and development and so many landowners, apart from those in south-west England where mining has been active

until recently, do not know whether they own the rights to the minerals as these were often retained by estates when the surface land was sold off. Thirdly many of the most prospective areas from a geological aspect are in areas of designated natural beauty such as National Parks, as these are often underlain by harder, older rocks which are generally prospective for mineral deposits. Fourthly there is no requirement to record and report any mineral activity and ensuing results so there are no systematic records of previous work.

To counter these drawbacks to exploration the UK government attempted to nationalise mineral rights in the late 1960s in the same way that the rights to energy minerals were already reserved to the nation. However, the legislation was not enacted and to compensate the Government set up three initiatives to assist mineral exploration. These form the only publicly available information on mineral exploration in Britain.

1. Mineral Exploration and Investment Grants Act 1972 (MEIGA) 1971–1984
2. BGS Mineral Reconnaissance Programme (MRP) 1973–1998
3. BGS Regional Geochemical Survey Programme (RGSP) 1970–2014

The MEIGA programme offered UK-registered companies a grant of 35% of allowable expenditure on approved mineral exploration projects, subject to a range of conditions. A number of MEIGA-supported projects were carried out in North Wales as described below (Fig. 1). The BGS (British Geological Survey – then called the Institute of Geological Sciences (IGS)) MRP was intended to provide background information on areas considered to be prospective so that companies could concentrate on specific targets, rather than have to look at large areas with accompanying problems of access and mineral rights ownership. The BGS carried out a number of MRP projects in North Wales, particularly in Anglesey. The RGSP began in Northern Scotland in 1972

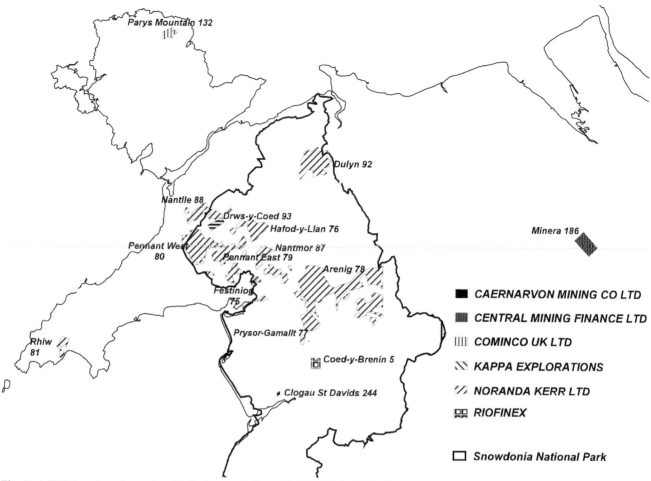

Fig. 1   MEIGA projects (reproduced with the permission of the British Geological Survey ©NERC. All rights Reserved)

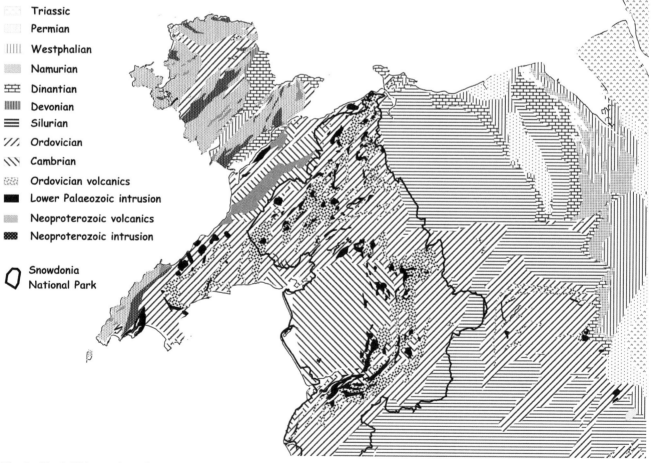

Fig. 2   North Wales geology (based on DiGMap GB-625 with the permission of the British Geological Survey)

and is now known as the Geochemical Baseline Survey of the Environment (G-BASE). It has just completed the geochemical survey of the whole of Great Britain by collecting stream sediment, water and soil samples at a density of about one per km^2 and analysing them for up to 50 elements. The results are published in a series of atlases.

North Wales has a complex geological history (Fig. 2). The oldest rocks are the various NeoProterozoic igneous and sedimentary rocks of Anglesey and the Lleyn Peninsula which have aggregated in complex ways along a SW–NE grain and whose history is still being unravelled. These are followed by the Cambrian muds and grits of Snowdonia and Harlech, later intruded by various igneous rocks. These are overlain by Ordovician rocks, predominantly muds and grits but with a major volcanic episode in late Ordovician times culminating in the 14 km x 7 km Snowdon caldera which spread ash and other debris over a wide area. This was followed by quieter Silurian times with the deposition of more sediments before the major Caledonian tectonic episode folded, compressed and cleaved the sediments to form the slates for which the region is so well known. These are overlain in Anglesey and along the North Wales coast by Carboniferous limestones, sandstones and coal measures. Metalliferous mineralisation has been discovered in the past at many locations throughout North Wales with economic (at the time) deposits of copper, lead, zinc, manganese, gold, iron and baryte. However, since the closure of the Parc zinc mine in 1962 there has been no base metal production in the region and only a few sporadic small-scale workings of the Dolgellau gold deposits.

Coed y Brenin

Following the discovery in 1963 of the major Bougainville porphyry copper deposit on the eponymous island in the South Pacific the major mining company RTZ started investigations in Britain in 1965 to see if any similar (though older) deposits were 'on its doorstep'. A literature search led to the old Turf copper mine north of Dolgellau in North Wales where the passage below from Dewey and Eastwood (1925) intrigued the RTZ geologist (Dr M.B. Mehrtens) with the following passage:

> Andrew Ramsay … stated that 'It was in this country, more than half a mile west of Dol-y-frwynog, that the once famous Turf Copper Mine was situated in the heart of the talcose schist, which almost everywhere contains much iron-pyrites in small crystals, scattered through the rock, together with specks of yellow sulphide of copper. Very small veins of this ore also intersect the mass. A peat bog occupied the greater part of the bottom of the valley. The turf was pared off the surface and burned in kilns, and being partly saturated with some compound of copper a large residue of valuable copper was left in the ashes. Many thousand pounds' worth were thus extracted. The neighbouring hills were afterwards burrowed in all directions in search of the great lode, or bunch, from whence the copper was supposed by sanguine adventurers to have been carried in solution to the peat. It was never found and probably does not exist; the water that percolated through the rocks, and rose in springs, having more probably carried the copper, in the form of a sulphate, from those minute quantities of the sulphide that are more or less diffused through the mass of the hill that overlooks the Turf Copper Mine, in the

peat-moss of which the copper was diffusedly deposited. The only trace of the ancient workings consists of the remains of a kiln where the turf was burnt; the walls of this kiln are partly vitrified and partly covered with a skin of copper slag. Scattered over the moor are wide stony spaces where the turf has been removed for treatment.

> W. Jory Henwood described this copper works. He says it was a deposit of turf of some 70 acres which received the drainage of an extensive common and of a long level on a vein of quartz, in which were found several masses of copper pyrites weighing some tons each. The chief repository of the copper was a bed of peat of about 18 inches or 2 feet in thickness, consisting of dead grass mixed with great quantities of rotten oak and hazel wood. Beneath the peat there was a bed of stones a few inches in thickness, many containing iron-pyrites in abundance, and some thinly incrusted with the green carbonate of copper. A second bed of peat underlies this and also affords copper, but so scantily that it has not been wrought.

> Some of the lower portions of the upper peat-bed were so rich in copper that they were carried to the Swansea smelting works in the condition in which they were extracted. Some of the leaves are said to have been covered with a thin pellicle of bright metallic copper; nuts were coated in like manner, and on being broken open afforded also a kernel of the same; and I was informed that copper was in some cases deposited between the fibres of the wood, so that on being cut it exhibited alternate layers of vegetable matter and of metal.

> In one year 2000 tons of ashes were sold at a profit of about £20,000. Turf which would not yield more than 2½ % of copper in the ashes was considered too poor to be wrought and an enormous quantity was left untouched in Henwood's time. (Dewey & Eastwood 1925)

The area was underlain by a late Cambrian granite intrusion into Cambrian sediments (Fig. 3). Following a field reconnaissance in 1966 to confirm the old reports Riofinex commenced negotiations in 1967 to acquire the mineral rights and in May 1968 stream sediment and soil sampling began around the area of the old Turf works (Rice & Sharp 1976). This soon proved that a substantial area showed copper enrichment. An induced polarisation (IP) survey showed some of the classic pyrite halo and drilling began in January 1969. The Coed y Brenin forest gave its name to the deposit. As was the custom at that time exploration drilling was carried out under 'the 28 day rule' whereby a General Development Order (GDO) stated that planning permission was not needed for minor developments, including drilling, provided they lasted no more than 28 days. It was not entirely clear whether core drilling to substantial depths, or drilling successive holes in the same general area, was within the spirit or definition of the GDO. In the event no planning permission was applied for from the local authority (Merioneth County Council), which was therefore unaware of the developments. Permission to drill was simply obtained from agreeable landowners, including the Forestry Commission. This was then the normal way of operating in Britain. Merioneth Council did send an officer to investigate in the summer of 1969 but was apparently told by the drilling crew that their hole would be finished in a week. He took that to mean the whole drilling programme and not just that particular hole and so no further action was taken

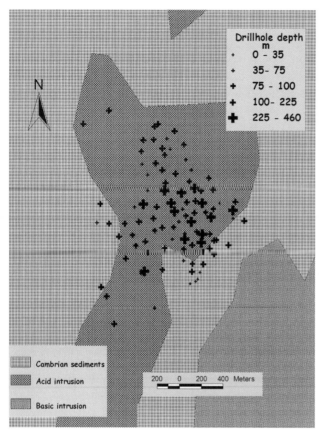

Fig. 3 Plan showing the layout of holes at Coed y Brenin (derived from MEIGA data and DiGMap-625 with the permission of the British Geological Survey ©NERC. All rights Reserved)

while drilling continued. RTZ formally told the local council of their interest in the area at the end of 1969 and the two sides met in January 1970. RTZ submitted a paper to the Council in April 1970 on 'Exploration at Coed-y-Brenin' by which time 24 holes had been drilled in the area. Later that month RTZ applied to Dolgellau Rural District Council for planning permission to drill holes up to 450 m at Coed y Brenin. This was passed to Merioneth County Council which decided that it was of national importance and should be 'called in' by the appropriate Minister, in this case the Secretary of State for Wales, to whom it was sent at the end of July 1970. Drilling continued until October 1970 when the Secretary of State instructed RTZ to cease, by which time a further 24 holes had been completed (Searle 1975).

A public enquiry was held over four days at Dolgellau in December 1970 by which time various conservation organisations and the media had become interested in the development and turned it into a *cause célèbre*. There was some debate over the remit of the enquiry. Was it just to decide over permission to drill exploration boreholes or would granting this imply permission for eventual mining? The former course was taken, but, following the completion of the enquiry, no judgement had been issued by the Secretary of State by July 1971 when the Mineral Incentive Scheme (MEIGA) was announced. RTZ applied for MEIGA assistance with drilling in August 1971 and was given permission to continue with work at Coed y Brenin (MEIGA AE5). A further 40 holes were drilled to June 1972 making a total of 110 holes for 14,139 m, including some additional geotechnical holes during studies for a proposed tailings dam (Fig. 3). The maximum depth drilled was 1500 feet. The 'ore expectancy' of the deposit was calculated as 198 million

short tons at a grade of 0.33% copper with minor molybdenum (a common association with porphyry copper mineralisation as shown in Fig. 4). Traces of gold were recorded during metallurgical testing but with gold at $35 per ounce and analysis for gold at very low concentrations costly and time consuming the drill cores were not routinely analysed for gold.

Whenever the geological work at Coed y Brenin was suspended the geological team carried out reconnaissance in other parts of Britain. In North Wales these areas included the Llysdulas estate north-east of Parys Mountain in Anglesey, Mynytho on the Lleyn Peninsula and several areas in the Merioneth volcanic belt and around Mynydd Gribau in the Conwy valley. Most soil or stream sediment anomalies were attributed to contamination from old workings but some areas in Merioneth were followed up with geophysics, especially around Aran Fawddwy where a narrow, intense electromagnetic anomaly was found. All this work was discontinued when the main Coed y Brenin project was abandoned.

The project had now become somewhat embarrassing to RTZ which announced in April 1973 that it was abandoning any further work as the deposit was too small and low-grade to warrant development (*New Scientist*, 26 April 1973, p. 196). Since then it has been the focus of some academic studies, including one by Owen Miller of Aberdeen University who found sporadic traces of gold in some of the core samples, including one sample with 3 g/t (Miller 1993).

The graphic borehole logs and some reports written after August 1971 under the MEIGA scheme, together with significant amounts of core including around ten complete holes, are available in the BGS National Geoscience Records Centre at Keyworth, together with additional pre-MEIGA reports and other data.

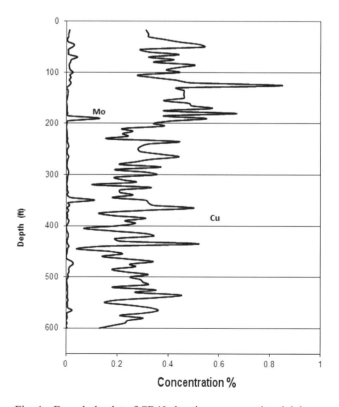

Fig. 4 Downhole plot of CB40 showing copper and molybdenum values (derived from MEIGA data with the permission of the British Geological Survey ©NERC. All rights Reserved)

The whole affair highlights the problems of a planning, legislative and cultural environment with no experience of modern mineral exploration and development or the tools to understand or manage it effectively.

Parys Mountain

The Parys Mountain copper deposit, near Amlwch in northern Anglesey has been mined since Bronze Age times with the main production occurring between 1768 and 1820. By the 1950s the area was almost derelict with only minor production of less than 1 ton of copper per week from a precipitation plant near the Dyffryn Adda adit (Audsley and others 1961). Exploration using modern techniques (mainly diamond drilling) to investigate the major enigmatic mineralisation associated with two large open pits – the Great and Mona opencasts at Parys Mountain – started in 1955 and has carried on almost continuously since then (Table 1). The geological map by Greenly in the 1890s shows a NE–SW trending syncline with Silurian mudstones separated from Ordovician shales by a 'felsite' intrusion (Fig. 5). The syncline is truncated at its south-western end by an enigmatic mass of quartz – the White Rock. The mineralisation was considered to be 'epigenetic' – that is occurring after the solidification of the igneous rocks present and lithification of the sediments. Little is known of the mineralisation worked from 1768 to around 1820, with the production of perhaps 130,000 tons of copper metal, but it appears to have consisted of quartz, pyrite and chalcopyrite veins and impregnations of the host rock. Later workings from shafts also tried to extract massive lead-zinc mineralisation, known locally as bluestone, but it was difficult to separate the fine-grained lead and zinc minerals from each other.

Anglesey Mining Exploration Ltd, a subsidiary of New Consolidated Gold Fields, looked at the prospect in 1955 under the direction of W. Manning who published an account of the deposit in the IMM symposium volume (Manning 1959). In 1956 Gilbert McPherson compiled a geological report on the Parys-Mona ore deposit for Sir Chester Beatty's Selection Trust which was interested, but did not carry out any exploration. In 1960 the flamboyant Canadian entrepreneur William (Bill) Richardson then entered the scene. He was invited to Anglesey by Sir John Lomax, agent of the Marquis of Anglesey, who met Richardson in South America when they were both involved in mining ventures (*Liverpool Daily Post*, Tuesday 22 August 1961). In 1961 Bill Richardson invited his friend Pat Hughes, who controlled the Irish-Canadian Northgate Exploration Ltd, in concert with another Canadian group, Union Minière of Belgium, and the London group who previously held the prospecting rights from the Marquis of Anglesey (who owned the mineral rights) to form Anglesey Copper Mines (UK) Ltd. Northgate raised $150,000 to spend on the ground acquired by Bill Richardson (*Mining Journal*, 15 Sept. 1961). Anglesey Copper Mines drilled 11 surface boreholes (M1 to M11) during 1961–62. Initial exploration, under the direction of Gordon W. Moore, consulting mining engineer for Northgate, was again for copper-bearing ore; the fine-grained copper-lead-zinc 'bluestone' mineralisation was not considered important. The Northgate target was mainly the downdip extension of the Carreg-y-Doll Zone – a prominent silica-rich horizon dipping to the north and containing predominantly copper mineralisation in swarms of quartz veinlets. This extension was known as the Northern Copper Zone. Northgate dropped out of the project in 1962 to con-

Table 1   Summary of companies and drill holes at Parys Mountain 1955–2010

Dates	Company	Hole numbers	Metres
1955–1957	Anglesey Mining Exploration Ltd		
1961–1962	Anglesey Copper Mines (UK) Ltd	M1–M11	3554
1966–1967	CIGOL	C1–C4	1656
1967	British Titan Products	R1–R5	183
1968–1970	CIGOL	H1–H36	9785
1970	CIGOL and Preussag	H37–H46	2980
1971–1972	Intermine and Noranda	IM1–IM24	5380
1973–1975	Cominco / British Kynoch Metals	A0–A25	7184
1976–1981	Cominco	A26–A53	10154
1985	Anglesey Mining	AMC1–AMC10	5925
1988–1991	Anglesey Mining Shaft pilot hole	SP1	549
	Chapel Zone (CZ)	CZ1–CZ9	1544
	White Rock Zone (WR)	WR1–WR2	350
	Underground holes (PM)	PM1–PM125	10500
1997–1998	Garth Daniel Zone	AMC11–AMC14	2200
2005–2006	Garth Daniel Zone	AMC15–AMC19	2950*
	White Rock Zone	WD1–WD9	630*
	Upper Engine Zone	CZ10–CZ13	800*
2012	Great Opencast	AMC20–AMC21	558
	Pearl Engine House	AMC22–AMC24	558
	Upper Engine Zone	CZ14–CZ20	866
Total		**Surface**	**57806**
		Underground	**10500**

* Approximate figures

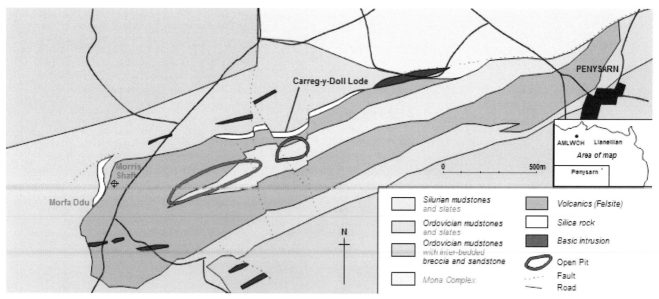

Fig. 5   Parys Mountain geology (after Manning (1959))

centrate on their newly discovered Tynagh copper-lead-zinc deposit in Ireland.

Following a four year hiatus, during which Bill Richardson tried to interest numerous companies in the project, Anglesey Copper Mines then had a complicated, and somewhat strained relationship with Canadian Industrial Gas and Oil Ltd (CIGOL), a subsidiary of Northern Ontario and Central Gas, who drilled 52 boreholes mainly into the Northern Copper Zone over four years from 1966. For instance, a report in 1969 stated that Hole H34 had intersected an average of 0.98% copper and 0.24 oz silver from 1148 ft to 1628 ft (*Mining Journal*, 25 July 1969). The Northern Copper Zone was estimated to contain 30 million tonnes of ore at a grade of 0.7% copper. In their final year CIGOL went into partnership with Preussag, much to Richardson's disgust. There is interesting correspondence in the BGS archives between Richardson and various persons in which he describes in colourful language his thoughts on the merits, and otherwise, of their exploration and the personalities involved.

The mineralisation is now known to be complex and occurring as a number of discrete orebodies separated by tens to hundreds of metres of barren host rock. There is a considerable amount of faulting and wall rock alteration by volcanic, mineralising and supergene processes as well as almost total cover of the original surface by spoil tips of varying age and thickness. This makes it difficult to carry out any form of geophysics or soil geochemistry, and to interpret the results. These normal exploration techniques have not been commonly used at Parys Mountain though CIGOL carried out an IP survey in 1967 that was used to target some drilling.

In 1966 and 1967 Robertson Research Company Ltd, the Llandudno-based consultants, carried out a pyrite exploration programme at Parys Mountain, with CIGOL's permission, for British Titan Products Co. Ltd. who were looking for a domestic source of pyrite as a feedstock for sulphuric acid for their ilmenite works at Billingham. Five short holes were drilled in the area north of the Great Opencast, though core recovery on the first hole was very poor. An estimate of a 'reserve' of 300,000 to 400,000 tons of rock with an average grade of 7–9% pyrite with some copper was made

(Wolfenden 1967). This was completely uneconomic at the time and only one block with 40,000 tons was considered to have a possibly economic grade of 24% pyrite. No further work was done.

CIGOL were succeeded by Intermine of Canada, in partnership with Noranda-Kerr who had become active in many areas of Britain, and 24 holes were drilled from 1971 to 1972 (Table 1). These were the first holes to target possible mineralisation beneath the open pits and were probably the result of Noranda believing they were dealing with a volcanic massive exhalative syngenetic deposit of the type then recently described by Sangster (1972) from Canadian deposits. These holes located a number of sporadic intersections of 'bluestone' with very variable assay figures for copper, lead and zinc. For example IM6 intersected 3.3 m at 6.9% copper, 4.5% zinc and 0.8% lead. However, it proved impossible, at the time, to correlate these intersections into an 'orebody' and both companies walked away from the prospect.

The area was then taken up by the major Canadian company, Cominco, who were looking at other areas of Britain, including the Craven Basin of Lancashire and the Devon Great Consols copper deposit in Cornwall.

A Cominco team, under the direction of Brian Young with David Owens and Richard Herrington, discovered the existence of a high-grade polymetallic ore deposit in the Engine Zone in 1973. This contained up to 3 or 4% copper as well as high grades of zinc and lead over widths of several metres and appeared to have a considerable strike length. It became the focus of attention as it provided a much more attractive target than the lower-grade Northern Copper Zone. Cominco, first in partnership with British Kynoch Metals and then alone, spent another eight years with MEIGA assistance (MEIGA AE132) patiently drilling 53 holes (A1–A53) to elucidate the structure of the complex mineralisation. On completion of this drilling campaign Cominco estimated that the deposit contained 4.8 million tonnes of mineralisation containing 1.5% copper, 3% lead, 6% zinc and small amounts of gold and silver. The complex geology of the deposit was not understood in detail at that time. The stratigraphy of the mine area consisted of a topmost unit of proven Silurian shales underlain by a thin

(200 m thick) unit presumed Ordovician lavas in contact with underlying presumed (from acritarchs) Ordovician shales. The whole Lower Palaeozoic package was unconformably underlain by PreCambrian Mona Schists along the Rhwc and Carmel Head thrusts. The lavas were presumed to be Ordovician (Caradocian) in age by comparison with the nearby Snowdonia Volcanic Formation and similar rocks in the Avoca copper deposit in Ireland (Wheatley 1971).

Chris Pointon and Rob Ixer published a major paper in 1980 when they showed unequivocally that the mineralisation was mainly synvolcanic and that the Carreg-y-Doll and Morpha Ddu [Anglesey Mining's spelling] 'lodes' were silica sinters or silica impregnations of the sea floor (Pointon & Ixer 1980). This was in direct contrast to the official Geological Survey view at the time that the mineralisation was epigenetic and formed during the Caledonian Orogeny (Nutt and others 1979). In 1981 Cominco's European focus changed to Turkey and work on Parys Mountain was suspended.

In 1984 Anglesey Mining, a wholly owned subsidiary of Imperial Metals Group of Canada, entered the scene led by Hugh Morris who had been an exploration director of Cominco and was familiar with the property. They acquired the rights to the Parys Mountain property and commenced exploration in May 1985, drilling six holes (AMC 1–6) totalling about 2500 m to confirm and extend mineral resources at the western end of the Engine Zone in the Morpha Ddu area. Planning permission for a shaft and underground mine was granted by Gwynedd County Council in April 1988 (*Financial Times*, 28 April 1988).

After spending around £1 million on preparatory work Anglesey Mining raised over £5 million by means of a share

offer in May 1988 to develop the deposit to a production decision. This involved sinking a 4.75 m shaft (capable of being used for production) together with underground development and underground drilling. The shaft was sunk to only 300 m of its proposed 500 m depth due to cost considerations. A level was driven from the shaft at 275 m depth for around 1 km with subsidiary drives into the White Rock Zone and to test the shale-volcanic contact (Fig. 6). Bill Charter and Clyde Leys were the project geologists and Bill Hooley the mine manager.

Over 100 short underground holes and around a dozen surface holes were drilled at this time to complement the underground development. Around 2000 tonnes of ore averaging 1.5% copper, 3.0% lead and 6.5% zinc were processed in a pilot plant which contained much equipment salvaged from the recently closed Gwynfynydd gold mine near Dolgellau. These proved that the ore was easily processed and could yield good recoveries. 200 tonnes of concentrates were sent to Avonmouth for smelting.

The proposed mine would process 400,000 tonnes of ore per year with an output of 25,600 tonnes of zinc, 12,120 tonnes of lead, 5840 tonnes of copper, 810,000 ounces of silver and 5250 ounces of gold (*Financial Times*, 26 May 1988).

In November 1990 the final feasibility study for Parys Mountain confirmed Anglesey Mining's in-house work and stated that production could start within a year, following construction of a mill and the extension of underground developments. Total 'reserves' (all categories) were stated as 6.4 million tonnes at 2.3% copper, 5.3% zinc, 2.6% lead, 39 g/t silver and 0.2 g/t gold (*Mining Journal*, 23 Nov. 1990). In October 1991 Hugh Morris stated that financing was expected to be complete by the end of 1991 with mine

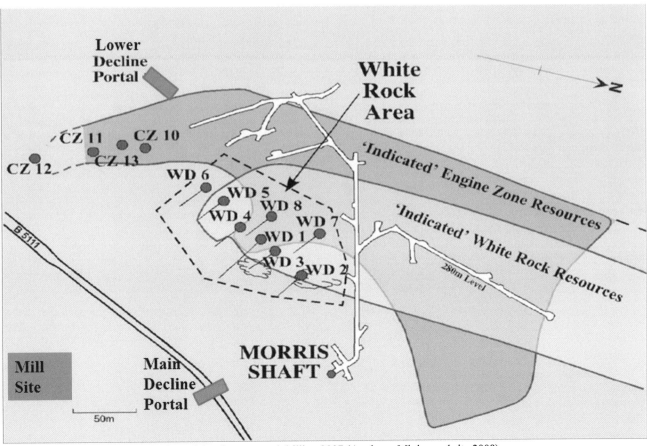

Fig. 6   Plan of 275 m level with planned development and drilling 2007 (Anglesey Mining website 2008)

and mill construction starting in January 1992 to reach full production by early 1993 (*Northern Miner*, 21 October 1991).

In 1992 Anglesey Mining raised a further £620,000 to secure its future for another three years and was looking for a joint venture partner to share the £25 million costs of developing the underground mine (*Metal Bulletin*, 13 Aug. 1992). However metal prices had declined and from then on Parys Mountain remained undeveloped though the Annual Reports of Anglesey Mining frequently mention talks with interested parties and several short periods of deep drilling and re-evaluation of the property were carried out. These included investigation of the possibility of developing small-scale gold extraction from some areas and the extension of the Engine Zone to the north-east with the discovery of the Deep Engine and Garth Daniel zones. A major advance in the understanding of the deposit came with the geochemical work of Tim Barrett and the structural work of Peter Tyler, both with the assistance of Ph.D. students due to Anglesey's support for and encouragement of academic studies of the deposit and its environment. Tim Barrett and Steve Tennant analysed 35 drill cores for a number of elements and used the results to erect a chemical stratigraphy which showed that the Parys volcanics, previously described as various types of 'cherty tuffites' could be split into at least four rhyolite lava units (Rhyolites A to D) and that Rhyolite B was the one associated with most of the mineralisation (Barrett and others 2001). This work was of great utility in understanding and correlating the geology with the mineralisation. Radiometric dating also showed that the Parys volcanics are of Lower Silurian age (436 Ma) and not Ordovician as previously assumed. The structure of the area was examined by Steve Westhead and then by Peter Tyler who was unhappy with the overturned syncline model originally proposed by Greenly in his 1919 Anglesey memoir and developed a homoclinal model with the entire volcanic and shale package surrounding the mineralisation being of Lower Silurian age within the remnants of a volcanic caldera which formed the northern and western boundaries of the deposit area (Tyler 2003).

In 2007 additional drilling was completed in the White Rock Zone and preparatory work started for a decline to access the mineralisation (Fig. 6). The company then anticipated five years production from the White Rock Zone followed by rehabilitation of the Morris Shaft and development of the Engine Zone deposit before extending east to the Garth Daniel and Deep Engine Zone areas.

In April 2008 Western Metals of Australia became interested in Parys Mountain and agreed terms with Anglesey Mining for its sale to Western Metals for 29.136 million Australian dollars (~£13.75 million). Western Metals paid Anglesey a non-refundable deposit of A$270,000 dollars to secure an exclusive right, for a period of up to 120 days, to carry out the due diligence review of the property. However, following the severe downturn in metal prices during the summer of that year Western Metals did not proceed and the property reverted to Anglesey Mining.

Anglesey Mining continued low-level studies of the deposit through the years of low metal prices and commissioned a review of the project in 2010. Drilling was restarted in 2012 to explore the possible extension of the Engine Zone to surface, provide information on the area below the

Great Opencast and explore the eastern boundary of the property to investigate the Northern Copper Zone near the New Pearl Engine House. The Engine Zone was shown to continue at good grades to within 180 m of the surface. The holes beneath the opencast intersected thin zones of low-grade mineralisation and the holes into the Northern Copper Zone proved the continuation of this mineralisation.

Parys Mountain remains an intriguing deposit with excellent potential for a significant mining operation.

Noranda exploration in North Wales

Noranda-Kerr, a medium-sized Canadian mining and exploration company, took advantage of the MEIGA scheme to investigate a wide range of areas throughout Britain in the early 1970s. These included a number of areas in North Wales (Fig. 1) where Noranda was interested in volcanogenic mineralisation (MEIGA AE 75–81, 87–88). The terms of the MEIGA scheme did not permit 'regional exploration' and so the Snowdonia project was split in multiple areas as shown on the map. The company's approach was to select areas where the Crown Estate or large landowners held the mineral rights to simplify access agreements and then carry out rapid, low cost reconnaissance exploration to determine whether the ground was worth more detailed investigation. In North Wales Noranda attempted to cover most of the outcrop of the Ordovician volcanic rocks of Snowdonia for volcanogenic copper-lead-zinc deposits of the type the company was familiar with in Canada and also looked at the Ordovician basic intrusive complex near Rhiw on the Lleyn Peninsula for copper-nickel mineralisation as the 1960s nickel boom was still in progress. As mentioned above (p. 106), they also joined with Intermine, another Canadian company, to investigate Parys Mountain as a possible volcanogenic deposit, rather than the accepted idea of epigenetic quartz-copper veins typified by the Northern Copper Deposit which had been the target of previous companies.

Noranda used stream sediment geochemistry as an initial screening tool for all the areas except Parys Mountain where the extensive mine waste cover rendered this technique ineffective. This enabled them to rapidly assess and compare the prospectivity of each area. In the event only the Hafod y Llan and Hafod y Porth areas in Cwm Llan, south-east of Snowdon, were determined to be worthy of follow-up with IP geophysics to investigate the contact between the Lower Rhyolitic Tuff Formation and the overlying Bedded Pyroclastic Formation. Seven short (<50 m) diamond drill holes were completed over a period of five months for a total of around 200 m using a man-portable Pac-Sac drill. The report by the site geologist mentions that the drilling caused no problems or protests in spite of being 'on the slopes of Snowdon' and when the Coed y Brenin controversy was at its height. Minor intersections of massive sulphide veins with copper, lead and zinc were found (Reedman and others 1985) but the project was abandoned when Noranda pulled out of Britain in 1973 as the exploration boom faded.

Drws y Coed

This ancient mining area consists of numerous workings on quartz veins with copper-lead-zinc sulphides in Cambrian quartzites and intrusives to the east of Nantlle. In 1957–58 Geolex Development and Mining, with MEIGA support

(MEIGA AE93), carried out dump sampling and examination of adits, as noted in the 1971–1974 reports of Kappa Exploration. Drws y Coed appears to have been Kappa's only project in the UK. The company employed a local geologist, R.C.B. Jones, to oversee work in 1973 by Watts, Griffis and McOuat who carried out very low frequency (VLF) and electromagnetic (EM) geophysics and recommended 10 diamond drill holes. Six holes totalling 675 m were drilled during 1973–74 at four locations including investigating the possible downdip extension of the main Drws y Coed deposit. No significant sulphide intersections were noted during the IGS logging of the cores which were then disposed of. However the IGS borehole logs are still preserved.

Minera

The major Minera lead-zinc mine worked several steeply dipping NW–SE veins over a strike length of about 4 km in Carboniferous Limestone. The limestone is unconformably underlain by Lower Palaeozoic rocks which are penetrated by some shafts. The mine was abandoned in the early 1920s because of low metal prices and the costs of pumping from 300 m depth. In April 1972 Charter Consolidated, then a major London-based mining company, authorised £15,000 for a detailed appraisal of the area. This showed that the Meadow Shaft was blocked at 74 m from surface while the New Minera Shaft was clear to 218 m from surface but then choked to the shaft bottom at 295 m. Charter then produced a phased plan to rehabilitate the mine and carry out further exploration.

Phase 1. Dewater to the 360 level, rehabilitate New Minera Shaft and 900 m of drives on the 320 and 360 levels plus sampling and 1640 m of underground diamond drilling.

Estimated cost £582,000 over 20 months.

Phase 2. Dewater to the bottom 430 level, rehabilitate the 380 and 430 levels, additional sampling and 800 m of underground diamond drilling plus geophysics and deep drilling from surface.

Estimated cost £305,000 over 6 months.

If successful this would be followed by a mine and plant development costing £2,640,000 over 21 months to recover an estimated 1.5 to 4 million tons of ore grading around 12.5% lead and zinc with a planned production of 180,000 tonnes of ore per year for a mine life of 10–15 years. The planned programme was never carried out, possibly due to the global slowdown in exploration and development during the mid 1970s.

However, interest in the property was revived in 1979 when Central Mining Finance (a wholly owned subsidiary of Charter Consolidated) planned two deep drill holes with MEIGA support to test the south-eastwards extension of the Minera Main Vein in the Main Limestone beyond and below the known workings (MEIGA AE186). The area had a complicated mineral rights situation with over 25 mineral owners in an area of 2 square miles (Fig. 7).

The target was the south-eastwards and in depth extensions of an orebody known from old records to contain around 12.5% combined lead and zinc. The drilling area was about 1 km south-east of the old workings. It was intended as a first stage reconnaissance to test the validity of the geological model and to see if any mineralised structures were big enough to warrant further investigation. The holes were planned to start in Coal Measures and then go through the underlying Namurian Cefn y Fedw Sandstone and Carboniferous Limestone before intersecting the mineralised zone adjacent to the Minera Fault and

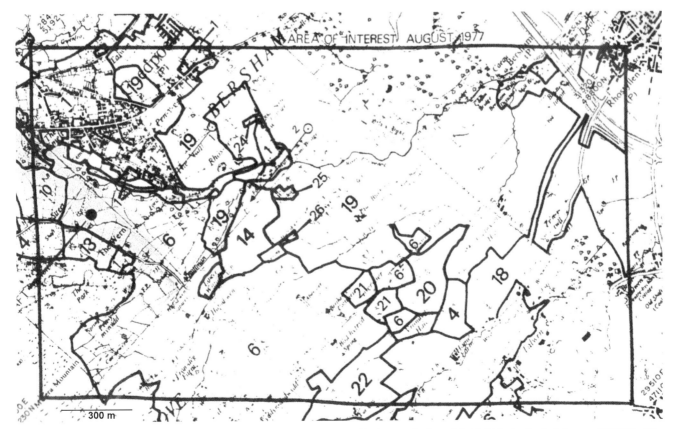

Fig. 7   Mineral rights in the Minera area MEIGA AE186 (reproduced with the permission of the British Geological Survey ©NERC. All rights Reserved)

passing into Silurian rocks. Because of the unknown nature of the ground Charter had difficulty in finding a company willing to drill the holes and eventually selected Drilling and Prospecting International (DPI) with cost per metre drilled plus a time cost for any non-drilling activities, such as wedging and cementing. The contractor estimated that the two holes would take around 20 weeks to drill. However, the first hole (M-1) was started in early January 1979 and was not completed until the end of July – a total of over 28 weeks. This was partly due to the severe winter with snow and freezing temperatures but mainly due to the borehole's inclination to veer to the right and steepen from its original 45° dip in spite of the use of repeated wedges to try to correct this. The hole was drilled to a vertical depth of 360 m in Coal Measures (downhole length of 460 m) before entering Namurian rocks and passing through an unexpected fault into the basal Carboniferous Limestone at 732 m. It entered Silurian mudstones at 865 m, about 130 m above the predicted depth of this formation. This was attributed to an upthrown block of Silurian strata between the Minera Fault and the fault at 732 m. The hole was stopped at 876 m.

An attempt was made to deflect the hole upwards to intersect the target area in limestone above the upthrown

Silurian block. Deflection was started at 560 m, initially using turbodrilling, but the hole was too small to provide sufficient fluid flow so conventional wedging was used with over 20 wedges at around 20 m intervals – a very expensive and time-consuming exercise which pushed the costs well beyond the original estimate. One wedge alone cost around £10,000 in time and materials. Silurian rocks were again intersected at 875 m before reaching the Minera Fault target area and the hole was stopped at 884.75 m (Fig. 8). Two additional holes were planned but were never drilled.

Dolgellau gold belt

Gold had been pegged at around $35 per ounce since the 1944 Bretton Woods meeting so there was little incentive to investigate the abandoned Dolgellau gold belt in the 1950s and 60s. There was a proposal by RTZ to investigate the Mawddach estuary for alluvial gold in 1970 which became mired in the Coed y Brenin controversy and was never pursued. However, George Hall, who had been working in the central Wales lead-zinc mining field since the 1940s, had always had an interest in the Dolgellau goldfield around the Harlech Dome and produced his seminal book on the area (Hall 1975) just as the gold price started to rise substan-

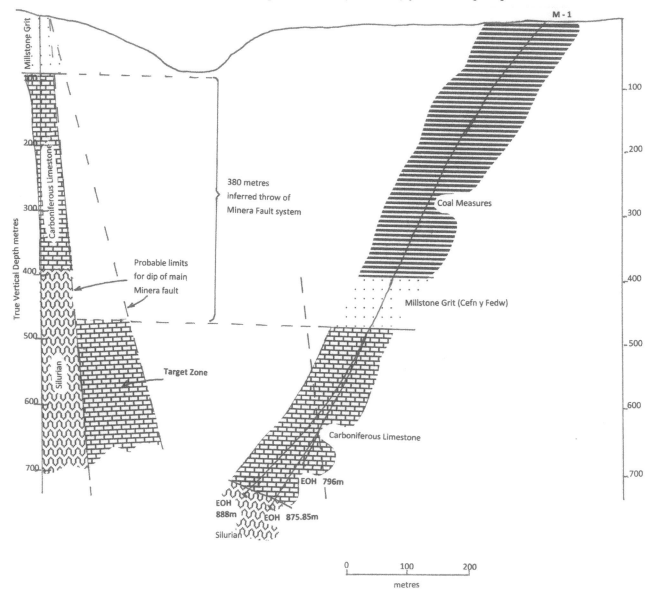

Fig. 8   Minera drillhole M-1 crossection (redrawn from MEIGA AE186 with the permission of the British Geological Survey ©NERC. All rights Reserved)

tially with the freeing of the gold price in 1971. When gold reached a peak of about $850 in 1980 the area became of interest to several companies. Gold generally occurred in small 'bonanza' high-grade shoots in quartz veins within shales of the Cambrian Clogau Formation, especially where it was intruded by dolerite sills (greenstones). A recent comprehensive evaluation of the geological structure of the area is given in Platten and Dominy (2009).

Clogau St Davids mine

This deposit was originally worked for copper until gold was discovered in the 1860s following the major Californian and Australian gold rushes. The mine had been largely dormant for many years until the Australian company Caernarvon Mining formed Clogau St David's Gold Mines Ltd in 1981 to investigate the eponymous deposit and was granted a Crown Mining Lease in 1982. The initial application for MEIGA support was over-ambitious with a proposed extensive laboratory testwork programme on the samples from trial mining of the quartz vein. It also included proposals for biogeochemical exploration for additional veins and sampling of adjacent waste dumps. A modified and less costly application was approved (MEIGA AE242) and exploration started in February 1983 directed by geologist John Rottenbury. The main thrust of the exploration was

to rehabilitate part of the Clogau mine near the Llechfraith adit entrance, including a winze or decline to the next level down, and drive back under the river to pick up the postulated downward extensions of several rich shoots recorded by earlier miners (Fig. 9). It was hoped that the main quartz vein would contain enough low-grade gold to pay for its development while the shoots would provide the profits. This did not prove to be the case.

Mining progressed as planned with development on No. 4 level extending 12 m east and 50 m west from the winze. Five to 10 tonne samples were taken at 0.5 to 1 m intervals but the sampling and milling of the vein caused great problems, as much of any gold present was 'free' and not locked in sulphides. It proved impossible to calculate an accurate balance of gold through the mill from the individual sample assay, the head grade assay into the mill, gold recovered in the mill and mill tailings assay. The average content of the vein was around 0.5 g/t though individual 5 tonne samples did contain as much as 8 g/t. The problems had still not been resolved by November 1985, at the end of the MEIGA scheme. However, Caernarvon floated Clogau Gold Mines on the London Stock Exchange Unlisted Securities Market (USM) in June 1984 with the intention of raising £2 million for further development. There was a report of a platinum find in 1985 – sometimes a sign of

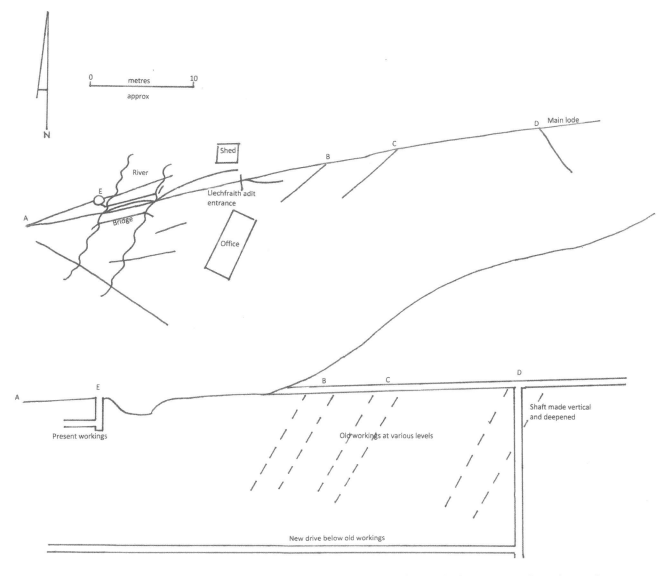

Fig. 9   Plan of Clogau Llechfraith adit development in 1983 (drawn by the author from a plan by Dr J. Rottenbury, deceased)

desperation in a small mining company (*Guardian*, 20 Oct. 1985). The Chairman and Managing Director resigned after continuing problems in 1985 and the company struggled on for a further two and a half years until the flotation money had all been spent with the recovery of 1150 grams (41 oz) of gold – an expensive venture (Hodgkins 1988). By 1988 Clogau Gold Mines, now Australian controlled, had developed interests in gold near Kalgoorlie in Western Australia (*Mining Journal*, 4 Nov. 1988) and at Le Châtelet in central France (*Mine and Quarry*, Oct. 1988).

Clogau gold mine was acquired by William Roberts in 1989 and produced small quantities between 1992 and 1998. The gold is now used for the 'touch of rare Welsh gold' in Clogau Gold jewellery. Tourism developments, including a cable car ride from Bontddu on the Mawddach estuary to the mine, were refused by the National Park Authority in 1989.

Cambrian Goldfields acquired a Crown Exploration Licence over Clogau gold mine in 1999 but met with considerable access difficulties after initial exploration. It also held two Crown licences from 2001 to about 2006 covering 150 km² of the Dolgellau gold belt including Prince Edward and Castell Carn Dochan.

Maestryfer mine near Clogau was worked by Chris and Terence Madden under the name of Stoic Mining from the mid 1980s (*Daily Mail*, 12 November 1994). This mine, like its bigger neighbour Clogau, always seemed to have the promise of great wealth just beyond the current working.

Carnon Holdings Ltd, during a phase of looking for opportunities outside its Wheal Jane tin mine in Cornwall, held a 400 km² Crown licence in 1989 from Dolgellau to Ffestiniog with excisions for Clogau and Gwynfynydd. Forty-seven mines or trials were sampled, the best results being 2.3 g/t at Prince Edward and 33.5 g/t at Llafar (<1 g/t elsewhere). The company disappeared in the early 1990s.

Gwynfynydd mine
Gwynfynydd mine was acquired by Mark Weinberg in 1981 on George Hall's recommendation and managed by George from 1981 to 1984 and subsequently by Nick Warrell who had formerly managed the short-lived Wheal Concord tin mine in Cornwall. The following brief description is taken from correspondence with George in 2001–2. The initial work was intended to be a zig-zag decline to intersect the junction of the Main and New lodes in the Clogau Shales below the old workings. Robertson Research remapped the surface and underground exposures around the mine lease. The mapping showed that the Clogau Shales, with some unworked quartz lodes – including one interpreted as an extension of the Chidlaw Lode which had been productive in the 1880s – were in a downfaulted block about 50 m across which was later called the Link Zone. The decline was suspended and a drive put across the block to the west on what was thought to be the Chidlaw Lode. George thought any gold would be in the footwall and therefore kept the footwall of the lode (which was in parts 20 m wide) diagonally across the drive from top left to bottom right. Several drill holes and a short cross-cut were used to prove the drive was on the footwall but no gold was found. More cross-cuts were used to drive along other lodes in the same Link Zone, also without success. Two years had passed without significant gold being found so in September 1983

George decided take 2 m off the apparent footwall of the Chidlaw Lode which revealed coarse visible gold in a quartz vein 5 cm wide. George describes the carbonaceous Clogau Shale 'as black as coal'. He remained convinced that there was not an 'average grade' of gold in the Dolgellau veins but that they consisted of thick veins composed of parallel ribbons of quartz with shale partings and accompanying pyrite, sphalerite and galena but no gold, with thin leaves of occasional bonanza gold on the footwall.

The rich shoot in the Chidlaw Link Zone produced 1659 oz from 3312 tonnes of ore between 1983 and 1990 at 'average grade' of 0.49 oz/t (Welsh Gold prospectus 1995).

Welsh Gold plc took over Gwynfynydd Gold Mine Ltd in 1992 and acquired a Crown lease for 21 years from January 1993. It was floated in 1995 for £1.3 million by Roland Phelps to develop the mine and to produce gold for pure Welsh gold jewellery in an associated retail operation. Wardell Armstrong assessed the mine as having proven reserves of 10,000 t, probable reserves of 24,000 t and indicated resources of 140,000 t with a proposed annual production of 5000 t/yr (Welsh Gold plc prospectus 1995).

In December 2008, Gold Mines of Wales (Operations) Ltd, a subsidiary of the Australian company Victorian Gold Limited, was granted a 125 km² Crown Exploration Licence covering the entire Dolgellau gold belt (Platten & Dominey 2009). In December 2011 Australian company Stellar Resources acquired 49.9% of Stellar Gold Mines of Wales Ltd whose subsidiary Gold Mines of Wales (Operations) Ltd held an exploration licence covering an area of 120 km² stated as containing the entire Dolgellau gold belt, including the historic Clogau gold mine. Stellar paid £100,000 cash plus shares then worth about £500,000. Stellar have subsequently stated that five geologists are working on the exploration and sampling of Clogau and have reported analyses of up to 749 g/t Au from 1 kg grab samples from various sections of the Llechfraith and Tyn y Cornel adits (http://www.stellar-resources.com/ accessed 14 Sept. 2014).

A Snowdon Consultants report by Dr Simon Dominy for Gold Mines of Wales in 2012 is said to state that the area could contain gold worth £125 million though he stressed this is a 'hypothetical or conceptual indication of likely tonnage and grade ranges of mineralised quartz lode which is not necessarily economic' (http://www.walesonline.co.uk/news/wales-news/could-wales-sitting-gold-reserves-2032666 accessed 14 Sept. 2014).

Mineral Reconnaissance Programme
The MRP carried out a number of exploration projects in North Wales (Fig. 10). The programme was intended to provide background geological, geochemical and geophysical data to assist mining companies in selecting favourable ground. It generally did not look at areas already being explored by companies to avoid conflicts of interest and accusations of favouritism.

The first, MRP 22, published in 1978, followed up zinc anomalies reported by Noranda in their 1972 MEIGA project of the same name in the Dulyn catchment northwest of Llanrwst. Noranda had thought they might be due to an extension of the Llanrwst mining field and recommended follow-up work though none was carried out. The MRP concluded that they were due to co-precipitation with manganese and a mineralisation link was unlikely.

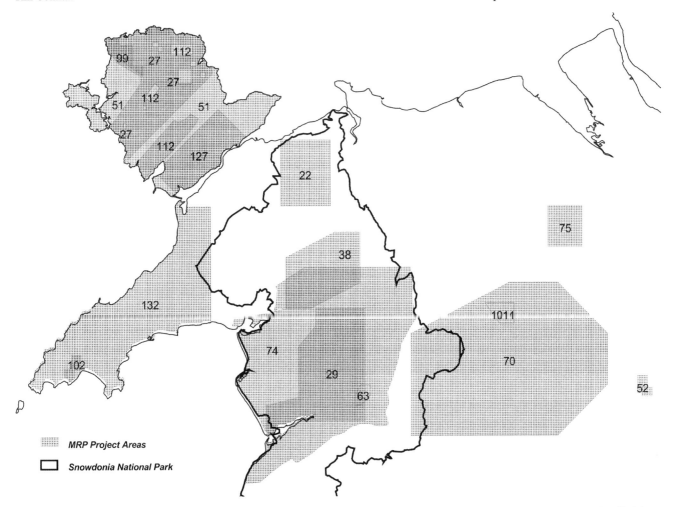

Fig. 10   Location of MRP projects in North Wales (reproduced with the permission of the British Geological Survey ©NERC. All rights Reserved)

This was followed in 1979 by MRP 27, the first of a number of investigations of parts of Anglesey. It carried out an airborne magnetic, EM and radiometric survey of the north and west of the island. The EM measurements were strongly affected by the numerous radio transmitters and there were no significant radiometric anomalies, but a number of magnetic anomalies were associated with Tertiary dolerite dykes, the Carmel Head thrust and possible mineralisation.

The eastern part of the Harlech Dome was then investigated by an integrated geological, geochemical and geophysical survey with additional surface exploration of numerous mines and trials (MRP 29). Possible extensions of the Coed y Brenin copper deposit were suggested and intrusion breccias associated with the Rhobell Fawr volcanism, such as the worked out copper-gold deposit at Glasdir (Fig. 11), were recognised as a potential target for further exploration.

The report also suggested that there were some areas of metal enrichment that could be due to stratiform mineralisation. Three of these, Benglog, Bryn Mawr and Penaran, were selected for follow-up. The Benglog area was investigated in MRP63 and some barium enrichment was found but no distinct targets were located. Bryn Mawr was selected as a drilling target but became the target of anti-nuclear and other protest groups and although permission to drill was obtained after a public enquiry the IGS decided not to continue as the safety of the drilling rig and personnel could not be guaranteed.

MRP 38 describes a gravity survey over the Tanygrisiau granite, near Blaenau Ffestiniog, which delineated its subsurface extension to the north-east. The granite is associated with minor sulphide mineralisation.

Additional baseline geochemical stream sediment surveys were carried out over the Berwyn Dome (MRP 70) and over the entire Harlech Dome (MRP 74) in conjunction with a gravity survey to investigate concealed structures and intrusions. The Berwyn survey found a number of weak metal anomalies and minor concentrations of gold grains in the Afon Tryston in the north-west of the area. These were followed up in MRP Data Release 1014 which confirmed the presence of gold but did not suggest that more intensive exploration should be carried out. The Harlech survey indicated that the Dolgellau gold belt could extend round the northern edge of the Dome towards Talsarnau – a view long expressed by the late George Hall. It also found numerous minor base metal anomalies with recommendations for follow-up investigations of a number of specific localities; however these are mainly in the Snowdonia National Park.

The MRP returned to Anglesey for a number of regional and local projects. MRP 51 was a reconnaissance geochemical survey of the whole island in the late 1970s with a few small follow-up soil surveys. It also included a useful listing of all the recorded mines, trials and mineral occurrences on the island. About one third of the island was not covered by the stream sampling due to poor surface drainage and contamination from Parys Mountain. MRP 99 investigated

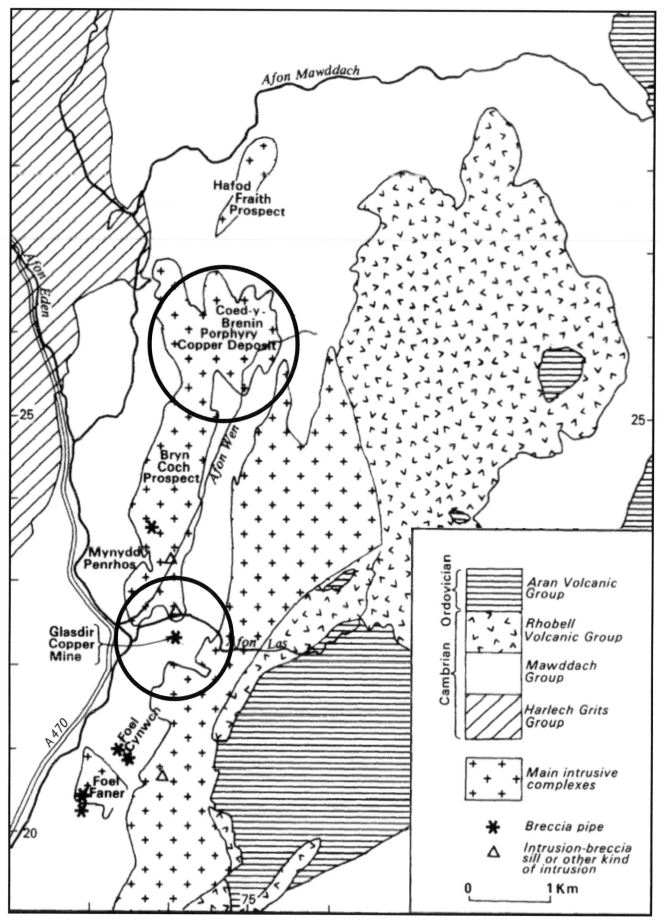

Fig. 11   Geological map showing the Coed y Brenin and Glasdir copper deposits (source MRP29) (reproduced with the permission of the British Geological Survey ©NERC. All rights Reserved)

the Ordovician rocks in the north-west of the island where a number of minor mines and trials had been worked. A number of soil geochemistry and IP geophysics traverses covered the north-west striking outcrop and 15 short boreholes were drilled to a maximum depth of 120 m. Copper, lead and zinc sulphides were found in veins in 11 boreholes. Unfortunately the report was published at a time when the Department for Trade and Industry (DTI), the programmes funding body, had a short-lived policy of issuing a summary report at the normal nominal price but charging £1000 for access to the full results so no metal values or intersection lengths are given. This resulted in minimal company interest in the report although the boreholes were successful in intersecting a number of base metal sulphide occurrences.

MRP 112 carried out a gravity survey of the island together with detailed geophysical and geochemical studies of selected areas. Gravity and IP geophysics surveys over Parys Mountain showed that the techniques could be used to examine the rest of the Ordovician area on the island. A number of areas were examined in more detail but no significant anomalies were found.

MRP 127 was a study of the Penmynydd basic intrusion in the south of the island on the southern side of the major Berw Fault to investigate the possibility that it was a layered intrusion which could contain copper and nickel mineralisation. Detailed gravity and magnetic surveys, combined with soil sampling, were carried out in 1990. No base or precious metal anomalies were found apart from minor enrichments in lead and barium which were attributed to minor veins in the thin cover of Carboniferous Limestone in part of the area.

Two projects on the Lleyn Peninsula examined the old Benallt and Nant manganese mines (MRP 102) and carried out a geochemical stream sediment survey (MRP 132). The Benallt survey investigated the possibility of extensions to the numerous, small and complex manganese orebodies in Ordovician mudstones between basic intrusions and lavas that had produced over 150,000 tons of ore. Unusually some of the manganese ore is magnetic and so detailed ground magnetic surveys were used to define potential new mineralisation. However five short boreholes to a maximum depth of 97 m showed that most magnetic anomalies were due to magnetic ironstone with very low manganese content and that it was unlikely that any significant manganese deposit remained undiscovered. The Lleyn geochemical survey was reconnaissance in nature and did not indicate the likelihood of any substantial mineralisation although there were indications of stratabound metal enrichment in Ordovician (Arenig) mudstones.

The MRP was subsumed into a wider Minerals Programme in 1998 and concentrated on syntheses of existing information within a GIS environment coupled with limited additional fieldwork. A report on the potential occurrence of mesothermal gold and volcanogenic base metal deposits in Wales combined geological, geophysical and geochemical datasets (Cooper and others 2000). Weightings were applied to each parameter such as distance from faults, rock type or presence of a mineral occurrence which were then combined in a GIS to generate a series of maps illustrating the potential for mineralisation of each type. As would be expected, the potential for gold was highest around the Harlech Dome, while that for vol-

canogenic mineralisation was highest in Ordovician areas especially Parys Mountain and around the Snowdon volcanic centre.

Conclusions

North Wales has been the focus of a number of exploration programmes for a variety of elements and deposit types due to its varied and attractive geology. The most important have been Coed y Brenin and Parys Mountain. The former attracted much attention and became a *cause célèbre* for opponents of any developments in national parks while the latter has suffered the vicissitudes of international metal prices and the problems of a complex orebody in spite of a supportive planning authority and local opinion. Much of the area lies within the Snowdonia National Park and although the development of small gold mines has been permitted it remains doubtful whether larger operations would be tolerated. Hopefully Parys Mountain will be developed as a major mine in the next decade.

This paper is only an overview of the exploration carried out in North Wales over the past 50 years and there are many aspects that deserve further study. Much useful information on mineral exploration in the area may have been lost due to the lack of any formal application or recording system apart from the MEIGA scheme between 1971 and 1984. Some companies have donated information to the British Geological Survey, but apart from the MEIGA records, there was no legal obligation to do so. Additional information on work in the Dolgellau gold belt may exist on the Crown Estate archive, but only the work carried out by Carnon referred to above is publicly accessible in the National Geoscience Records Centre. The BGS MRP reports and the G-BASE analyses remain the major sources of geological, geophysical and geochemical information on the area.

Acknowledgements

I would like to thank the late George Hall for informative letters and conversations. I would also like to acknowledge the many useful visits to Parys Mountain during both Cominco and Anglesey Mining exploration. In particular Ian Cuthbertson was always welcoming, helpful and informative. The MEIGA records at the National Geoscience Records Centre at the British Geological Survey in Keyworth contain much useful information of which only a small part has been used in this account. The BGS MRP reports are available on-line at http://bgs.ac.uk/mineralsuk/exploration/potential/mrp.html.

References

Audsley, A., Daborn, G.R., & Pearson, D., 1961. *The Recovery of Copper from Mine Water at the Parys-Mona Copper Mines, Anglesey*, Scientific Report, N.C.L./CON-2, Department of Scientific and Industrial Research, National Chemical Laboratory, Teddington, Middlesex

Barrett, T.J., MacLean, W.H., & Tennant, S.C., 2001. 'Volcanic sequence and alteration at the Parys Mountain volcanic-hosted massive sulfide deposit, Wales, United Kingdom: applications of immobile element lithogeochemistry', *Economic Geology* 96, pp. 1279–1305

Cooper, D.C., Rollin, K.E., Colman, T.B., Davies, J.R., & Wilson, D, 2000. *Potential for Mesothermal Gold and VMS Deposits in the Lower Palaeozoic Welsh Basin*, BGS Research Report RR/00/09, DTI Minerals Programme Publication no. 4

Dewey, H., & Eastwood, T., 1925. *Copper Ore of the Midlands, Wales, the Lake District and the Isle of Man*, Special Reports on the Mineral Resources of Great Britain vol. 30 (London: HMSO)

Hall, G.W., 1975. *The Gold Mines of Merioneth* (Kington, Herefordshire: Griffin Publications)

Hodgkins, J., 1988. 'The reopening of Clogau gold mine 1966', *Rock Bottom* 5, pp. 2–3

Manning, W., 1959. 'The Parys and Mona mines in Anglesey', in *The Future of Non-Ferrous Mining in Great Britain and Ireland* (Institution of Mining and Metallurgy), pp. 313–333

Miller, O.D.W., 1993. 'Precious metal mineralization associated with the Coed-y-Brenin porphyry copper system, North Wales', unpublished Ph.D. thesis, University of Aberdeen

Nutt, M.J.C., Ineson, P.R., & Mitchell, J.G., 1979. 'The age of mineralisation at Parys Mountain Anglesey', in *The Caledonides of the British Isles Reviewed*, Geological Society of London Special Publication no. 8, pp. 619–627

Platten, I.M., & Dominy, S.C., 2009. 'Geological mapping in the evaluation of structurally controlled gold veins: a case study from the Dolgellau gold belt, North Wales, United Kingdom', World Gold Conference 2009 (Southern African Institute of Mining and Metallurgy)

Pointon, C.R., & Ixer, R.A., 1980. 'Parys Mountain mineral deposit Anglesey Wales: geology and ore mineralogy', *Transactions (Section B) Institution of Mining and Metallurgy* 89, pp. B143–B155

Reedman, A.J., Colman, T.B., Campbell, S.D.G., & Howells, M.J., 1985. 'Volcanogenic mineralisation related to the Snowdon Volcanic Group (Ordovician) Gwynedd North Wales', *Journal of the Geological Society of London* 142, pp. 875–888

Rice, R., & Sharp, G.J., 1976. 'Copper mineralisation in the forest of Coed-y-Brenin, North Wales', *Transactions of the Institution of Mining and Metallurgy (Section B: Applied Earth Science)* 85, pp. B1–13

Sangster, D.F., 1972. 'Precambrian volcanogenic massive sulphide deposits in Canada: a review', Geological Survey of Canada Paper 72–22, pp. 1–43

Searle, G., 1975. 'Copper in Snowdonia National Park', in *The Politics of Physical Resources*, ed. P. Smith (Open University Press), pp. 66–112

Tyler, P.A., 2003. 'The Parys Mountain volcanogenic sulphide deposit, North Wales: a new interpretation', in *Europe's Base Metal Deposits*, ed. J.G. Kelly, C.J. Andrew, J.H. Ashton, M.H. Boland, G. Earls, L. Fusciardi and G. Stanley (Irish Association for Economic Geology), pp. 127–153

Wheatley, C.J.V., 1971. 'Aspects of metallogenesis within the southern Caledonides of Great Britain and Ireland', *Transactions (Section B) Institution of Mining and Metallurgy* 80, pp. B211–B223

Wolfenden, E.B., 1967. *Evaluation of Pyrite Deposits on Parys Mountain, Amlwch, Anglesey*, Report No. 123, Robertson Research Co. Ltd.

Copper, Lead and Slate: Technological and Social Change in the Extractive Industries of North-West Wales

David Gwyn

Abstract: Both copper and slate were extracted on a significant scale in north-west Wales from the late eighteenth century, and there is evidence to suggest that immigrant metalliferous miners brought with them skills that soon proved useful to the slate quarrymen. This paper will consider technology transfer between copper and slate from the 1750s to the 1820s such as the use of explosives and haulage systems, and will consider the population movements which might have led to the spread of these technologies. It will also consider the different challenges posed by copper-mining, as an industry with deep roots and a mobile workforce, and by slate quarrying, where demand was growing quickly but where there was little tradition of technical innovation.

Introduction

Two major extractive industries transformed the landscape and society of north-west Wales from the late eighteenth century into the late nineteenth. One was the search for metalliferous ores, primarily copper and lead, the other the quarrying of slate. (Fig. 1) Both have been extensively researched, yet gaps in our knowledge remain and many assumptions about them have remained unchallenged; both were conducted on an extensive scale, at least while demand was high, but thereafter went into a long-term decline. What this paper seeks to do is to ask questions about the relationship between them and to suggest that, between 1768 and the 1830s, copper mining may have provided the nascent slate industry with the skills-base and some of the technical knowledge, perhaps also the entrepreneurial confidence, that enabled it to develop. As such it is necessarily a speculative offering, but it is offered in the hope that others may be persuaded to undertake the more detailed research, in parish records and other sources, that might prove or disprove the case. I focus particularly on the lives and experience of the more skilled among the workmen as the agents of 'technology transfer' rather than exclusively on managers and agents, because there were quite clearly many other influences on the growing slate industry, not least the skills that the capital of Lord Penrhyn, Thomas Assheton Smith and other wealthy investors in the slate industry could bring to bear. But it is well worth while examining how informal contacts and population movements within the north-west Wales region might also have been a factor.

Copper mining had an ancient history in north-west Wales long before the glory days of the eighteenth century but it was a series of developments in 1768 that once again made it an industry of global significance. In that year the Vaynol estate re-opened its mines at Drws y Coed in the Nantlle valley and, even more significantly, low-grade but easily accessible copper ore was discovered on Mynydd Parys on Anglesey, where it was worked in two adjacent mines, the Parys and the Mona.[1] The Vaynol mines

Fig. 1   North-west Wales, showing principal locations mentioned in the text

enjoyed some success into the nineteenth century but Parys became astonishingly profitable until the end of the century.[2] Copper was also worked on the Great Orme, at the mouth of the Conwy river. Lead mines were opened, or revived, in two areas in the seventeenth century – in the Gwydir ore-field on the western bank of the Conwy valley, and around Llanengan on Penrhyn Llŷn.[3]

---

[1] 2 March 1786 was for years afterwards kept as the anniversary of the discovery. The archive of the Swansea copper smelters confirm that Parys moved into the export market around this time – NLW, MS 1510B, entry for 4 October 1769.

(For the Llanberis copper mines see Crew 1976.)

[2] For the Greenfield valley and the Parys commercial empire, see Harris 2003.

[3] Bennett & Vernon 1989, 6–7; Bennett & Vernon 2002, 1.

Fig. 2   John Warwick Smith's 'One of the Copper Mines Belonging to the Paris Mountain Company, Anglesea, 1790' shows the method of raising the ore from the opencast

Workforce

When Thomas Pennant visited Parys in 1778 he estimated that about 8000 people were 'getting their bread from these mines'.[4] They were a mixture of local Welsh and incomers, though as yet no attempt has been made to study their origins. The Cornish influx to Amlwch came later, but what is certain is that from 1768 onwards it was a teeming, overcrowded place, and that it was somewhere where there was good money to be earned. This is amply borne out by paintings of the mines, showing the labour-intensive nature of the work (Fig. 2).[5]

By contrast, until the very end of the eighteenth century, a far smaller number of people within the region made a living from the slate industry. Farmers undoubtedly worked convenient outcrops to re-roof a local house or the parish church as necessary, and perhaps more slate quarrymen than we might think are hidden as 'labourers' in parish records, but even in Nantlle, the longest-established and best-organised quarrying area, probably no more than a few hundred people made a living from slate by about 1790.[6]

The Ogwen valley (Fig. 3) is unlikely to have employed many more at this time, and Nantperis probably far fewer.[7] Detailed examination of the parish records for Maentwrog and Ffestiniog by Dr Michael Lewis suggests that the total number of active quarrymen in the area was at this stage no more than about ten.[8] They did include the famous Methusalem Jones, the Nantlle quarryman to whom the discovery of slate in the Diffwys gorge through supernatural revelation is credited. This was around 1760, but what is interesting is that Methusalem Jones was a peripatetic individual who ran several businesses, and spent several years in Amlwch. What he did there we do not know; he may have worked as a miner, but it is tempting to see Methusalem Street, attested from 1787, as something to do with him.[9]

For much of the eighteenth century, the most productive area of slate quarrying, one which exported throughout the Atlantic economy, was that of the Loire valley in France,

---

[4]   Pennant 1783, 281–282.

[5]   Rowlands 1981; Hope 1994.

[6]   This very rough estimate is based National Library of Wales, Glynllifon MS 84, ff. 56v–96v recording 130 men and women working at Cilgwyn, and Bangor University, Porth yr Aur MSS 27204–27209 (summarised by D.D. Pritchard in Caernarfon Record Office, XM 4874/6) setting out the position at the independent quarries nearby together with the unknown workforce at yr Allt Lechi, Cloddfa'r Coed, Cloddfa'r Lôn,

Galltyfedw and the surely aptly named 'Twll Cornwall', as well as those on the southern side of the valley. Bangor University, Porth yr Aur MS 30340 gives 50 men at Hafodlas, 50 at Pen y Bryn, 100 at Gallt y Fedw, 100 at Tal y Sarn and 260 at Cilgwyn.

[7]   Bangor University, Penrhyn castle 1970 records 80 quarrymen receiving instructions to set themselves up in partnerships of five or more men in the 1760s.

[8]   Lewis & Williams 1987; also research material ex info Dr Michael Lewis.

[9]   Unpublished research note by Dr Michael Lewis; see also Williams 1882, 81.

Fig. 3   Penrhyn slate quarry in the Ogwen valley kept no more than a few hundred men busy until the late eighteenth century, as in John Warwick Smith's painting, 'The Slate Quarries at Bron Llwyd' (undated), but had grown to be of vast size by the mid-nineteenth century (Yale Center for British Art, Paul Mellon Collection)

but national bankruptcy and revolution enabled the Welsh quarries to move into the ascendancy. In 1800 an experienced group of Lake District slate quarrymen, William Turner amongst them, became involved in Diffwys quarry at Ffestiniog, a partnership including the egregious lawyer John Evans took a crown lease of Cilgwyn, and Richard Pennant, Lord Penrhyn, began the construction of an iron railroad to connect his quarries to the sea.

Technologies
Blasting
The traditions of quarrying areas of the Arfon district of Gwynedd agree that it was at Cilgwyn in Nantlle that gunpowder was first used in the slate industry for shot blasting, though the local historian John Griffith 'Sylwedydd' suggests that even here it was little practised before about 1800.[10] Several theories have been advanced about when and by whom the technology was introduced, but each one points to copper mining practice. If Sylwedydd was correct, and there was little blasting before the turn of the century, it could be that John Price, as manager of Mona mine at Parys and one of the crown tenants at Cilgwyn, was instrumental in its widespread adoption. Dr Gwynfor Pierce Jones suggested that it might have been learnt from local miners as early as the 1730s, and that it could therefore have been a factor in the Nantlle area's pre-eminence in slate production in the early years of the eighteenth century.[11] Published sources record no activity at Drws y Coed this early, but a date in the 1760s is quite possible.[12] The introduction of

jumpers for drilling shot holes at Nantlle was credited to a 'man from Llanberis', who may have been a copper miner or may have been a slate quarryman.[13] Cilgwyn men took the skill of blasting to Ffestiniog and to Llanberis.[14]

Pumping, wind and steam power
The two copper mines on Parys mountain both went deep below the surface but were accessed from a low ridge. As a result, they could make very little use indeed of water for pumping, and had to find alternative energy sources very early on. The Mona mine stock list of 1788 refers to pumps valued at £22 18/- and 'water shafts', presumably a rising main,[15] which may have been powered by a windmill, since the same source includes a 'wind engine' valued at £178 13/-. A windmill – and there may have been several in the late eighteenth century – is depicted in John 'Warwick' Smith's watercolour of 1785, a small tower mill with vertical walls, believed to have been demolished by 1790.[16]

Most early slate quarries in the area were self draining, and even where they needed pumps it was generally possible to use water power to operate them. Penrhyn quarry had waterwheels and pumps by 1793.[17] The Nantlle quarries by contrast could in theory have made effective use of water

[10] Jones 1963, 137; Bangor University, Bangor MS 8277, 4; Sylwedydd n.d., 66.
[11] Jones 1996.
[12] Bick 2003, 44–52; Pritchard 1945, 358; 'Dewi Peris' 1896, 267.
[13] Lewis (ed.) 1987, 64.
[14] Owen 1868, 369; Williams 1882, 72, 135–136; Pritchard 1945, 358; Richards 1995, 47, on early rock-blasting; Williams 1892, 110, on the pre-eminence of the Cilgwyn quarrymen in rock-blasting.
[15] Bangor University, Mona Mine 3040.
[16] Pennant 1783, 279; Guise & Lees 1992, 138–139.
[17] Caernarfon Record Office, XM/1311/5 confirms water courses and waterwheels at the quarry in 1793.

Fig. 4   John Warwick Smith's painting 'The Lakes of Llanberis – from the Road from Caernarfon Going to Llanberis, Caernarfonshire', dated 1792, shows how the two lakes lent themselves to transport from the copper mines, located beyond Dolbadarn castle (centre), as well as from the slate quarries on the slopes to the left (Yale Center for British Art, Paul Mellon Collection)

power but suffered from the problem that they all depended on the one stream, which made co-operation between the different estates and quarry tenants difficult.[18] For this reason, wind power was used to pump in the Nantlle quarries from 1806 onwards, operating both small-scale timber structures and towers.[19] No traces are known to survive, though a sketch shows a substantial stone tower at Hafodlas quarry (Cloddfa'r Coed) in the early nineteenth century.[20] The very first steam pumping engine in the Welsh slate industry was also to be found here, installed in 1812 by a local artisan engineer, John Hughes of Pen y Groes.[21] Whether he had made his way to Parys, or for that matter one of Anglesey's coal mines, to see how such things functioned, is of course unknowable, but these would have been the only places within his Welsh-speaking environment where he could have taken advice about how to source, install and operate such a machine.[22]

Haulage
Early illustrations of the Parys mines show windlasses perched on flimsy platforms on the edge of the opencasts, hauling kibbles and sometimes men on hemp ropes. 'Turn Trees Rolls & Stages' worth £17 13/- are recorded at Mona

mine in 1788 and three 'hand-whimseys' are recorded at Parys mine in 1815 along the edge of the opencast. Horse gins are also evident from early paintings.[23]

One slate quarry which would both have needed such a system was Cloddfa'r Coed in Nantlle, a deep and steep-sided pit. It is no surprise that it is here that we first read of a whim, in around 1790 when one Michael Owen is recorded as having introduced the Independent cause to the valley by praying near it.[24] Cloddfa'r Coed had nine whims by the 1820s, and Cilgwyn five by 1821.[25] The memoirs of Robert Williams, recalling developments of the 1820s in his native Nantlle district, distinguish between hand-operated *tyntris* (turntrees) worked in conjunction with wheelbarrows, and horse-powered *chwimsis* (whimsies) used with railways, and also refer to winding a *cibl* (kibble). This English-derived terminology strongly suggests direct influence at artisan level from copper mining practice.[26]

---

[18] Gwyn 2002.

[19] Bangor University, Porth yr Aur MSS 27514, 27937, 27037, 27059, 27087 and 29479.

[20] National Library of Wales, TAOI PB01261.

[21] Hafodlas quarry formed part of Hafodlas farm, but was known colloquially as Cloddfa'r Coed ('the quarry of the woods'). See Gwyn 2002.

[22] John Hughes never became proficient in English – Bangor University, Carter Vincent Additional 3538, p. 47, and McChristie 1838.

[23] Rowlands 1981, 22–24. John Price, the Mona Mine agent by the 1790s, was also involved with slate quarries at Cilgwyn in Nantlle, in Ffestiniog, and at Cefn Du in the Nantperis area from 1800; see Rowlands 1981, 40, and Bangor University, Schedule of Porth yr Aur papers. Bangor University, Mona Mine MS 3040; National Library of Wales, PZ 3209 Al/I-A115 (Julius Caesar Ibbetson: Paris Mine: aquatint after watercolour, 1795).

[24] Rees & Thomas 1873, 227.

[25] Bangor University, Porth yr Aur MSS 27447, 27465 and 29694. Porth yr Aur MS 27824 refers to hand-wound rope-ways at Cilgwyn in 1813.

[26] Williams 1900, 88–89.

Transport

Copper ore was boated down the Peris and Padarn lakes while the Llanberis mines were active,[27] under the auspices of some formidable female haulage contractors, of whom Margaret ferch Ifan (1702–1793) was the best known. It is hard to imagine that the Dinorwic slate quarries could have adopted boat transport as effectively as they did once they moved into capitalised production in 1788 without existing knowledge of boat building and management. That year, the quarries on the north-eastern side of the lakes were leased by the Vaynol estate to a partnership which abandoned the old packhorse route through Llanddeiniolen parish in favour of using boats. Slates destined for the Vaynol estate's harbour at y Felinheli were landed at Penllyn, whereas slate for Caernarfon was boated down to a stockpile at Cwm y Glo, on the opposite side of the lake.[28] This trade made use of perhaps between 16 and 22 vessels, some purpose-built and directly operated by the quarry partnership, others owned by independent contractors, some of them possibly existing lake boats (Fig. 4).[29]

Contract work

The decline of the Parys mines in the early nineteenth century made available within the region a surplus of skilled and hard-working men who could be called on to carry out contract work as and when needed. A number of instances are known.

One is the re-building of Madocks' cob on the Traeth Mawr, after the breach of 1812, when workmen from Parys were drafted in – including Thomas Edwards, the *hwntw mawr* (big south-Walian), who was convicted of the murder of Mary Jones of Penrhyn Isaf, and hanged at Dolgellau on 17 April 1813.[30]

Another was the construction of the Festiniog Railway between 1832 and 1836. One 'HR' carved his name on a cutting wall together with the word 'AMLWCH' and the date '1833' (Fig. 5). He was presumably working for James Smith, a local contractor and road builder who had been awarded the contract to build the formation of the railway on 22 December 1832, but who quickly came to grief.

Fig. 5   A graffito presumed to be carved by an Amlwch labourer engaged on construction of the Festiniog Railway (courtesy Andy Carey)

Smith, as a road builder, might well have been able to find employment for Parys miners who were out of work, and it is quite likely that they would have been found on road-building contracts throughout Anglesey, Caernarvonshire and Merioneth. Anglesey men – some from Holyhead, but some from Amlwch – were among the two hundred men who were at work when the Festiniog Railway Company went ahead using direct labour in 1834.[31]

Additionally, the traditions of several Blaenau families suggest that when the slate industry expanded in the 1860s, with the need to drive levels, Amlwch miners responded to the call. They would have been well qualified for this sort of work, which required a different skill from the actual quarrying for slate. Some are believed to have married locally and settled down in Blaenau.

Conclusions

There is some evidence for the transfer of skills and technology from the teeming, peripatetic world of the copper and lead miners and the more rooted world of the slate quarrymen, and enough has been said to suggest that a detailed search in parish records would tell us much more. How many of the early slate quarrymen were Anglesey-born, and what was their parish of birth? Is there any evidence that specialist workers in the slate industry came from Anglesey – men for instance who might have known how to operate a pump or a steam engine? We do not know; but perhaps enough has been said here to suggest that anyone prepared to work through the maze of local and regional archives – records of births, marriages and deaths, local and chapel histories, bastardy bills and the earliest government census – might well be able to tell us how the industrial revolution in north-west Wales was made.

Bibliography

Beazley, E., 1985. *Madocks and the Wonder of Wales* (Aberystwyth: Welsh Books Centre)

Bennett, J., & Vernon, R.W., 1989. *Mines of the Gwydyr Forest, Part 1: Llanrwst Mine and its Neighbours* (Cuddington: Gwydyr Mines Publications)

Bennett, J., & Vernon, R.W., 2002. *Metal Mines of Llanengan* (Warrington: Gwydyr Mines Publications)

Bick, D., 2003. *The Old Copper Mines of Snowdonia* (3rd ed.) (Newent)

Crew, P., 1976. 'The copper mines of Llanberis and Clogwyn Goch', *Transactions of the Caernarvonshire Historical Society* 37

'Dewi Peris', 1896. 'Chwarelyddiaeth', *Y Genhinen* XIV 4, pp. 267–268

Guise, B., & Lees, G., 1992. *Windmills of Anglesey* (Painscastle)

Gwyn, D., 2002. 'An early high-pressure steam engine at Cloddfa'r Coed', *Transactions of the Caernarvonshire Historical Society* 63

Harris, J.R., 2003. *The Copper King: Thomas Williams of Llanidan* (Ashbourne: Landmark Publishing)

Hope, B., 1994. *A Curious Place: the Industrial History of Amlwch (1550–1950)* (Wrexham)

Hughes, S., 2000. *Copperopolis* (Aberystwyth: Royal

---

27 Bick 2003, 113.
28 Bangor University, Porth yr Aur MS 29087 (permission to build a new road from Llanddeiniolen to Port Dinorwic, 1788) and 29084 (letter announcing improvement to the harbour on the Menai Strait at y Felinheli, 1793).
29 Illsley 1979, 97–98, p. 94.
30 Beazley 1985, 177, 191.

31 Lewis 1997, 11.

Commission on the Ancient and Historical Monuments of Wales)

Illsley, J.S., 1979. 'Trade and transport on Llyn Padarn', *Transactions of the Caernarvonshire Historical Society* 40

Jones, E., 1963. *Canrif y Chwarelwr* (Denbigh: Gwasg Gee)

Jones, G.P., 1996. 'The Economic and Technical Development of the Slate Industry in the Nantlle Valley' (unpublished Ph.D., Bangor University)

Lewis, M.J.T. (ed.) 1987. *The Slate Quarries of North Wales in 1873* (Maentwrog: Snowdonia National Park Study Centre)

Lewis, M.J.T., 1997. 'Archery & spoonerisms' *[Festiniog Railway] Heritage Group Journal* 51

Lewis, M.J.T., & Williams, M.C., 1987. *Pioneers of Ffestiniog Slate* (Maentwrog: Snowdonia National Park Study Centre, 1987)

McChristie, T.T., 1838. *The Trial of Thomas Williams Esq.* (London)

Owen, R., 1868. 'Cloddfeydd llechau Ffestiniog', *Y Traethodydd*, pp. 353–385

Pennant, T., 1783. *Tours in Wales* (London)

Pritchard, D.D., 1945. 'Aspects of the slate industry; the expansionist period (1790–1877), XI', *Quarry Managers' Journal*, Feb. 1945

Rees, T., & Thomas, J., 1873. *Hanes Eglwysi Annibynol Cymru 3* (Liverpool: Swyddfa y 'Tyst Cymreig')

Richards, A.J., 1995. *A Gazeteer of the Welsh Slate Industry* (Llanrwst)

Rowlands, J., 1981. *Copper Mountain* (Llangefni)

Sylwedydd, n.d. *Chwarelau Dyffryn Nantlle a Chymdogaeth Moel Tryfan* (Conwy)

Williams, G.J., 1882. *Hanes Plwyf Ffestiniog* (Wrexham)

Williams, R., 1900. 'Hunangofiant chwarelwr, 8: dadblygiad chwarelyddiaeth', *Cymru*, pp. 88–89

Williams, W., 1892. *Hynafiaethau a Thraddodiadau Plwyf Llanberis a'r Amgylchoedd* (Llanberis)

The Hunter Machines

Graham Isherwood

Abstract: This paper looks at the stone working machines of father and son James and George Hunter and their application and use. These include: James' original stone planer and his sleeper block boring machine; their large replaceable tool saws; George's further development of the replaceable tool and his association with William Fothergill Cooke in the north Wales slate industry, where wider uses such as decorative dressing, undercutting and tunnelling were developed. Many Hunter machines were manufactured by Archibald Munro & Co. of the Arbroath Foundry and are considered to have been a major factor in the expansion of the Scottish granite industry. Until the use of diamond saws became widespread, the Hunter saws and their derivatives were the only machines which could handle large stone with comparative ease.

Introduction

Between 1835 and 1882 James Hunter and subsequently his first son George developed a series of stone dressing and cutting machines for use in the quarrying and masonry industries. This paper concentrates on the innovation of the replaceable stone-cutting tool insert which George used in his stone cutting and tunnelling machines and the use of those machines in the quarries of north Wales and elsewhere.

Lack of space prevents inclusion of biographical information, some patent drawings and an account of development and patents of the machines by Archibald Munro and his later associates after 1867.

The planing machine (1835)

James Hunter was born in Arbroath about 1806. Around 1827, while working for his father, a reed and shuttle maker, he was engaged by Lindsay Carnegie of Kinblethmont to superintend works on his estate at Leysmill (which included a sawmill) and the mechanisation of the Leysmill quarries.[1] Much of the stone at Leysmill was not of the best quality for pavement work and required a lot of hand dressing and time to make it saleable; in the early 1830s James set about trying to develop a mechanical means of planing it smooth. With Carnegie's encouragement, the machine was perfected and patented in 1835.[2]

Referred to by James as a 'Power Stone Planer', it was manufactured by the Munro Company, of Arbroath Foundry. It was a great success and was described in the journals of the time and at meetings of important institutions. A working model of it was displayed at the Adelaide Gallery in London[3] and at the Great Exhibition of 1851. The machine was widely adopted in the pavement quarries of Arbroath and elsewhere in the country as well as in Sweden.[4]

The planing machine drew on the various technologies with which James was familiar. It combined the reciprocating action of a manual wood plane, the basic hand tools of the mason and regulated its action with mechanisms to be found on a weaving loom. It consisted (Fig. 1) of a reciprocating box girder frame about 18 feet long supported by pairs of wheels on pedestals either side of the working area. This was somewhat over 6 feet wide to accommodate the stone carrying tables which moved under and at right angles to the girder frame.

In the centre of either side of the frame was a vertical slide, with screw adjustment, which carried what James called 'cant blocks'. Each cant block carried two tools, one for each direction of cut; the 'roughing' tools were on one block and the finishing tools on the other. The tools, which were essentially the same as the mason's roughing punch and broad finishing chisel, were mounted in bores at the bottom of the cant blocks, with rotational adjustment of the tool provided by a geared sector and worm.

The cant blocks were pivoted so that they could tilt to lower into action the appropriate tool for the direction of cut and raise the other clear. A rod connected each cant block to a cross bar which passed through short slots in the girder frame sides towards one end. This was attached to a sliding bar which was free to move on the axis of motion of the frame. The bottom of this bar carried a rack, which meshed with a pinion driven from the main gearing. The movement of the bar in the frame tilted the cant blocks between their two positions.

The planer was driven from line shafting via flat and crossed belts to two loose pulleys. A double clutch mechanism allowed either pulley to be connected to the gear train to provide forward or reverse motion with a neutral central position in which neither clutch was connected. The clutch lever could either be operated manually, or, once the planer was in operation, automatically from one direction to the other at the end of each stroke.

Starting from rest with a fresh stone and the girder fully over to one side, manually engaging the clutch caused the pinion under the girder to turn, this would move the rack over its short travel, tilting the cant blocks and the tools into their working position ½ to 1 inch below the unplaned surface of the stone to be worked on. Further rotation of the pinion would then drive the girder forward, and engage the stone with the roughing tool. As the girder reached the end of its 6 foot stroke, a stud would strike the clutch lever and reverse the drive. The final pinion would rotate in the opposite direction and move the rack bar to its other extreme position, tilting the cant blocks the other way and bringing the other tools into position with further rotation driving the girder back towards its starting position. At the end of the return stroke, a second stud would strike the clutch lever, the drive would again be reversed and the cycle would con-

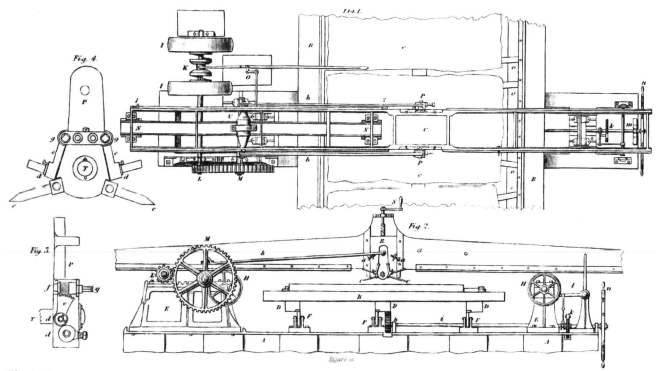

Fig. 1   James Hunter's 1835 'Power Stone Planer' (Patent no. 6794) (*Prize-essays and Transactions of the Highland and Agricultural Society of Scotland*, 1837)

tinue until the clutch was moved manually into the 'neutral' position.

The stones were carried under the girder frame on iron reinforced wooden tables which ran on fixed wheels, very similar to the arrangements for timber saws. On the underside of each table was a rack which engaged with a pinion and shaft immediately below the girder. The shaft was connected to a ratchet and pawl arrangement at the opposite side of the planer to the drive gearing, the pawl being attached to a lever operated by another stud on the reciprocating frame, thus advancing the table beneath the girder at the end of each double stroke. The ratchet could be disengaged and the table wound on or back using a hand wheel.

The planer exemplified several of what were to become the characteristics of the Hunter machines.
- the tools were easily replaceable
- the action of the machine emulated the actions of a mason
- it enabled working of stone which would otherwise have gone to waste
- it worked on stone where the amount requiring removal was not a factor, that is, the basic value of the material was low, it was the finished product which had the value

James added a lathe to the table which thus enabled him to use the planer to turn stones to produce vases, and even church fonts.[5]

The block dressing machine (1838)
In the 1830s many railways used stone blocks to support the rails, instead of timber sleepers. These had to be dressed to give a flat seating on the top, and holes bored for wooden plugs which enabled the rail 'chairs' which held to the rails to be fastened down. In 1838 James patented his next invention, a pair of machines (patent numbers not known) which mechanised the two jobs.[6] These were again a great success, but the days of stone sleepers were quite short.

Both machines were operated manually by repeatedly winding on and off a large diameter handle, similar to the weighted lever of a printing press, and used coarse drill bits and scrapers which again 'chipped' off small fragments of stone to achieve their end, much as the masons did.

The stone cutting machine (1855)
In the late 1840s George Hunter joined his father in the quarry workshop. The 1851 census gives his trade as 'Mechanic'. Between them they worked on the next invention, a saw to cut stone blocks.

It is not hard to see how the 1835 planer could be made to cut stone. With the table advance disengaged, by lowering of the vertical slide the roughing tools would gradually cut a coarse slot across the stone. However, the form of the tools was not ideal for this purpose and neither was the way in which they were held. What was required was a new tool which would not jam in the slot it was cutting.

We do not know exactly how the Hunters arrived at their final tool, but we can make some educated guesses. The first is that the trial machine was a heavily modified planer, and thus that the initial cutter movement was reciprocating rather than circular. The tool holder had to be narrower than the cutting head of the tool so that it could follow the tool along the cut without jamming. The tool had to be easily replaceable and able to withstand the impact of the cutting/chipping action. The arm that supported the tool holder had to be of a similar thickness to the tool holder and tall enough to clear whatever depth of rock the tools were intended to cut. The arm – a modified cant block – would have to be able to hold two tool holders, one for each direction of cut. We can thus conjecture that the trial machine had a single vertical slide, and a single cant block, vertically longer than before, with at the bottom two sockets of some kind to receive both tool holders and their tools. The final patent referred to using malleable iron as the material into which the tool holders fitted, so that if it was damaged by contact

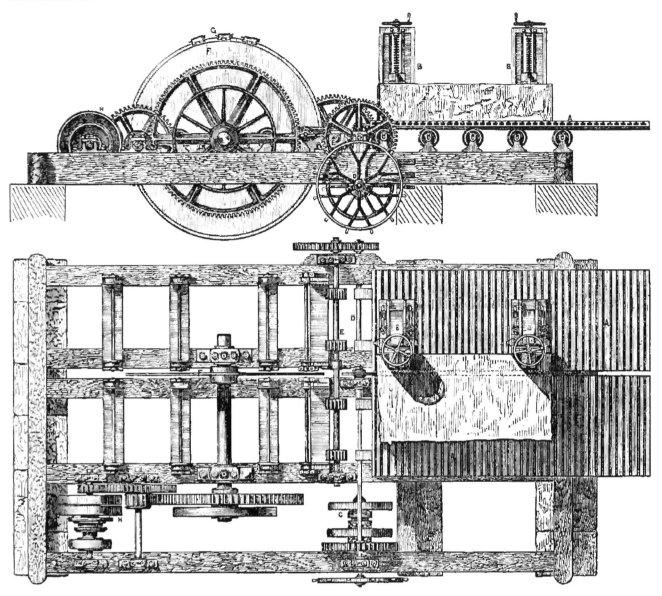

Fig. 2   James and George Hunter's 1855 'Stone-Cutting Machine' (Patent no. 913) (*Practical Mechanics Journal*, 1859)

with the rock it could easily be reshaped. Presumably many types of tool holder and tool shapes were tried before the final form was adopted. One might imagine that a circular form of tool seemed subject to least wear, and had the additional advantage that, as the working edge became blunted, it could be turned in its socket and used a second or even a third time before removal for sharpening.

After much trial and the assistance of the Munros again, the new 'Stone-Cutting Machine' (Fig. 2) was patented in 1855.[7] It is said that most of the work in developing it was due to George – which may have come about because of James' loosing a leg in an accident in the sawmill, from which he is reported to have suffered to some extent for the rest of his life.[8]

The machine resembled a conventional circular saw for wood, the axle of the 'cutting disc' being mounted below a movable table. The significant part of the invention was not that it was a circular saw for stone – that had been tried before – but that it had replaceable steel teeth, similar in shape to a golf-tee, which were fitted in sockets round the edge (Fig. 3). It cut faster, more easily, and much more quietly than any previous saw,[9] and again was widely publicised in both the local press and via syndication across the country.

Gearing was needed to reduce the speed of line shafting to that of the disc. The Hunters had determined, probably from their planer experiments, that the best tool speed was between 20 and 30 feet per minute. The cutting disc of the first machine was 11 feet in diameter, suggesting a rotational speed of around 1 revolution per minute. The tool holders were spaced on the periphery so that there was room between them to insert or remove a tool from its holder without disturbing any others. Thus the tool holders were at least 6 inches apart, giving 24–30 tools on a disc of this size.

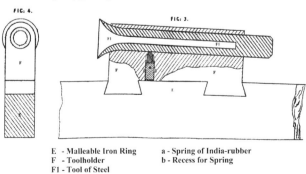

E - Malleable Iron Ring   a - Spring of India-rubber
F - Toolholder   b - Recess for Spring
F1 - Tool of Steel

Fig. 3   James and George Hunter's 1855 tool holder and tool (Patent no. 913)

The iron tables were slotted to take clamps for holding down the stones. Each table was driven by a pair of pinions which engaged with racks on their undersides so that the tables, one either side of the cutting disc, moved in unison. The patent also provided for a pair of supporting wheels under the table bearing on each side of the disc near its periphery to keep it aligned correctly.

The prototype was demonstrated at the Leysmill quarry, and cut through stone at 7 horizontal inches per minute. Two men were required to attend the machine, 'their principal work being the adjusting of the stone being operated upon, the taking of it away, and the looking out for another'.[10] Another comment was 'it requires no skilled person to work it, as any labourer can turn or replace the tools, they being completely self adjusting'.[11]

George, presumably because of his father's injury, appears to have worked as a 'mobile installer' for the planing and then the cutting machines, travelling as necessary to install and set up the machines, and probably teaching those who were to use them to operate and maintain them. Consequently, in 1856 George found himself in the Forest of Dean where the owners of the Bixslade quarry, having heard of the cutting machine and travelled up to Arbroath to see one in action, had then had one built for them by one Goodfellow 'of the same town'.[12] (Which town is meant is not clear.) When the installation was complete, the quarry owners asked George to stay on and manage the works, so he settled in nearby Coleford.

In the following year (1856) James died, his obituary referring to the effect of the loss of his leg mentioned earlier.[13]

The ridge dressing machine (c. 1855)
Just before his move to the Forest of Dean, George had devised a further machine, for 'Ridge Dressing' – that is, to cut the stones used for the ridge of a roof, basically an inverted V. This employed two saws at right angles, and could make ridge pieces directly from stone blocks.[14] Apparently only two were manufactured, naturally by Munros. I have been unable to find any patent application for this.

While in the Forest of Dean, George kept in contact with the Munros, possibly still acting as a peripatetic installer and technical instructor, and worked on his scheme for a universal stone working machine which could do almost anything with stone that had previously been done by hand.

The universal stone working machine (1862)
George's new stone working machine was patented in April 1862.[15] The patent describes three machines. Two, a stone cutter and a planer, were variations of the same machine. The third was a 'rubbing table'. The patent also describes a new form of the tool. All three machines combined Hunter cutting tools with planing tool boxes which allowed the pronounced curved 'lay' formed by the cutting tool to be planed off in the same operation if required.

All three machines had a pair of columns which carried a beam and drive shaft across the work table. The machine heads and/or planing tools were mounted on this beam.

In the first two machines in the patent (Fig. 4, top), the height of the cross beam could be adjusted by coupled screwed shafts on each column, driven by the machine gearing. No such arrangement is shown for the third machine, though there may have been provision for it.

In the first machine, two cutting heads, driven by the cross-shaft, carried cutting discs. These could be independently set, using a worm and wheel and detachable handle, to any angle relative to one another and to the stone to be worked on. The drive to the cutting disks was via a bevel gear, keyed to the cross-shaft and free to move along it with the cutting head, which drove a bevel gear on a short intermediate shaft on the rotational axis of the cutting head, which in turn drove a bevel gear on the cutting disk shaft.

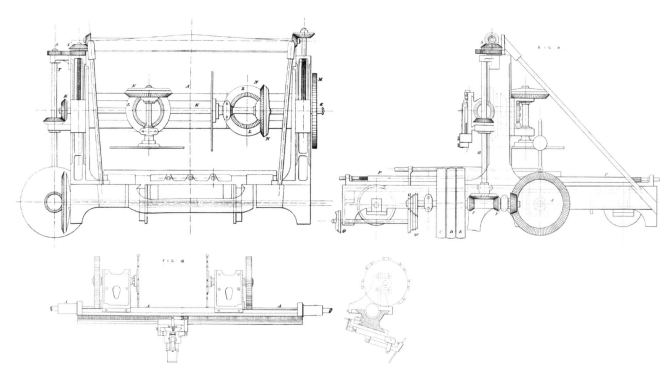

Fig. 4   George Hunter's 1862 stone cutter: end (top left) and side (top right) elevations. The side elevation shows the planing tool mounted on the rear of the cross beam. Below is plan and side elevation of the alternative beam arrangement. (Patent no. 942)

The planing toolboxes were carried on the other side of the beam and could be moved from side to side, their positions being adjusted by means of a handle on each toolbox which turned a pinion engaged with a rack along the length of the bar.

The table was provided with two separate drive mechanisms, one as a separating nut on a screwed shaft beneath the table driven at one of four speeds via multi-step pulleys, and the second using pinions to mesh with a rack or racks beneath the table for faster movement or returning the table after a cut. The machine was intended to be capable of cutting and dressing circular stones, and the drawing shows a turntable but omits a means of driving it.

The patent drawing omits, either by accident or design, various essential components, such as the reversing mechanism on the drive pulleys, details of the table driving mechanism and a clutch to disengage the drive to the screws that raised the beam. Furthermore the lettering on the drawing does not entirely correspond to that of the patent text. It is possible that the drawings were based on parts of several machines and in the process something was lost.

A limitation of the machine was that the diameter of the bevel gears on the disc shafts would limit the depth of cut under the gear. Also, the space taken up by the disc shafts limited the separation of the hubs and thus the largest width that could be cut.

The patent provided for an optional beam arrangement that omitted the facility to angle the cutting discs (Fig. 4, bottom). This utilised a different beam and the discs were mounted on short axles, at the other end of which was a gear wheel, almost the same size as the disc, driven by a smaller pinion on the drive axle as before. The beam could be rotated about the axle so as to bring either the discs or the planing tools to bear as required. The machine had the same limitations as the first machine with regard to the size of the pinions, separation of the discs etc.

The third machine had a horizontal disc on a vertical shaft above the table. A keyway on the drive shaft to the cutting head suggests that the height of the cross-member between the two standards, and hence the height of the cutting disk above the table, was adjustable. Again a fixed tool allowed for the lay made by the cutters to be planed off. The table appears to have a separating nut beneath it on a screwed shaft (Fig. 5).

The new tool form was horseshoe shaped instead of circular. It was made by bending a piece of flat steel and was the first of continuous developments intended to make the tool easier and cheaper to produce as well as easier to replace. A modified form of tool holder was also described which allowed a certain degree of movement of the tool-holder in its location.

The first machine was demonstrated in Munro's Arbroath Foundry yard to an invited crowd of quarrymasters, builders and other dignitaries from the local area, Forfar, Dundee and as far afield as Edinburgh. George, naturally present at the launch, among the usual toasts that accompanied the luncheon, remarked that 'he had done his part, the builders would not (he hoped) fail in doing theirs.'[16]

One can imagine that in George's hands the machine would probably do everything that its inventor claimed for it. However, one can equally imagine George darting about it, adjusting this, moving first this lever and then that and so on, like a master magician, and that the effect on the observers would have been of a very versatile machine but one not easy to use in a practical environment by ordinary labourers.

The machine continued to be demonstrated for almost a month. So impressed were the Association of Builders from Dundee that they proposed and indeed set up a 'Dundee Stone-Cutting Company, Limited' to purchase and use one and then more of George's machines to supply the building trade. George actually had an engagement 'for a lengthened period to erect several of his machines on the Continent, and was about to depart this country for that purpose' when he was prevailed upon by the builders of Edinburgh to remain for a year 'in order to superintend the erection of the machines which they have ordered, and also to superintend the erection of those to be procured by the Dundee Association'.[17]

I have not been able to trace either company. Either George's 'continental travel' was a bit of kite flying, or else he must have had a very good and flexible arrangement with his employers at Bixslade.

The first machine went to the Duntrune quarries near Dundee, where it joined one of George's original ridge dressers.[18] Such was the interest generated by the press reports of the machine that the Liverpool and Birkenhead Slate and Slab Company, which had opened a slate quarry in 1859 at Braich Ddu, near Ffestiniog, the slate rock of which was proving extremely hard to work, made contact with the Munros, and through them with George.[19] The

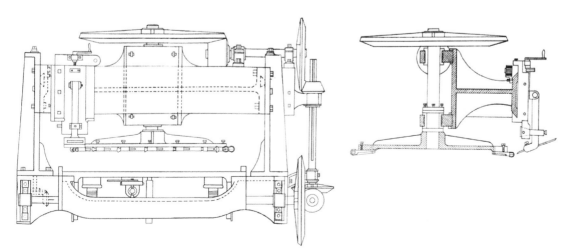

Fig. 5   George Hunter's 1862 rubbing table: end elevation and cutting head section (Patent no. 942)

Duntrune machine proved itself capable of dealing with a sample of the difficult slate rock, and on the strength of that, the company made George an offer to go and take management of their quarries and 'to work his machine in them'.

The directors, having seen George demonstrate the machine, ordered two machines from Munros; however they wisely decided to have one configured simply for stone cutting, the other mainly for planing. The stone cutter had discs 2 feet 6 inches in diameter (at least one newspaper account gives the diameter of the discs of the first machine as 4 feet, the same as on the next machine, described below).

By early December 1862 both machines were ready and had been tested at Munros 'in every way'. The company was completely satisfied and on 12 December George left Arbroath for Maentwrog in the Vale of Ffestiniog.[20] George now had the opportunity to see his new machine at work in the real world at first hand, and had the company order a second machine – but it seems he had learned his lesson as it appears that what he now designed was the forerunner of what we might call the 'classic' 'Hunter saw' (George did not call them saws until later, generally referring to them as 'stone-cutting machines').

The 'Hunter saw'

The new machine (Fig. 6) was drastically simplified. The cutting discs were mounted directly on the axle, which was carried on standards at a fixed height above the table, with the drive gear outside the standards. It seems likely that the dual table drive was replaced by a simple screw feed. The

discs could be positioned at any location across the width of the table and it was possible to have more than two discs. The new machine for Braich Ddu had no less than four discs each 4 feet in diameter carrying 28 tools each. It was described as 'the largest machine of the kind yet made'.[21]

At Braich Ddu George came to the notice of William Fothergill Cooke, the inventor, with Charles Wheatstone, of the electric telegraph. Cooke had sold the patent for the telegraph to the Government and received a great deal of money which he invested first of all in moving to Aber Iâ, the present day Portmeirion, near Portmadoc, and setting up home there, and then by investing in the slate quarries, which were experiencing a boom period.[22] He began with the Maenofferen Quarry in 1861, and then the Hafodlas Quarry at Bettws y Coed in 1862.[23] The work of George's machine at Braich Ddu was widely reported in the mining and national press and talks on it were given to such as the Liverpool Polytechnic Society.[24] Cooke probably encountered George soon after he arrived in the area – most of the English people in the area naturally congregated, and the two probably hit it off from the start.

The first tunnelling machine (1864)

While at Maentwrog, in 1864 George patented a tunnelling machine designed to cut a circular tunnel into rock. This, like his other machines, used replaceable tool teeth.

The machine (Fig. 7) consisted of two main parts, a four wheeled carriage, which ran on 2 foot gauge track and carried three pairs of screw jacks which were intended to fix

Fig. 6   The classic 'Hunter saw' by De Winton – seen here at Delabole Quarry (British Geological Survey catalogue number P200504, Reproduced with the permission of the British Geological Survey ©NERC. All rights Reserved)

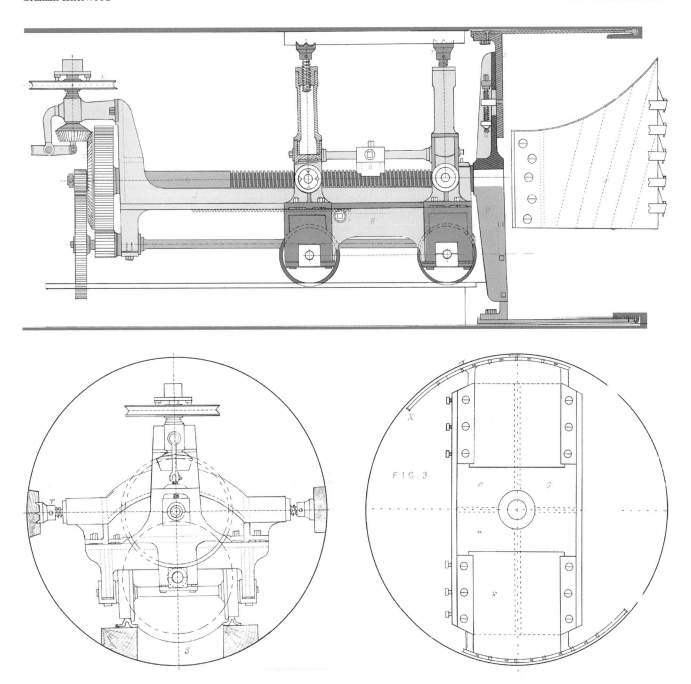

Fig. 7   George Hunter's 1864 tunnelling machine: side elevation (top), rear elevation (bottom left) and front elevation (bottom right) (Patent no. 1244)

the carriage to the sides and roof of the tunnel being cut, and a sliding platform which was able to move through the carriage. The platform's rear end supported a wire rope pulley, a clutch and gearing to drive a long screwed shaft which also passed through the carriage to the front of the platform where it was supported by a bearing. At the end of the shaft was the 'chuck', a casting about 5 feet across which supported a pair of slides on the ends of which were fixed the cutting segments. These were curved and extended about 30 inches in front of the chuck. Their front edges each had five toolholders and teeth of the conical form. The chuck and the segments made up the cutting head. The slides were adjusted by means of short screwed shafts so that the actual width of the tunnel being cut could be adjusted in a range from about 5 feet 6 inches to 6 feet 6 inches. A rod above and parallel to the screwed shaft was fixed to the carriage. This carried a half nut which could be clamped down onto

the screwed shaft. Thus, with the carriage clamped to the tunnel, rotation of the shaft would also advance the cutting head into the rock. A rack on the underside of the platform meshed with a pinion on a shaft extending to the right-hand side of the machine. A detachable handle on the squared end of this allowed the platform and its cutting head to be withdrawn when the half nut was released from the screwed shaft.

In operation, the rail track was laid in the tunnel with sufficient clearance between the end of it and the working face for the cutting head to revolve. With the 'chuck' horizontal, the machine was pushed forward until the cutters almost touched the rock face. The carriage was then clamped in position, the clamping screws being either extended directly onto the rock or onto timber beams between the clamps and the rock. The rope drive would be tensioned and then started up. The clutch would be engaged and the cutting head would begin to revolve. The half nut would be screwed in and actual cutting begun. The cutting advance into the rock was about 5 to 8 inches per hour, so it would take about 3–5 hours to cut a 2 feet deep groove into the rock face. Although the speed of advance seems very slow, the actual cutters would be working at their optimum speed of 20–30 feet per minute, and working in a path 6 feet in diameter meant the head was rotating at between one and two revolutions per minute. Hence it was cutting a groove the width of the cutters nearly 19 feet long and 5 to 8 inches deep each hour, a rate of removing rock of between three and four inches per minute, which was a typical rate for the Hunter machines. Although the segments could go deeper, markings left in extant tunnels suggest that 2 feet was the usual advance; perhaps a 'core' deeper than 2 feet was more difficult to remove.

At the end of the cut the half nut would be released and the rack used to withdraw the cutters from the groove. From marks on extant tunnel walls, it would appear that the head continued to revolve as it was withdrawn. Once clear of the cut and with the chuck horizontal, the drive clutch would be disengaged, and the segments drawn in slightly to avoid them catching on the walls as the machine was withdrawn. How the workmen got to the rock face to begin the work of removing the core is unclear. With the chuck vertical there was a space about 18 inches wide at best and about 4 feet high between the chuck and the tunnel walls through which a man might pass. However, as the chuck had to be horizontal to clear the rail track it would seem that the machine would have had to be withdrawn to a wider part of the tunnel, or even to the start of the tunnel, to allow the work to commence. Once the core had been removed – an opera-

tion which could take several hours in itself – and the waste cleared, the machine could be run forward again, clamped up and the next core cut. The use of the rail track and the problem of removing the core appear to be major weaknesses of the machine.

Although the patent drawing shows that the main screw was capable of being run out about 4 feet – the half nut appears to have been capable of only about 2 feet of travel along its own rod. The intention may have been not to advance the rail track and platform after the first cut, but just reposition the nut and make a further cut.

This first tunnelling machine patent was submitted in the May of 1864 and sealed in November.[25] However, unlike previous machines that preceded their patents, the first machine was not constructed until the following year, the press reporting in August 1865:

> Messrs Munro, of the Arbroath Foundry, have just finished the construction of a large and powerful machine, which it is intended to employ in tunnelling through slate quarries in Wales. The machine, the only one of its kind which has yet been made, cuts into the solid rock. An experiment was made with it on a stone wall in Messrs Munro's yard. It cut a large ring in the wall five inches deep, in less than five minutes. … The manufacture of these machines for the Welsh quarries has of late considerably increased the iron trade of Arbroath.[26]

As with the Braich Ddu machines, it was probably despatched by sea to Portmadoc and then taken up the Festiniog Railway to Duffws. It seems most likely that it was tested at Maenofferen by invitation of Cooke, who would have provided the finance for its construction. There

Fig. 8   Trial tunneller level, Maenofferen Quarry

is a short single bored tunnel, about 30 feet long, in a small chamber on Floor 2 along the strike of the vein almost vertically under the later back-vein incline engine house (Fig. 8). There is also a trace of the start of a second bore next to it. The bore shows no evidence of any anchor marks in the walls and, in the absence of any other candidates, seems a good choice for the initial trial, although that does not rule out the possibility that other trials have been removed by quarrying.

The double tunneller (1865)

Cooke and Hunter submitted their first joint patent, for a development of the tunnelling machine, before the end of 1865.[27] To improve the 'stability' of the machine it was a 'double' tunneller, with two contra-rotating heads mounted at the front of a single broad frame, and was intended to cut two bores at the same time. Although it was possible for the bores to overlap one another slightly by setting the two chucks to be at right angles to one another and setting the segments at their maximum extension, it is not thought this was actually done.

The machine was driven by a small water turbine mounted on the frame immediately behind the heads. Belting and a gear train reduced the speed of the turbine to the usual slow speed of the cutting heads. No provision was made for the heads to advance separately from the frame; instead the frame was supported and guided by rollers bearing on the tunnel walls, roof and floor. The lower rollers were arranged to leave the bottom of the bores clear, so that debris from the cutting operation and also from the eventual core removal could be passed beneath the frame. This idea was somewhat restricted as the left-hand tunnel floor was occupied by the water supply pipe to the turbine. This had a telescopic section where it connected to the machine to accommodate its forward movement during the cutting operation. The rest of the pipe was made in short sections to allow it to be progressively extended as the tunnel advanced – and dismantled whenever the machine had to be withdrawn. The outfall from the turbine washed over the faces of the cores and brought the debris to the floor.

The cutting segments themselves were modified from the 1864 patent by having three additional tools mounted on their leading side to widen the cut made by the front tools as the machine advanced, thus making it easier to back the cutters out from their full depth at the end of a cut and avoid jamming. The segments were otherwise of the same dimensions as in the 1864 patent – about 30 inches deep. Although the main patent drawing shows a fixed width chuck, an inset shows the same width adjustment method as before.

The machine was advanced by a shaft drive taken via a clutch from the left-hand chuck shaft to a worm at the rear of the frame. This drove a shaft across the width of the frame via a worm wheel and clutch. This shaft had hooks on it to enable chains to be attached. At the left-hand end of the hooked shaft was a squared end for fitting a handle to allow it to be turned manually. To start a new cut, a short hole was drilled immediately in front of the working face in the triangular area or 'nib' between the actual bores, and which had been cleared by hand. A short anchoring rod was placed in this hole and a chain and tackle connected between it and the hooked shaft at the rear of the machine. In operation the rotation of the hooked shaft tightened the

chain and tackle and thus advanced the machine. When the usual core depth of about two feet was reached, the main and advancing clutches were released and a separate chain tackle anchored behind the machine was used to draw the machine clear of the face and allow access to the cores. The patent suggested that the cores were extracted by 'wedging or small blasts'. The 'nib' between the cores at top and bottom was also removed by hand. The patent allowed for, but did not show, the possible attachment of a drill at the centre of each chuck to make holes in the centre of each core to assist the removal process.

At least one machine was constructed, presumably by Munros, and tested in a Welsh quarry, where it was photographed (Fig. 9). The strata shown in the photographs is inclined and typical of Ffestiniog, so it seems almost undeniable that they were in Maenofferen, although the location is unknown – it may well have been in the lower part of what is often called the 2½ or Davy Jones' quarry; this was subsequently worked out which would have destroyed any remains. The machine in the photographs differs slightly from the patent drawings: it has the adjustable chucks, the water feed to the turbine follows a slightly different path and also supplies two hose pipes which were directed into the cuts, and the rearmost stands for the shaft driven by the turbine belt appear to be adjustable. The two photographs show different diameter belt pulleys and gears, so perhaps they were experimenting with different ratios to find those which gave the best results.

While the machine certainly gained in 'stability', by which the inventors appear to refer to a tendency for the original machine to twist in the bore, and did not require any track, the need to dismantle the turbine feed pipes every time the machine had to be moved by more than the depth of a cut, together with the awkward chain tackle advance, were factors against it, and it did little to improve access to the cores.

Cooke gave an illustrated talk to the Royal Society for the Arts in 1867 and described this (and other) developments, saying of the double tunneller

> One form includes in its construction two parallel borers, cutting two tunnels each 5ft 4in in diameter, side by side, and freeing two cores weighing more than two tons each at every cut. … From one core, and that one the first ever cut by that machine, 23 slabs of more than one ton in weight were made, besides a considerable number of slates. Its rate of progress in cutting is eight inches per hour, and the depth of cut allowed by the cutting-blades is twenty-one inches forward. This machine has penetrated many yards into the solid slate bed, and is destined, I fully believe, to revolutionise the present system of quarrying that valuable material.[28]

The patent drawing has no scale. The diameter given probably corresponds to the smallest diameter setting of the chucks, which would give the greatest forward speed as the cutter path would be that much shorter.

The patent also included a sketch of a single bore tunnelling machine fitted with two concentric cutting heads, the inner core rotating in the opposite direction and at a higher speed than the outer to provide 'stability'. It was intended to use similar anchoring methods to the 1864 patent machine, with a similar screw advance to the cutting head. Again it is not thought likely that it was ever constructed.

Fig. 9   George Hunter and W.F. Cooke's 1865 double tunneller (Patent no. 3297). Note the change of the first reduction gear between the two photographs. (Courtesy David Pollard)

Further tunnelling machines (1866)

The double tunneller was followed very rapidly in 1866 by a joint patent describing four different machines: an 'overcutter', an 'undercutter' (both for extracting the rock in the quarry by machine) and two tunnelling machines.[28]

It would appear that one or both of the men had been looking at recent developments in coal cutting machines and had spotted a possible application of Hunter's tools. However, the problem with those machines, especially when used for undercutting a seam of coal, was that the maximum distance a circular cutter could be inserted was rather less than its radius because of the presence of the driving axle and its support. George's solution, which he applied to both to the tunnelling and the undercutting machines, was based around the idea of driving the cutting disc on its inside edge.

The first two machines (the undercutter and overcutter) used a thicker cutting disc than previously, allowing for three or more rows of tools instead of one. The disc was hollow with gear teeth cast on its inner periphery. A pinion meshed with these teeth and was driven by a shaft through a strong concentric trunnion. This was bolted to two circu-

lar plates which supported the cutting ring and allowed its rotation.

In the 'overcutter' (Fig. 10) the trunnion extended on both sides of the cutting ring and was supported by a pair of bearings. A gear train reduced the speed of a wire rope drive – the turbine seems to have been abandoned, although was included as an optional power source in the specification – to the usual tool speed of 20–30 feet per minute. The cutting ring was mounted vertically along the centre line of the machine, which ran on rails for guidance. A worm wheel sector was fixed to the trunnion so that rotation of the worm could lower the cutting ring into the rock beneath the machine. The off centre drive meant that the ring could cut into the rock to something like ⅔ to ¾ of its diameter. When this was reached, the machine would be allowed to move forward using any of the anchoring methods available, or even by attaching a rope to the front of the machine and leading it round a pulley to a counterweight truck running down an incline or even the face of the quarry; this would be assisted by the tendency of the ring to pull itself into the cut. The patent drawing shows a variable speed belt drive

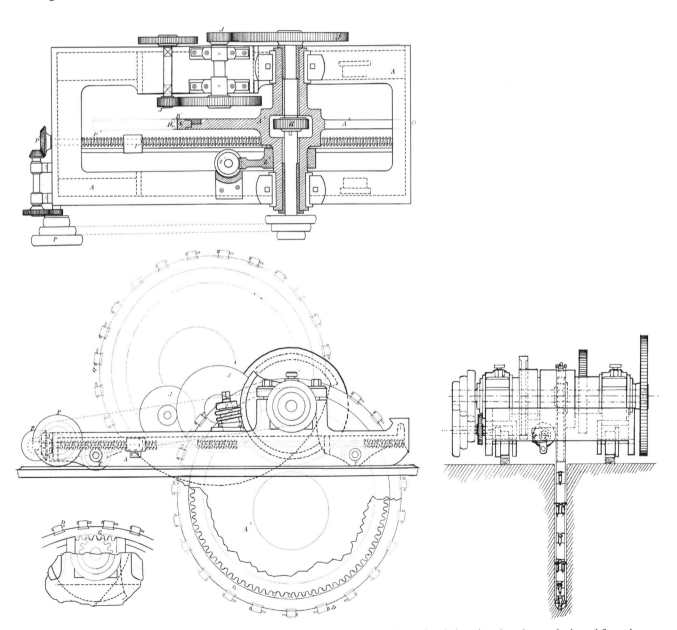

Fig. 10   George Hunter and W.F. Cooke's 1866 overcutting machine: plan and side and end elevations based on and adapted from the patent drawings (Patent no. 433)

from the main disc shaft via a bevel gear to a feed screw running the length of the supporting frame. On this was a captive nut to which could be attached a chain or rope. If the machine was working 'downhill' then its own weight would carry it forward, regulated by a rearward rope to the nut. If working horizontally, or 'uphill', then a forward rope fastened to the nut and anchored somewhere in front would enable the machine to pull itself forward.

At the end of the cut, the worm could be used to extract the cutting disc from the slot, the machine returned to the start, the tracks moved over and another run started. Not explained in the patent was how the tracks were constructed so that the cutting disc could move between them; perhaps they were intended to be in pairs, one either side. The specification also mentioned the possibility of having multiple discs on the same axle.

The 'undercutter' was intended to work with its cutting ring horizontal, like a coal cutter. In this case the trunnion could only extend on the upper side, the lower end being level with the circular infilling sheet and thus the trunnion needed to be that much wider, being supported on only the upper side. The machine was in two parts, the lower carriage, which ran on rails, had to be anchored in place during cutting so as to oppose the tendency of the cutting ring to try and pull itself into the cut and pull the machine towards the rock face being undercut. This tendency did not matter in the overcutter since the effect was to hold that machine more securely onto its track. The cutting ring was supported by a massive bearing which was attached to an upper frame along which it could slide for about 12 feet. Once the ring had cut to its full depth – Cooke said that a 3ft 4in. diameter ring could cut into the rock to a depth of 2ft 3in. – then the ring could advance along the slide frame for 12 feet. At the end of the cut the cutting ring was unclutched from

the slide frame – it would appear the usual divided nut and screwed shaft was used to advance the cutting ring bearing – and the carriage unanchored, allowing both the carriage and frame to be advanced by the 12 feet, the ring remaining in the cut. The carriage was then clamped, the divided nut screwed up and the cut continued. Unfortunately the patent drawings do not include the undercutter – so its appearance is still somewhat in doubt. George Hunter's 1882 patent, to be described later, does show some detail of what may have been a developed form of it.

Thus by the deployment of both over- and undercutting machines the intention was to mechanise the extraction of rock from the quarry without the wasteful use of explosives.

The third application of the internal gear arrangement was for a new type of tunneller. The main limitation of the previous tunnelling machine patents had been the massive chuck which carried the cutting segments which effectively blocked access to the core until the machine was fully withdrawn from the tunnel. This machine was not a trepanner like the earlier machines, but instead used rotating drums which carried on their surface the usual tools in rows of twos and threes (Fig. 11). These were staggered so that a whole row did not strike the rock at once. The drums, one large one flanked by two smaller ones, were mounted on a common axle across the front of the machine. The larger drum was about 6 feet in diameter and 3 feet wide, the smaller ones 3 feet. The drums were driven by a pair of pinions which meshed with teeth cast on the inside of the outer edges of the larger drum. The effect of the three drums was to cut a cruciform shaped tunnel. The pinions were driven via the usual long gear train from the rear of the machine frame. The frame ran on flanged wheels which were intended to run along the top corners of the lower part of the tunnel – the machine in effect making its own roadway. The lower

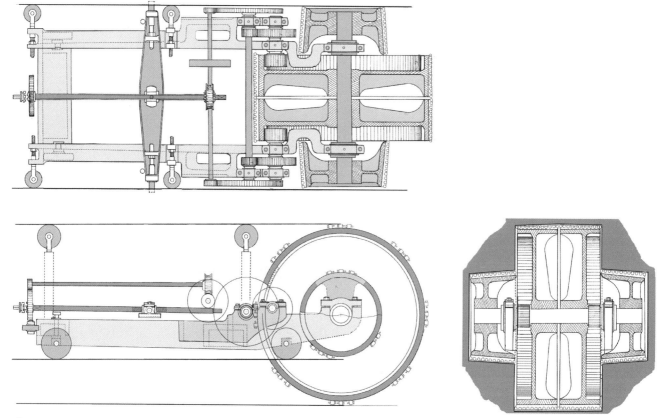

Fig. 11   George Hunter and W.F. Cooke's 1866 'Self-Roadway' drum tunneller: plan, and side and end elevations (Patent no. 433)

part of the tunnel was also intended to facilitate the removal of debris by a scraper or similar contrivance.

A new form of anchorage was proposed. In this a strong girder was positioned across the centre of the machine. At each end was a short but strong screwed shaft which could be wound outwards beyond the sides of the machine into pre-drilled holes in the sides of the tunnel. At the centre of the girder was the usual divided nut arrangement which could be clamped onto a screwed shaft which ran the length of the machine and was driven from the gearing. Due to the usual slow speed of work, there would have been ample time for men on the frame to drill the next two holes while the machine advanced. When the girder had reached the end of its travel, the nut was undone, the bolts withdrawn and the girder slid forward to the new position and bolted up.

Two alternative arrangements were proposed. In one the outer pair of drums were replaced by segments of the same diameter. In another, the centre portion of the main drum was omitted. This meant that the machine could only advance up to the main drum axle. At this point additional cutters, mounted on the inside of the drum and cutting inwards were gradually extended, severing the rock. The advantage of this is not at all clear.

Although this section of the patent is often referenced in modern literature on the history of tunnelling machines, probably because it was a 'face cutter' rather than a trepanner, as far as we know it was never actually constructed.

The fourth application of the edge drive was to a trepanning tunneller (Fig. 12) – the example given in the patent was a double version with the two cutting rings rotating in opposite directions. Little detail was given other than that the cutting ring was used rather than the 'chuck' of the earlier types. Three cutting segments were attached rather than two, presumably to give a more even turning movement or perhaps an increase in cutting rate, but were otherwise similar to the form used on the 1865 double tunneller, although they had no adjustment.

The cutting ring was supported radially and axially by rollers mounted on a fixed ring round which the cutting ring revolved. An annular steel plate kept debris away from the rollers and the gear teeth on the inside of the cutting ring. At the bottom and to the rear of the fixed ring was a roller running on the bottom of the tunnel to prevent the ring grounding on the tunnel floor.

Two pinions, one on each side of the cutting ring, meshed with the internal teeth of the ring; their shafts passed through bearings in the support ring towards the rear of the machine. A second fixed ring supported the rear ends of the shafts where bevel gears connected them to the main reduction gearing. The two fixed rings were connected by channel sections bolted to the rings and through which the drive shafts passed. The channels also carried mountings for the rollers at the sides of the machine which bore on the tunnel walls. No details of anchorage or the means of advancement were shown; presumably, being a double tunneller, a similar method to the 1865 patent could have been adopted, or more likely the cross-girder and bolts of the drum tunneller described above.

The advantage cited for this tunneller was that the open centre of the ring made access to the cores and their removal easier – although this disregarded the fact that the waste. would still have to be manhandled past or over the gearing.

Cooke exhibited photographs of both the undercutter and overcutter in his 1867 talk to the Royal Society of the Arts, so examples of both were certainly constructed. However the only references to a ring tunneller refer to a single bore machine.

Such a machine under construction at Munros Arbroath Foundry in April 1867 was described as follows:

> The tunnelling machine is constructed to cut a tunnel seven feet in diameter. It cuts thirty inches into the rock, and then has to be removed in order that the block of stone which has been cut may be taken out of the opening made. The machine has been constructed for Messrs Hunter & Co., of Merioneth, in Wales, and is to be employed at the Meneforan [sic] Slate Quarries, and it is supposed that it will excavate pieces of slate rock weighing about six tons in an hour and a half. The principal parts of the machine are three rings, two of which are fixed when it is in operation. On the front ring, which is a revolving one, there are three semicircular steel plates, on each of which are four cutting tools. The front ring is fixed on two round parallel bars which travel through the two fixed rings, and guide the revolving ring into the rock. The machine is driven by a wire rope 5-16ths of an inch in diameter, and the motion is communicated to the front ring by two horizontal shafts and by spur and bevel gearing and a feeding screw. The engine by which the

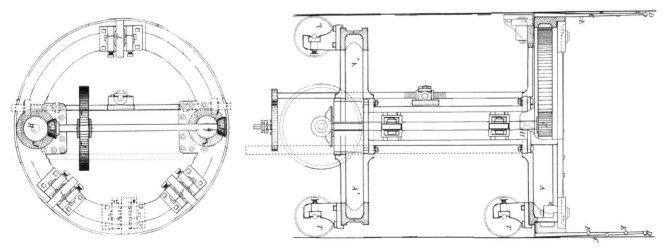

Fig. 12   George Hunter and W.F. Cooke's 1866 open centre tunneller: rear (left) and side (right) conjectural elevations based on drawings for Patent no. 433

machinery will be wrought is of six horsepower, and has been constructed to suit the machine.[30]

Cooke later described the machine in his May 1867 talk to the RSA:

Other photographs represent another form of the tunneller, which is now being erected in a quarry of the ffestiniog Valley. It will cut a single tunnel six feet nine inches in diameter, and penetrate twenty-eight inches at each cut. The principle explained in the 'under-cutting' machine is employed here, only the solid central holder, for the axle plate, is here open in the centre as a ring, round which the cog-toothed cutter ring revolves; and the latter, instead of carrying the movable tools on its periphery, in the same plane, carries three segment blades of steel, projecting forward at the extremity of which a series of cutting tools are fixed, as in the saw blades. The carriage of this machine is fixed in the tunnel immovably by bolt-screws, and the massive working parts gradually screw themselves forward as the cutters penetrate the rock. The open passage is preserved through the centre of the ring frame and ring-cutter, to the front of the work, even whilst the machine is in action; owing to this, the core, after cleaving up, is more readily removed than that from the double tunnelling machine. This machine will excavate more than five tons at a cut … It must be remembered that these machines were made expressly for slate rock tunnelling, and have not yet been tried on sandstone or limestone rock for tunnelling purposes, which may offer fresh difficulties.[31]

Cooke's account suggests that the carriage was fixed to the rock and the cutting head moved forward – which could either refer to the type of anchorage used for the drum tunneller, or to something more akin to the original arrangement used on the 1864 machine.

Further stone-cutting machines (1866)

1866 also saw the publication of the next of Cooke and Hunter's patents, this time concerning the stone cutting machines.[32] This was the next part of the partners' long-term aims of streamlining the whole stone working operation, from quarry to builder's yard. The patent now embodied George's modification and simplification of his 1862 patent, but added more features to it to make it more efficient.

The basic arrangement of the cutter shaft over the work table with two or more large diameter cutting discs mounted on it and the main gearing outside the shaft stands was retained. Instead of the table being directly coupled to the feed screw by dividing nuts it was free to move and was driven by loose pins which coupled the table to a cross bar driven by the feed screw. At the end of the cutting operation, the pins could be removed and the table quickly returned to the starting position to be unloaded and reloaded with fresh stone, while with the drive reversed, the bar could return to the start, albeit more slowly, thus dispensing with the need for separate fast and slow drive mechanisms.

The loose table meant it was possible to have more than one table in use in a 'merry-go-round' arrangement. If overhead cranes were arranged at either end of the machine, then when one table of stones had been cut and the pins removed, it could be unloaded by one crane and moved clear of the machine and placed on a parallel track to be returned to the start, while an empty table was moved into position by the other crane and loaded (Fig. 13). During these operations the bar could be run back. As soon as the bar was in position, the pins for the next table could be inserted and cutting recommenced.

The partners proposed that several machines should be placed in a line, so that the tables could run on from one

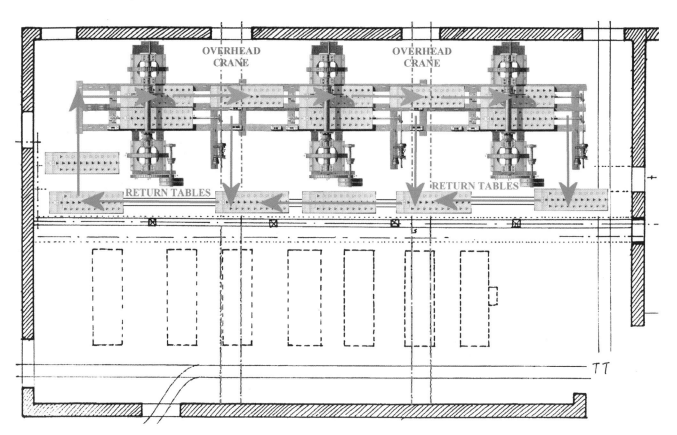

Fig. 13   George Hunter and W.F. Cooke's 1866 'production line' concept (Patent no. 2192), based on author's sketch of Hafodlas mill

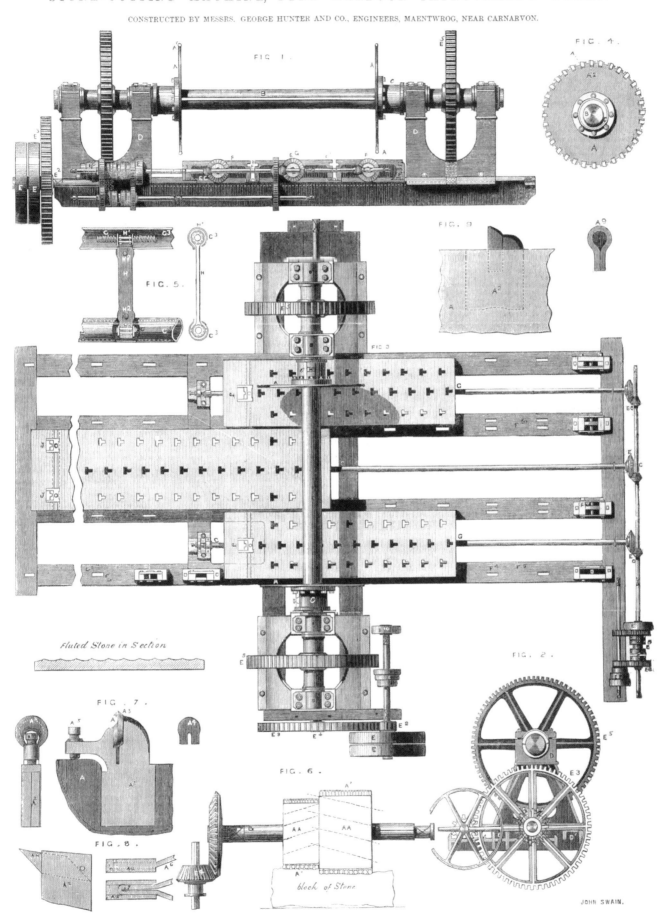

STONE-CUTTING MACHINE, TYNE HARBOUR IMPROVEMENT WORKS.

CONSTRUCTED BY MESSRS. GEORGE HUNTER AND CO., ENGINEERS, MAENTWROG, NEAR CARNARVON.

Fig. 14   George Hunter and W.F. Cooke's 1866 stone cutting machine (Patent no. 2192) (*The Engineer*, Dec. 1866)

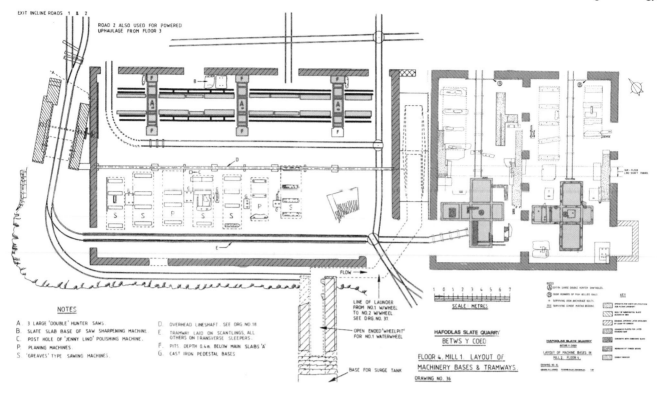

NOTES

A. 3 LARGE 'DOUBLE' HUNTER SAWS.
B. SLATE SLAB BASE OF SAW SHARPENING MACHINE.
C. POST HOLE OF 'JENNY LIND' POLISHING MACHINE.
P. PLANING MACHINES.
S. 'GREAVES' TYPE SAWING MACHINES.

D. OVERHEAD LINESHAFT. SEE DRG. NO.18
E. TRAMWAY LAID ON SCANTLINGS, ALL
    OTHERS ON TRANSVERSE SLEEPERS.
F. PITS. DEPTH 0.4 m. BELOW MAIN SLABS 'A'.
G. CAST IRON PEDESTAL BASES

HAFODLAS SLATE QUARRY
BETWS Y COED

FLOOR 4. MILL 1. LAYOUT OF
MACHINERY BASES & TRAMWAYS.

DRAWING NO. 36

Fig. 15   Hafodlas mill at Bettws y Coed, showing remains with Hunter saw beds emphasised (from Griff R. Jones, *Hafodlas Slate Quarry*, 1998)

onto the next. Thus between each pair of machines, stones could be repositioned, unloaded or a new set loaded, and any empty tables craned off to the return track. A further development allowed for a much wider space between the standards so that two or more tables could be accommodated side by side. The patent drawings show three tables, each with independent screw drive. In this case, one table could be being loaded, another unloaded and the third operated on, all at the same time, depending on requirements. One, two or three pairs of cutting discs could be used.

If it was necessary to work on a block that would not pass under the drive axle, the cutting discs could be slid to the standards, and the axle removed. The standards were then angled slightly so as to keep the return side of the discs clear of the cut – the thin sliver of rock which was trimmed off had to be broken away by hand before it reached the standards.

A further development of the 'production line' approach was to use a large continuous roller chain to advance the tables in place of the screwed shafts.

The patent introduced tools made from steel punchings, a circular one being the simplest. This required a new type of holder, but the tools could be produced in large numbers quickly and cheaply. Another tool form was a trapezium of steel, which was folded and sprung into its holder.

The patent also included an improved form of the turntable machine of 1862 for making grindstones etc.

The patent drawings, which naturally showed all the modifications in one, were used by *The Engineer* to illustrate the first machine, undoubtedly built to the patent, for the Tyne Harbour Commissioners (Fig. 14).[33] It seems likely that the patent drawings were based on that machine, but with additions to illustrate the full extent of the patent. For example, although the drawings show a three table version, accounts of the actual machine only refer to one table.

The machines were intended to cut blocks for the new breakwaters at the mouth of the River Tyne and were suitably massive. The first machine, supplied and installed in 1866, had two blades 7 feet in diameter, the discs being ¾ inch steel plate with 44 tools and holders, the tools being set alternately to left and right to make a cut 1¼ inches wide

Fig. 16   Slate blocks exhibiting the characteristic Hunter saw 'lays', mill building, Hafodlas Quarry, Bettws y Coed

at a forward speed of between 3½ and 7 feet per minute to a depth of 2 feet 9 inches. The rotational speed was some 1½ revolutions per minute at a cutting speed of 5 feet per minute – which would give a tool speed of about 33 feet per minute. Some accounts give the maximum depth of cut as 3 feet 2 inches and the number of tools as 33. A tool speed of 44 feet per minute was quoted in one account but this seems rather high given that there were 44 tools as well – perhaps there was some confusion between the number of tools and the tool speed itself. The main axle was 12½ inches in diameter and 14 feet between the standards. Other details include a table 11 feet by 8 feet, 8 foot diameter main gears and the total weight of the machine was about 26 tons. George was paid some £700 for it.[34]

The slate quarries in which, as Cooke put it, 'I have a considerable interest' seem to have been used as demonstration sites for the various machines. As noted above, the tunnelling machines seem to have been demonstrated at Maenofferen, and there was certainly a stone cutting machine there as well. It is possible that an attempt was made to demonstrate the 'production line' approach at the Bettws y Coed Slate and Slab quarry – otherwise known as Hafodlas. Two Hunter machines had been installed in the first part of the slate mill, constructed in 1863, so we can reasonably assume that these may have been to the 1862 patent, while the second and larger part of the mill, completed in 1867, was host to no less than three 'double Hunters' arranged in a line along the north wall, with overhead cranes in between them and a parallel flanking tramway.[35] Again, these were almost certainly constructed to the 1866 patent – although the number of tables per machine is not known. Given the size and arrangement of the foundations the machines could have accommodated a pair of tables across their width (Fig. 15). This part of the mill was constructed using a very large number of cut blocks of considerable size, many showing the characteristic Hunter tool cutting lay (Fig. 16). The foundations for the two machines in the older part of the mill are much 'squarer' in outline than the later ones which would seem to support the idea of them being 1862 patent types, the evidence of many blocks which have been cut on all four sides, and in some cases apparently then smoothed off also supporting this.

The 1866-type machines at Hafodlas are thought to have had 4 foot diameter cutting discs, some typical values for these being given by *The Engineer* as 14 feet between standards, the discs ⅜ inch thick and capable of cutting 15 inches thick rock at up to 6 inches per minute.[36] Other cutting machines made at this period included some with 4 discs, in which case they were made with 16 feet between standards and cut at 3 inches per minute when all four blades were in use, or 6 inches with only two. One at least, with four discs, was made for the 'Dolledellar' quarries – presumably Dolwyddelan.[37] This is confirmed by the auction notice for the 'Lledr Vale Quarry' in August 1869 which included a Hunter saw, 4 blades 2 feet 9 inches diameter with table 12 feet by 9 feet 9 inches, a small Hunter saw with one blade and table 5 feet by 4 feet 7 inches and two Hunters planing machines with tables 9 feet 6 inches by 9 inches (which must be an error).[38]

So well did the first Tyne machine do its job that two more were ordered, the first being of even larger proportions, with a disc 13 feet in diameter and mounting no less than 68 (some accounts say 70) tools. Each disc was 1⅜ in. wide, making a cut 2 in. wide and weighed 2¾ tons. This time the tools were set alternately in ones and twos. The main axle was 15½ inches in diameter and 23 feet long. The standards were 9 feet high, the bed 30 feet by 20 feet, the table driving screws 3½ inch diameter at 1 inch pitch and drove the table at 4½ inches per minute. The machine weighed 60 tons.[39] It was supplied in 1867 and George received £1500 for it.[40] The third machine was supplied in 1868 and was apparently identical to the first. It was despatched from Arboath in August 1868 on board the sloop *Cochrane Henry*.[41]

Meanwhile there had been a revival of interest in George's cutting machines in his native area. The *Dundee Advertiser* reported in July 1866, referring to the 1862 patent machine:

At the preliminary trials the machine gave much promise of success, but it was found afterwards that the machinery was far too complex for ordinary purposes, and, as more than one practical man remarked, 'It tried to do too much, and the consequences was that it did nothing properly.' … the difficulties which were encountered in introducing the machine discouraged those who were convinced of its practical usefulness, and by and bye the scheme dropped out of view, so far as this district was concerned.

The machine, however, had been found to be very useful in the slate quarries of Wales and elsewhere in England, and the Messrs Munro continued to make large numbers of them for use there, and by that means the idea was kept alive, while the inventor was enabled, on seeing the machines in actual operation, to make such suggestions for their improvement as would make them suitable for general use. Still, no attempt was thought of to utilise the invention, so far as regarded the freestone of Forfarshire, until a few weeks ago, when Mr Langlands, who lately entered on the tenancy of the Duntrune quarries, conceived that such a machine might be made available for cutting and dressing the stones taken from his quarries. Impressed with this idea, and having in remembrance the former attempts of a similar kind which had been made, he opened communications with the Messrs Munro, and these gentlemen stated to him that he might make trial of a machine at their works in Arbroath, but that this would be done at his own risk. The trial was made, and was so far successful that he had one of the machines erected in his quarries; and, from his experience of it during the past few days, he is confident that it will fully answer the purpose for which it is required, and that while it will save him a large expenditure of money, it will also enable him to supply the demands made upon him for stone with far greater rapidity and regularity than with the old method of hand cutting.[42]

The machine had a pair of 3 foot 9 inch diameter discs each with 22 tools and was described as: 'one of the smallest and lightest which the Messrs Munro have yet made … is 6 feet wide, and can cut a stone 9 feet long and 17 inches thick'.

The machine being successful, other quarries soon followed suit – by July 1867, the Carmyllie quarries had two machines in operation, with a third in course of erection; one had two discs, the others four each.[43]

Munros were not the only manufacturers to produce machines to Hunter and Cooke's patents. Thomas and DeWinton of the Union Foundry, Caernarfon, took them up, as did Humphrey Owen of the Vulcan Foundry, also of Caernarfon, probably soon after George had successfully introduced them at Braich Ddu. De Winton supplied Hunter machines to the Prince of Wales Quarry, Cwm Pennant, in 1865, to Pen yr Orsedd Quarry, Nantlle, in 1868 and, at a later date, to the Delabole Quarry in Cornwall.[44]

Cooke's tunnelling machines (1867)

In his May 1867 paper to the RSA on the tools and machines, Cooke described his partnership with George:

> As ... my own name is united with Mr Hunter's in several recent patents, ... my share has chiefly consisted in extending the application of the movable tools and tool holders (the real essence of his invention) to fresh and wider fields of usefulness, whilst the onus of adapting the machinery to each novel application, and in so doing producing an entirely new result, has fallen upon the inventive genius and mechanical skill of Mr George Hunter.[45]

He also explained the necessity, irrespective of the machine configuration, for the cutter to rotate in the opposite direction to the feed, so that 'each tool slides smoothly at first into the groove formed by the preceding tool, and then cuts boldly out' at the surface of the slab. If this arrangement is reversed

> the tools will come aplomb on the stone with a jarring blow, and tend to drag it into the cutter, when the result may be the crumpling of the blade, or the stripping off of the tools from their holders.

Cooke soon followed this by a new patent on his own behalf, which was originally deposited in September 1867, and not sealed until the following March – but which related to the joint tunnelling machines.[46] In it Cooke described some of the problems which had occurred using them:

> When using this machine I have found that after causing the machine to cut forward a distance into slate or stone and form an annular groove therein, the time occupied in removing the central core by hand through the middle of the machine is about three times as long as the time taken by the machine to cut the groove into the slate or mineral, and consequently the machine was idle for 9 hours out of every 12

He then described his solution to this problem, which was to drive multiple tunnels in parallel, whose bores intersected one another. The tunneller being used first in one, then retracted and moved to the second, then to the third before being returned to the first and so on, thus with three tunnels, the tunneller should be in almost constant use. To achieve this, he described the use of a traverser (Fig. 17) to move the tunneller sideways after it had worked on each bore, along with alternatives using one or many turntables. The matter of transferring the rope drive from tunnel to tunnel was included. He then described the way in which quarries could be worked using these multiple tunnels on each floor, joined by shafts in conjunction with the over- or undercutting machines, arrangements which he claimed 'in practice have worked most satisfactorily'. He related the operations both to quarries in which the rock was vertical or nearly so, as at Penrhyn and Llanberis, inclined, as at Ffestiniog, and horizontal as at Bath. He also proposed, though without a drawing, using spring loaded cutters attached either to the

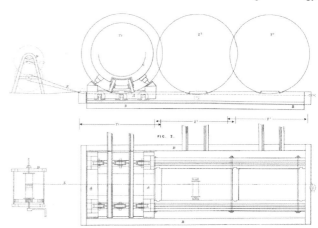

Fig. 17   Cooke's 1867 tunneller traverser (Patent no. 2580)

cutting segments themselves, or to non-cutting segments mounted on a second lighter machine, which could open out at the back of a core and, cutting inward towards the centre, make it easier to detach.

In late 1867 or early 1868 Cooke's enthusiasm led to an investment in the Llanberis Slate Company Limited which was to cost him dear. The company was already somewhat dubious, and had expended a large amount of shareholders' money to little profit by developing the Gallt-y-Llan slate quarry, near the end of Llyn Peris.[47] At a meeting of shareholders the situation was described in this way:

> ... the attention of the board had been directed to the tunnelling machine patented by Messrs. Cooke and Hunter, and the directors, therefore, deputed their colleague, Mr. Elliott, who had strongly advocated its employment, to watch its action. The tunnelling machine having been practically tested at the Maen Offeren Quarry, it was proved capable of forming a tunnel 7ft. in diameter at the rate forward of 9 feet per diem, and of producing in its progress a large proportion of rock available for slate making. According to the calculations made by the patentees, the process of making a tunnel on their system, through good slate rock, leaves a large profit on the operation, in addition to the prospective returns to be obtained from the mass of rock thus unroofed ... Negotiations were, therefore, opened with Messrs Cooke and Hunter ... these gentlemen offered to waive all claim for licences and royalty in consideration of 1800 shares being allotted to them, £4 10s per share being considered as paid on each share, leaving Messrs Cooke and Hunter with a liability of £1000, which they agreed to pay ...[48]

Cooke was to join the board of directors. One machine was already on site and at work in January 1868 but the company failed in November 1868. At the auction which followed no mention was made of any tunnelling machine or machines.[49] The auction of the site only raised £1000, the plant and machinery a paltry £141. It is possible that only one tunneller was on site. Was it perhaps the Maenofferen machine which had been 'transferred' to speed up activities, with the other new machine or machines to follow? In that case it would not have been company property but Cooke and Hunter's, and so could be removed. If construction of the new machine or machines had begun, then the cost of it would have fallen on Hunter and Cooke, with no return possible. What is fairly certain is that by accepting the shares they also accepted the financial liability attached to them when the company failed, quite apart from any expenses they had entered into regarding new machines which were left on their hands. It is thought that Cooke bore the major financial burden of this.

In the same year, 1868, at Maenoffren one of the tunnelling machines was used to try and drive a tunnel eastwards from the old Cwmbowydd workings, leaving the strange 'quadruple bore' tunnel known ever since as 'Cooke's Level' (Fig. 18).[50] A contemporary account reports:

> I noticed that the orifice of the tunnel was very peculiar. In shape it seemed formed by the outline of four circles the circumferences of which intersected each other. The boring of this was perfectly smooth. Mr Owen explained to me that when commencing the level they had been induced to try a patent boring machine, whose action was the rotatory movement of a circle of knives. I afterwards saw the remains of the ponderous machine, like a huge mammoth cast-iron skeleton. After proceeding a few yards its use had been abandoned, because the cost of working it more than quadrupled the cost of the manual labour necessary for doing the same amount of work. Nor would it cut through granite.[51]

Whether this was simply meant as a demonstration of the overlapping tunnel idea, an attempt to convince the Maenoffren board to purchase a machine made for Llanberis, or even a trial of the spring cutters to help detach the core we may never know.

Although information is lacking, I can imagine that Cooke financed almost all the development work and the various prototype machines. I doubt that Hunter had very much money of his own, so it is quite possible that the 'late' appearance of George's 1864 patent tunneller was due to it being converted into reality only through Cooke's enthusi-

asm. The stone cutting machines were a clear financial success, but the quarrying machines definitely not.

The Patent Stone Working and Tunnelling Machinery Company Limited (1870)

In 1870 Cooke founded 'The Patent Stone Working and Tunnelling Machinery Company Limited' to set up and use the saws in London where there was, he claimed, no end of building work which could be supplied.[52] This may have been a formalisation as a limited company of Cooke and Hunter's existing partnership in an attempt also to reduce any future financial liability. The company had a capital of £40,000 in 4000 shares of £10 each.[53] A wharf was purchased on the south bank of the River Thames at Nine Elms in Battersea, it is thought at Downey's Wharf on Downey's Dock Road, and the long established company of Powis, James & Co. of Victoria Works, Battersea, who made woodworking machinery, were licensed to manufacture the patent machines. No sooner had the company been set up than Cooke's situation became so dire that a committee of his friends was set up to look after his finances, and took over his shares in the company.[54]

Also in 1870 (or possibly a year or so earlier) Cooke withdrew from a major role in both the Maenoffren and Bettws companies, staying on as an ordinary Director and became, with George, tenant of the Abercwmeiddau Quarry, near Corris. George moved from Maentwrog to Aberdovey.[55] We don't know how long their association with Abercwmeiddau had been going on, but the tunnelling machine was certainly used there (Fig. 19), as was the undercutter, for both were lying there, abandoned when the quarry was offered for sale in 1871. A report described the tunnels as 7 feet 4 inches diameter, 150 yards long across the vein, with a similar tunnel and cross level at a higher level and a vertical shaft between them.[56] This would seem to suggest a serious trial or demonstration of their proposed methods of quarrying had been attempted.

The stone moulding and planing machine (1870)

Cooke and Hunter's next, and last, joint patent was in 1870. This was primarily a development of the 1866 cutting machine patent for using barrels to cut profiles in stone.[57] In it the massive barrels were abandoned in favour of individual rings of varying diameters which could be assembled along the axle to give the required profile. Once these had removed the bulk of the material, then a steel profile cutter could smooth the resulting shape. It was a return to the roughing and finishing approach of the 1835 planer, but with greater flexibility. The patent allowed for several variations including the replacement of the horizontal axle with a vertical spindle to one side of the moving table. The table could be inclined at an angle to the cutting spindle for more effect. Another variation provided for a pair of spindles, one on each side of a central table, but mounted with the usual large diameter cutting discs, which cut to within an inch or so of one another.

Several machines were produced to the patent by Powis, James & Co. and appeared in their catalogues and those of their successors James, Western & Co. from 1873 onward. It is possible that the patent was produced specifically for them.[58, 59]

Cooke now returned to Surrey, and George moved to

Fig. 18 The quadruple bore 'Cooke's Level', Floor B, Maenofferen Quarry

Fig. 19   Inside the double tunneller level, Abercwmeiddau, Corris Uchaf (courtesy Stephen Thorpe)

Battersea, London, presumably to be close to the stone works at Nine Elms and to the James, Western & Co. works.[60] Cooke's enthusiasm for London was justified when the Patent Stone Working Machinery Company reworked Portland stone salvaged from Robert Mylne's Blackfriars Bridge

In 1871 the Civil and Mechanical Engineers Society visited the works and were impressed with the machinery. The Engineer reported in detail on the works and concluded:

> For what they undertake – and their work embraces a very varied range – the stone working machinery of Fothergill-Cooke, and Hunter seems decidedly satisfactory.[61]

Despite this positive report, in 1874 the the Patent Stone Working and Tunnelling Machinery Company was wound up and the plant and machinery sold off.[62]

The double-sided moulding machine (1876)
In 1876 George produced his last stone-moulding machine patent, based on multiple tools on duplex spindles which could act on both sides of a stone at the same time.[63] The patent was again apparently used by James, Western & Co., on whose behalf it had perhaps been devised.

The 1882 tunneller and cutting machines
With the closure of the Patent Stone Working works and the probable downsizing of James, Western & Co's Victoria

works (it seems very likely that in the latter case it was the stone-working department that was first to go), by 1881 or 1882 George had no work and cast about for employment. The result appears to have been his dusting off some 'unfinished business' with the tunnelling machines and in 1882 George's last patent appeared.[64] It looks and reads very much like an uncompleted patent of about 1868, intended to follow Cooke's patent for the traversers, but now updated to allow for the application of compressed air to drive the tunneller. This tunneller was not a ring machine, but rather a reversion to the chuck type with a concentric differential screw gear to drive it (Fig. 20). The 'three-armed' frame with its gearing above its centre line was held in place by conical-ended jack screws and its claimed advantage was that it provided 'great convenience' for the removal of the bored core.

This patent also gave considerable details of the undercutting machines. These now had two discs, either one being removable and both capable of being repositioned on the shaft, and could cut above or below the machine or even both at the same time.

The patent illustrated several variations on the undercutter theme. All used a pair of end frames connected by a pair of substantial rods along which the cutting disc carriage moved. The main drive shaft and a feed screw were carried in bearings in the frames. At one end the drive shaft was driven by a pair of belt pulleys at right angles to one another, coupled by bevel gears – presumably so that the belt drive could be in either direction. At the other end the

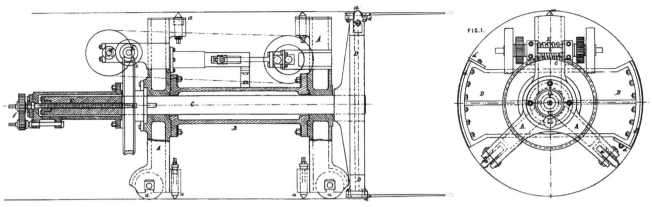

Fig. 20   George Hunter's 1882 tunneller: side and front elevations (Patent no. 3138)

main shaft drove the feed screw via belts and pinions to give the appropriate ratios. At the bottom corners of each frame were mounting points for some form of clamp, to fix the machine in position in the workings.

The first variation (Fig. 21, top) is suggestive of an undercutter design created before the internal gearing of the 1866 patent was developed. The cutting disc frame was mounted on the rods, and connected to the feed screw by the usual dividing nut. A sliding pinion keyed to the main shaft drove a second pinion mounted on the cutting frame on a short shaft which had at its other end a worm screw.

This drove a worm wheel on the vertical shaft which carried conventional cutting discs at either end. In this version there was no provision to swing the cutting discs outward, they could only move along with the cutting frame parallel to the rods of the main frame.

The second variation (Fig. 21, bottom) utilises the same type of drive arrangements as the 1866 undercutter. The cutting disc frame was driven by a sliding worm gear on the main shaft, driving a worm wheel which drove a vertical shaft which terminated in the internal gears which drove the cutting rings. Pivoting on this shaft were two independ-

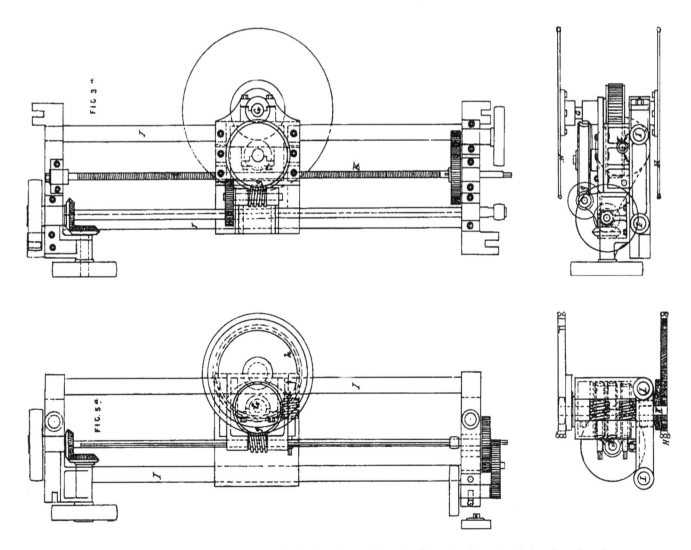

Fig. 21   George Hunter's 1882 undercutters: first version (top) and second version (bottom), plan and end elevations (based on patent drawings, Patent no. 3138)

ent trunnions which carried the eccentric support rings. Manually operated worms drove worm wheel sectors to swing the cutting rings in and out of the rock.

A third variation provided for a machine in which a conventional cutting disc was mounted in a vertical plane at the end of a long shaft. This was preceded by a 'chasing cutter' which cut a slot in which the cutting disc shaft and boss could move along.

A fourth variation provided a different frame arrangement for working in the side of a pit.

These variations fit well with the methods of quarrying proposed by Cooke in his 1867 patent, so to what extent they were modified from what George may have intended to patent in say 1868 is difficult to say. However, given that the tunneller was adapted for compressed air, perhaps that was the limit of the modifications to the undercutters as well.

What happened to George after this time is not clear, but it is possible he eventually found work with the North Eastern Railway Company and moved to York as a result. The year of his death is uncertain but is possibly 1887.[65]

Machines subsequent to 1887

The production of 'Hunter saws' did not cease with their inventor's death. Following F.J. Barnes', of the Portland Stone Co. Ltd, takeover of the Stone Working & Quarry Co. (Portland) Ltd, in September 1891, he renamed it the Portland Stone Quarries, Steam Saw Mills, Masonry & Turning Works. He then modernised the 'Station Works' and had a Hunter saw installed. In a publication giving an overview of the Portland stone industry, which was published in 1896, there are references to a Hunter saw installation, and also to Messrs. Webber & Pangbourne using a 'dry' circular saw, a term sometimes used for a Hunter. It also contains a picture of this saw – which certainly looks like an under-table axle Hunter saw.[66]

In 1896 the Oakeley Slate Quarries at Blaenau Ffestiniog were constructing a new 'slab mill' and to equip it they ordered a pair of Hunter saws from De Winton's. De Winton's proved difficult and a further order went to Owen's foundry.[67] They supplied a pair of apparently conventional saw tables but with a Hunter type blade. However, later inventories are confusing; some describe them as 'screw-fed, gear driven', which is certainly a Hunter, although the same inventories call them 'single Hunters' or 'semi-Hunter' and even 'Hunter-portable'. The Owen machines were described as 'for large slabs' with no mention of the blade type; perhaps they were reverted to a large steel type saw?[68] I suspect that they were simply single bladed Hunter saws, perhaps with the saw axle below the table top, as in a conventional slate saw. Inventories for Hafodlas in 1906 use a similar nomenclature; they refer to 'large double Hunter', 'small double Hunter', 'extra large double Hunter', and 'small single Hunter' machines. Unfortunately the distinctions which these titles imply are no longer clear.[69]

By the beginning of the twentieth century, although some Hunter type saws were still to be found in various quarries around the country, they tended to be referred to as 'dry saws', the names of Hunter and Cooke being almost forgotten. It was only in north Wales, and in Ffestiniog in particular, that the name Hunter was remembered. As late as May 1957 an old Hunter blade from the Votty and Bowydd Quarry was photographed for the Oakeley Quarry magazine

Caban,[70] Hunter saws by then having been long displaced by diamond tipped saws.

There are very few pictures of the various machines, most illustrations being taken from the patent drawings, although, as remarked above, a pair of photographs of the 1865 double tunneller exist. There are a couple of photographs of the smaller version of the 1866 saws as used in Graig Ddu (Manod) Quarry in Ffestiniog and at the Delabole Quarry in Cornwall (Fig. 6), a postcard of the under-table axle saw in the Prison quarry workshop in Portland, and an illustration of one in use at another Portland stone works, but that is all.

Conclusion

Modern works on the history of tunnelling machines often mention the machine from the 1866 joint Hunter and Cooke patent. Unfortunately, it is the one machine that it is almost certain was never constructed and, although circular bores cut by their other machines can still be found in the quarries of Maenofferen and Abercwmeiddau, their creators and their actual machines go unremarked. Had the tunnellers and over/undercutters been tried in something like chalk or sandstone, and in a more visible locality than north-west Wales, perhaps Hunter and Cooke would have been associated with the first Channel Tunnel attempt rather than the inventors Brunton, Beaumont and English.

If the Hunter saw was so successful in cutting slate slabs why was it not more widely adopted? The circular 'iron saw' invented by John Whitehead Greaves, of the Llechwedd Quarry in Ffestiniog, was noisy and the blades required frequent re-sharpening, typically twice or more a day. However, a basic two disc Hunter saw cost around £200, approximately ten times the cost of an 'iron' saw. Even as late as 1914, when the Hafodlas machinery was valued, a Hunter saw was worth four times as much as a conventional saw.[71] Furthermore, the Hunter saw worked best when dealing with thick blocks, not the relatively thin and easily handled blocks needed by the slate makers. Hunter saws almost always required the services of an overhead crane to handle their work. Also, the distinctive 'lay' of the Hunter tools gave the blocks a rough edge which was not liked by the slate makers, who preferred a relatively smooth surface to lay their chisels along the grain.

Let us leave the last word to Manfred Powis Bale, one time manager of Powis, James & Co. Writing in 1884 in what he claimed was the first book on stone working by machinery he said:

> As many of the latest forms of machines and cutting tools for working stone have been based on Messrs Hunter and Cooke's patents, ... we think they are fully entitled, as we have before remarked, to be considered the forerunners of modern stone-working by machine. As regards the earlier constructors of Stone-Working machinery of which we have any reliable records, the names of James Tulloch of London, and Mr James Hunter of Forfarshire will always hold a foremost place.[72]

Acknowledgements

I must give credit to the late Rodney Weaver who started this particular hare running way back when we were surveying Hafodlas in the 1980s; also to the staff of the then Patent Office Library and their successors, the Intellectual

Property Office Sales Department, who were able to provide copies of all the various Hunter, Cooke and Munro patents. I should also like to thank the various members of AditNow.co.uk for their photographs of Hunter tunnel locations and for our long-running discussions on the subject.

References

1   Obituary of James Hunter, *Glasgow Herald*, 15 June 1857, quoting *Arbroath Guide*.

2   Patent no. 6794 of 1835, 'Improvements in the Art of Cutting or what is commonly called Facing and Dressing certain kinds of stone'.

3   *Mechanics Magazine* issue no. 665, 7 May 1836; *Morning Chronicle*, 2 June 1836 and 13 Sept. 1836.

4   Obituary of James Hunter (ref. 1 above).

5   Obituary of James Hunter (ref. 1 above); *Mechanics Magazine* issue no. 636, 17 Oct.1835, pp. 38, 43.

6   *Mechanics Magazine* issue no. 780, 21 July 1838; *Minutes of the Proceedings of the Institution of Civil Engineers*, vol. 2 (Jan. 1842), pp. 146–148.

7   Patent no. 913 of 1855, 'Improvements in Stone-cutting machinery'.

8   Obituary of James Hunter (ref. 1 above).

9   *Caledonian Mercury*, Edinburgh, 16 July 1855, quoting *Arbroath Guide*.

10 *ibid.*

11 *Mechanics Magazine*, 27 Dec. 1856.

12 *Hereford Times*, 11 Oct. 1856.

13 Obituary of James Hunter (ref. 1 above).

14 *Practical Mechanics Journal*, 1 Oct. 1859, pp. 176–177; *Fife Herald & Kinross Strathearn & Clackmannan Advertiser*, 1 April 1862.

15 Patent no. 942 of 1862, 'Improvements in machinery and tools for cutting, sawing and planing stone, marble and slate'.

16 *Dundee Advertiser*, 1 May 1862; *Dundee Courier and Argus*, 5 May 1862.

17 *Dundee Advertiser*, 20 May 1862; *Dundee Courier & Argus*, 13 June 1862.

18 *Dundee Advertiser*, 12 Dec. 1862.

19 *ibid.*

20 *ibid.*

21 *Carnarvon & Denbigh Herald*, 25 July 1863; *Mining Journal*, 23 Jan. 1864; 30 April 1864; *Dundee Courier*, 18 April 1864.

22 *North Wales Chronicle*, 15 June 1861.

23 Griff R. Jones, *Hafodlas Slate Quarry* (1998), pp. 14, 98–99, 100–102.

24 *Daily Post*, 3 Feb. 1863.

25 Patent no. 1244 of 1864, 'Improvements in apparatus for cutting marble, stone, slate and coal'.

26 *Paisley Herald & Renfrewshire Advertiser*, 19 Aug. 1865.

27 Patent no. 3297 of 1865, 'Improvements to machinery for cutting or getting slate, stone, coal and other substances'.

28 *Journal of the Society of Arts*, 17 May 1867, p. 423.

29 *** New note *** Patent no. 433 of 1866, 'Improvements in machinery used in cutting stone, slate, and other minerals, and in forming tunnels, galleries and roads'.

30 *Dundee Advertiser*, April 1867.

31 *Journal of the Society of Arts*, 17 May 1867, p. 423.

32 Patent no. 2192 of 1866, 'Improvements in machinery and tools for cutting slate, stone, marble and other minerals'.

33 *The Engineer*, 14 Dec. 1866.

34 Tyne Improvement Commissioners Accounts: Newcastle upon Tyne, Literary & Philosophical Society, N 125 via Hazel Fleming.

35 Jones, *Hafodlas*, *op. cit.*, pp. 14, 98–99, 100–102.

36 *The Engineer*, 14 Dec. 1866.

37 *Dundee Advertiser*, 4 April 1867.

38 *Carnarvon & Denbigh Herald*, 14 Aug. 1869.

39 *The Engineer*, 14 Dec. 1866.

40 Tyne Improvement Commissioners Accounts (ref. 32 above).

41 *Dundee Courier & Argus*, 17 Aug. 1868.

42 *Dundee Advertiser*, July 1866.

43 *John o'Groats Journal*, 18 July 1867; *Dundee Courier & Argus*, 15 April 1868.

44 A. Fisher, D. Fisher & G.P. Jones, *De Winton of Caernarfon* (Garndolbenmaen: RCL, 2011), pp. 90–91, 93.

45 *Journal of the Society of Arts*, 17 May 1867, p. 420.

46 Patent no. 2580 of 1867, 'Improvements in Tunnelling and Quarrying Slate and other minerals, and in Machinery used for those purposes'.

47 *Daily News*, London, 8 Oct. 1863; *North Wales Chronicle*, 12 June 1867, quoting the *Mining Journal*.

48 *Mining Journal*, 4 Jan. 1868.

49 *North Wales Chronicle*, 28 Nov. 1868.

50 Brunton's plans of the Maenofferen & Votty Quarries, 1870s, author's collection.

51 *Carnarvon & Denbigh Herald*, 1873, reprinted in *The Slate Quarries of Wales in 1873*, ed. M.J.T. Lewis (Maentwrog: Snowdonia National Park Study Centre, 1987), pp. 43–44.

52 *Journal of the Society of Arts*, 17 May 1867, p. 419.

53 Share certificate: Dolgellau, Gwynedd Archives, Z/DP/5/485 1873.

54 Geoffrey Hubbard, *Cooke and Wheatstone and the Invention of the Electric Telegraph* (Routledge & K. Paul, 1965), p. 137.

55 1871 census.

56 Report of John Inray, CE, quoted in Sara Eade, *Slate Below: a study of Corris* (2012), pp. 38–43.

57 Patent no. 1202 of 1870, 'Improvements in stone-cutting apparatus'.

58 Powis, James, Western & Co. Catalogue 1873, Part II: Reading University Rural Life Collection, tr_scm_p2_b527.

59 Western & Co. Catalogue 1878: Reading University Rural Life Collection, tr_scm_p2_b705.

60 1871 census.

61 *The Engineer*, 21 July 1871, p. 37.

62 *The Standard*, 5 May 1875.

63 Patent no. 3740 of 1876, 'Improvements in stone working apparatus'.

64 Patent no. 3138 of 1882, 'Improvements in Tunnelling and Quarrying Slate and Apparatus therefor'.

65 *York Herald*, Jan. 1887.

66 David Pollard, pers. comm.

67 Transcriptions of Oakeley Slate Quarries manager's reports, author's collection.

68 Various inventories 1927–1933, author's collection.
69 Report written by Moses Kellow of the Croesor Quarry, in Jones, *Hafodlas, op. cit.*, pp. 32–33.
70 *Caban* (the house magazine of the Oakeley & Votty Slate Quarries Company Ltd.), May 1957.
71 Jones, *Hafodlas, op. cit.*, p. 57.

72 M. Powis Bale, *Stone Working Machinery and the Rapid and Economical Conversion of Stone* (Crosby Lockwood, 1884), pp. 43–49, also descriptions of Hunter machines etc., pp. 51, 54, 62, 81–83, 100–102, 131–135.

Appendix

Patents referred to in this paper

Year	Number	Patentee(s)	Patent title	Machines
1835	6794	James Hunter	Improvements in the Art of Cutting or what is commonly called Facing and Dressing certain kinds of stone	planing machine (the 'power stone planer')
1838	[?]	James Hunter	[?]	block dressing machines
1855	913	James Hunter George Hunter	Improvements in Stone-cutting machinery	stone cutting machine
1862	942	George Hunter	Improvements in machinery and tools for cutting, sawing and planing stone, marble and slate	universal stone working machine
1864	1244	George Hunter	Improvements in apparatus for cutting marble, stone, slate and coal	tunnelling machine
1865	3297	W.F. Cooke George Hunter	Improvements to machinery for cutting or getting slate, stone, coal and other substances	double tunneller
1866	433	W.F. Cooke George Hunter	Improvements in machinery used in cutting stone, slate, and other minerals, and in forming tunnels, galleries and roads	undercutter, overcutter and two tunnelling machines
1866	2192	George Hunter W.F. Cooke	Improvements in machinery and tools for cutting slate, stone, marble and other minerals	stone cutting (sawing) machines
1867	2580	W.F. Cooke	Improvements in Tunnelling and Quarrying Slate and other minerals, and in Machinery used for those purposes	tunnelling machines
1870	1202	W.F. Cooke George Hunter	Improvements in stone-cutting apparatus	stone moulding and planing machine
1876	3740	George Hunter	Improvements in stone working apparatus	double-sided stone moulding machine
1882	3138	George Hunter	Improvements in Tunnelling and Quarrying Slate and Apparatus therefor	tunneller and cutting machines

Electricity in the North Wales Slate Industry

Tim Oulton

Abstract: This paper traces the history of the use of electricity in the North Wales slate industry and the equipment used. It covers the use of electricity from 1854 (the earliest reference so far found) through the development of early private and public supply systems to present day use of standard industrial equipment. It highlights pioneering work in the use of AC in the industry and shows how the slate industry stimulated the development and use of electricity in parts of North Wales ahead of a great many parts of the UK including London.

Appendices describing typical quarry electrical practice and equipment and giving details of some of the electrical contractors to the industry are provided.

Introduction

Prior to the use of electricity, the main sources of power in the larger slate mines and quarries were water wheels and steam generated from rail-borne coal. In smaller or remote quarries water wheels and horse power sufficed. Oil engines were used in several of the more remote quarries including Moelferna, Hendre Ddu and Aberllefenni. Producer gas from coal or coke used directly in a gas engine was used by Penarth quarry and also extolled by others. None of these were ideal to the main power requirements of a slate quarry, where pumping and underground winding were needed. Water wheels and steam were, however, the main sources of power throughout the Welsh slate industry before 1900 and in many cases long afterwards. Some underground power was provided by compressed air generated directly from these sources. Quarries such as Rhosydd, which was remote from an electricity supply or a supply of coal, continued the use of water power alone until near its closure in the 1930s.[1]

Electricity first began to have commercial possibilities in the UK in the last quarter of the nineteenth century. The earliest industrial users were mainly railways and tramways where the separation of the prime mover from the point of utilisation was particularly attractive. That feature was of equal or greater attraction to mine managers so initial electrical developments tended to be in the underground quarries. However, the advantage of lighting to extend working hours in winter and the instant availability of motive power at start of work time clearly appealed to all quarry managers, so development soon also started in the bigger surface quarries.

Elcctricity would clearly be attractive to a manager reading about its use on railways[2] as well as urban street tramways. Action was likely held back by concerns over reliability and the difficulty in finding expertise and contractors in a fairly remote area.

The object of this paper is to put into the public domain such information as the author knows about the subject and he stands ready to be corrected on any matter. Contemporary spellings for place names are used where these are appropriate. The author has used a number of secondary sources and quoted the original source where that is known, few have been checked; that forms part of the on-going research and they are quoted in this paper as best available evidence to date.

Early uses of electricity in the quarries

It is likely that the first use of electricity in a quarry was not for power but for shot firing. It is possible that Penrhyn quarry purchased a 'Galvanic Battery' for that purpose in 1854.[3] The electrical system of firing multiple shots would clearly be safer and attractive in a quarry requiring the blasting of large quantities of rock at one time.

Telegraph and telephones were also used early in the quarries. It is likely that Penrhyn had an internal telephone link to Port Penrhyn in 1888. Oakeley quarry had a private circuit connection to their wharf office in Portmadoc carried by the Festiniog Railway (FR) on their poles, for which the Festiniog had to obtain a licence from the Post Master General. That probably began as a telegraph circuit soon after the Festiniog telegraph system was established in 1872. The quarries would likely have used the public telegraph service provided by the Festiniog long before the Post Office was able to provide a service. When development of the FR telephone system started in 1897 the quarries asked for a service and an FR drawing of 1909 shows eight quarries and a slate merchant connected to the Blaenau FR telephone exchange and nine quarry wharfs or offices and a slate merchant to the Portmadoc exchange.[4]

---

1   M.J.T. Lewis and J.H. Denton, *Rhosydd Slate Quarry* (Mold: Adit Publications, 1994), p. 61.

2   The Giant's Causeway Tramway opened in 1883, Bessbrook and Newry Tramway in 1895 and both the Liverpool Overhead Railway and the Douglas and Laxey Coast Electric Tramway in 1893.

3   Eric Foulkes, pers. comm. Until a firm reference is found for this there must be some doubt. Only the Daniell, the Grove and the Bunsen cells had been invented at this date; all were highly unsuited to this application, but it is just possible they were used.

4   Drawing in the Ffestiniog Railway Archive (in Caernarfon Record Office); Norman Pierce, unpublished research; John Wagstaff, article in Ffestiniog Railway *Signals* magazine, 1973, based on research in the Ffestiniog Railway Archive; unpublished research by Plas Tan y Bwlch Study Centre Industrial Archaeology group.

The first power systems

Llechwedd quarry was one of the first to have made recorded experiments with electricity for power when, in 1889, they ordered a 7.5 kW DC dynamo to be driven by a 25 hp turbine. By the end of the year they had made provision and were enquiring for a more powerful machine.[5] The same reference records that at that time they were experimenting with an electric rock drill which was working well by the end of the year. It also records that they had an electrically driven fan for ventilation working in 1890. It has been reported that they used the power for pumping and mill driving but an 1898 inventory says that they had two machines for pumping and lighting only.[6]

Oakeley had four small schemes in the 1890s. The three main ones were direct driven by steam engines using existing boilers. One in Bonc Coedan mill provided lighting, one near the top of K Trwnc provided power to pumps on M and N floors and one at Twr Babel drove an electric incline underground specially designed by East Amos & Anderson of Erith in Kent. A fourth scheme in the Middle Quarry mill in 1899, driven from the line shafting, was for an electric rock drill trial.[7] Both Cilgwyn and Dorothea also seem to have had small systems for lighting and possibly pumping before 1900.[8]

The next significant development was the commissioning of Dolwen power station by Yale Electric Power Co. in 1902. The Dolwen scheme provided 180 kW at 560 volts DC to provide power to the town of Blaenau Ffestiniog as well as to Votty and Bowydd quarry.[9] Power at Votty quarry was used for three inclines and pumps and also a supply from Votty drove a 10 hp mill motor at Llechwedd. An inventory by Moses Kellow in 1914 for lease valuation of Votty equipment lists five motors by Sandycroft, who were the contractors for Dolwen. I think it is quite likely that four, of 179 kW capacity in total, were the originals driving the New Robey incline and three pumps. The inventory also lists a battery and booster set which was probably also part of the original provision to cover peaks from the haulage.[10]

This may have been the first electrification for power on any substantial scale in a slate quarry. The town scheme is reputed to have been the first public electricity supply derived from water in North Wales and pre-dated a public supply in some of the towns on the North Wales coast and even most of London.[11]

By 1900 it must have been clear to quarry managers that electricity had potential for the industry and development began to gather pace. In 1902 the manager at Cilgwyn was reported in *The Quarry* and the *Slate Trade Gazette* as having a system used for pumping and a rock drill and that there was an intention to use it for a cableway hoist. No technical details are given and there are doubts about the nature of the scheme.[12]

Also in 1902, the Inspector of Mines report records that Hafodlas quarry near Bettws y Coed was using electricity generated by water power to drive their mill. This seems to be the earliest use of electric mill driving but technical details are unknown.

By 1904 Maenofferen had commissioned a 275 kW, 500 volt, DC scheme capable of providing a considerable proportion of the power requirements of the quarry.[13] This appears to have been the first instance of a quarry relying on electricity for all aspects of its business. The prime mover was intended to be two Pelton wheel water turbines with steam standby. However, it may have been commissioned with steam only, possibly because the civil works were not complete, but water power was subsequently the prime mover during its lifetime. That system incorporated a battery to cover peak loads. Because lead-acid batteries have a substantially higher terminal voltage on charge, a booster was provided to keep the battery in good condition and maintain constant voltage on the system. Such systems were by then becoming common for urban tramways and DC domestic distribution systems. The steam plant was later removed, probably after 1912 when supply was taken from North Wales Power and Traction (NWPT) and the quarry was able to regulate its generation to available water.

In the same year Llechwedd are reported as experimenting with a 'Marvin-Sandycroft' electric rock drill.[14] Electric rock drills are again reported in use there in 1926.[15]

After negotiations with Yale came to nothing, Llechwedd went ahead with their own scheme, commissioned in 1906

---

5   Unpublished research on Charles Warren Roberts letter book (Meirionnydd Record Office, Llechwedd Collection Z/DBE) by Plas Tan y Bwlch Practical Industrial Archeaology course.

6   Meirionnydd Record Office Z/DBE/3002, an inventory of 1898, records one 15 hp and one 10 hp dynamo, apparently turbine driven with a 'costly switchboard' providing power for pumping and lighting.

7   Graham Isherwood, pers. comm., after his research in the Oakeley Slate Quarries Co. Ltd Collection (Meirionnydd Record Office Z/DAF).

8   Alun Richards, notes in the Plas Tan y Bwlch Archive (at Plas Tan y Bwlch, Maentwrog).

9   Dewi W. Thomas, *Hydro-Electricity in North West Wales* (Dolgarrog: National Power, 1997), pp. 39–43. This book is useful for matters of the 1930s onward but lacking and inaccurate in information on early quarry schemes. The many photos, though interesting, are very poorly reproduced.

10   Graham Isherwood, pers. comm.

11   Gordon Woodward, 'Hydro-electricity in North Wales 1880–1948', *Transactions of the Newcomen Society* 69B (1997),

pp. 205–236. At least one date in this reference is incorrect according to primary sources; however, information from it is quoted as best available and most seems reliable. Additional information on provision of power to North Wales towns can be found in Emile Garcke, *Manual of Electrical Undertakings*, vol. 45, 1948/9; and on London from Leslie Hannah, *Electricity before Nationalisation* (London: Macmillan, 1979).

12   There is some suggestion that this might have been an AC system and the generator is recorded by the late Dr Gwynfor Pierce Jones as a 50 Hz unit of 1901. I do not believe it was an AC system, as Kellow claimed to be the first to use AC in 1904 and this was not challenged as far as I know; if it was AC, technical journals would have taken a lot more interest. The contractor was GEC and it is likely that Bruce Peebles were the first to supply AC equipment in Britain in 1902. However, Alun Richards records without reference that they 'had problems with the AC winder' in 1906. Further research is needed. It is possible that Cilgwyn took an AC supply as soon as it arrived at Pen yr Orsedd, next door, in 1906. They certainly built a new power house then, but do not appear on the 1910 North Wales Power and Traction (NWPT) trading account of 1910 (Thomas, *op. cit.* (n. 9 above), p. 53).

13   Inspector of Metalliferous Mines report 1904, Section V, General remarks p. 35.

14   *Ibid.*

15   Unpublished research by Plas Tan y Bwlch Practical Industrial Archeaology course, *op.cit.* (n. 5 above).

re-using Maenofferen's water supplemented from a third reservoir. Their power station, Pant yr Avon beside the A470 (SH697468), is still in use as a power station and still contains its original plant, though that is now out of use, superseded by modern AC equipment. The original plant comprised two Pelton wheels, each driving a 250 kW DC generator.[16] By 1905 the system at Llechwedd was interconnected with the Yale system to enhance security of supply and the Maenofferen system was added in 1911.[17]

Development of AC systems

Up to about 1903 quarry managers had little choice; if they wanted to use electricity, it had to be DC as the development of DC equipment in Britain had outstripped AC.

In North Wales the challenge was taken up by one Moses Kellow. He was a Cornish engineer who became manager of Croesor quarry, a medium size undertaking in Cwm Croesor. Educated privately and at Davies Grammar School, he was taught geology by his father and must have been well read.[18] He considered a DC scheme but decided to electrify his quarry on the AC system; it is possible he had seen a copy of the Thompson text book.[19]

AC had been used in 1899 at the Frongoch lead mine near Aberystwyth but that failed for financial reasons and was sold up before the system had time to show the potential of AC electrification.[20] That scheme was a lavish system designed by Italian engineers using AC motors supplied at 2300 volts 50 Hz.[21]

Kellow, in 1902, drew up notes of what he wanted to do and seriously considered a DC scheme. His calculations, believed to be extant, showed that a DC scheme would be very inefficient, so he opted for the little tried AC.[22] Kellow said that he had great difficulty finding manufacturers or contractors (though Bruce Peebles could have supplied him by the time he was ready to order) and that he had to go to Europe, where development was more advanced, to find what he wanted.[23] Eventually, in 1904, he had continental

equipment working but there were teething problems and the scheme was not fully operational until early 1906.[24] His system consisted of a 375 hp Pelton wheel turbine driving a 250 kW 2750 V 40 Hz alternator in a power station (SH648459) on the opposite side of the valley to the quarry.[25] The building survived as a youth club hut and has now been returned to use as a power station with modern plant.[26] Kellow used the power for mill driving, winding, winches, pumping, lighting and to provide power to an electric locomotive running on DC through a motor-generator set. The scheme included arc lighting in working chambers, the first and probably the only time substantial lighting was provided in the underground work places. He also had a supply to his own house.

Kellow was a bit of a showman and liked to publicise his own work, and maybe was not quite the pioneer he claimed to be. However, there is no doubt that the paper he read to the Institution of Civil Engineers about the scheme in 1907[27] had considerable influence and he received the Telford Prize for it. There is little doubt too that Kellow went to more expense than needed to achieve his objective but the example of Croesor must have stimulated interest in AC systems and most subsequent developments used AC. It is clear from the letter books that many came to see the installation. It is also clear from the letters that he had many disputes with contractors; one ended up in court.[28] His system provided all the power Croesor needed until closure. A public supply was only provided post closure when the quarry was used as an explosive store.

Development of a public electricity supply

In 1906 the only public electricity supplies in North Wales were the DC schemes in Blaenau Ffestiniog and in some of the coastal towns. There were also a few small-scale village systems, mostly installed by Richard Edwards.[29] Some of these supplied quarries but probably only for lighting. In that year the North Wales Power and Traction Co. commissioned Cwm Dyli power station.

Cwm Dyli was innovative in being one of the earliest power stations to generate at high voltage AC and to be designed primarily for industrial loads. NWPT was incorporated in 1903 with wide ranging statutory powers to provide power for electric railways and public and industrial supplies.[30] See Appendix II below, under North Wales Power Co. Ltd, for more details.

In order to raise the capital to build Cwm Dyli they needed some of the larger quarries to agree to take a supply; Oakeley, Pen-yr-Orsedd and Dinorwig did so and the 4 MW project went ahead in partnership with Bruce Peebles as main contractor. There were four 1500 hp Ganz Pelton wheel turbines, each driving a 1 MW Bruce Peebles generator of the rotating field type, designed by Ganz, generating at the transmission voltage of 10 kV. The initial scheme

16 Thomas, *op. cit.* (n. 9 above), p. 29.

17 Woodward, *op. cit.* (n. 11 above), p. 215.

18 Moses Kellow, autobiography, Bangor University Library, ref. MSS 5276.

19 The late Rodney Weaver, pers. comm. The text book in question is thought to be Silvanus Phillips Thompson, *Polyphase Electric Currents and Alternate Current Motors* (London: E. and F.N. Spon, 1895).

20 David Bick *et al.*, *Frongoch Lead & Zinc Mine*, British Mining 30 (Northern Mine Research Society, 1996), pp. 50–51; Richards, *op. cit.* (n. 8 above).

21 E.H. Davies, *Machinery for Metalliferous Mines* (London: Crosby Lockwood, 2nd ed. 1902), pp. 496–498, which includes a wiring diagram of the installation.

22 Adrian Barrell, 'The Croesor File' (unpublished research document, a copy of which is in the Plas Tan y Bwlch Archive). The file includes quotes from original letter books and papers held in various public and private collections.

23 Moses Kellow, 'The application of hydro electric power to slate mining', paper read to the Institution of Civil Engineers 1907: minutes of the proceedings, part 4, January 1907, pp. 50–74 (copy in Caernarfon Record Office in box Llechi). Kellow's claim of operation without problems is at variance with Barrell, *op. cit.* (n. 22 above), who quotes from original letter books about problems such as a burnt out armature on the exciter in 1906 as well as problems governing the turbine in order to give tight control of speed and hence of frequency

which controlled the speed of all the motors in the quarry.

24 Barrell, *op. cit.* (n. 22 above).

25 Kellow, *op. cit.* (n. 23 above).

26 https://www.rwe.com/web/cms/en/312580/rwe-innogy/sites/hydroelectric-power-station/united-kingdom/sites-in-operation/cwm-croesor/ (accessed 17 July 2014).

27 Kellow, *op. cit.* (n. 23 above).

28 Barrell, *op. cit.* (n. 22 above)

29 Thomas, *op. cit.* (n. 9 above), pp. 5–13.

30 Thomas, *op. cit.* (n. 9 above), pp. 45–53.

provided transmission lines to Blaenau Ffestiniog, Nantlle and Llanberis. Other villages near the lines were also eventually provided with domestic supply and a NWPT trading account of 1910 indicates payment from Pen-y-Gwryd and Pen-y-Pass, so the hotels at those locations must have benefited from the transmission lines passing their doors.[31]

The DC public supply in Blaenau Ffestiniog was eventually linked to the NWPT supply with rotary converters as were the DC schemes in several coastal towns by 1924.[32]

AC schemes in the quarries

The 1906 Oakeley scheme was particularly interesting in that they were said at the time to be one of the largest industrial users of the AC system in the UK. The main step forward was the successful design by Ganz of an AC motor for winding on big inclines.[33] The largest used at Oakeley were 200 hp, 200 rpm induction motors with wound rotors and liquid resistance starters, built by Bruce Peebles to a Ganz design. They were used on multi-track surface inclines. Smaller motors of the same type were used on the underground inclines. Oakeley used AC motors thoughout, some 1900 hp in total, for mill driving, pumping and compressors as well as inclines.[34]

Pen-yr-Orsedd adopted electricity as soon as supply was available, with Bruce Peebles as main contractors. They signed up for a trial period in 1906 at a discount price and permitted Bruce Peebles to use their installation for sales publicity. They installed about 750 hp of motors for mill driving and for their 'Blondin' winding ropeways but are reported as finding it 'unreliable', though they seem to have used electricity as prime motive power from that time on.[35]

Although Dinorwig signed up for supply in 1906, they seem to have made less use of it, probably for lighting and possibly to drive one of their two mills. Dinorwig records for the period are lost and the only information the author has is the NWPT account copy of 1910.[36]

When a public supply was available, other quarries began to take advantage of it. Maenofferen connected their DC system to the public supply in 1912 by means of a 200 kW rotary converter.[37] This probably allowed them to dispense with the battery and the standby steam plant. Metering was provided to allow them to export power to NWPT as well as import. Llechwedd finally connected its system to the public supply in 1931 with a rotary converter, having previously used a 160 kW oil engine driven generator to cover peak loads and water shortage.[38]

Penrhyn took a supply in 1912 for their 'Blondins', chain inclines and new mills.[39] At about that time Penrhyn were changing their slate producing methods to a centralised mill system and electricity became their main source of motive power. Their Chief Engineer, G.K. Paton, wrote a paper in 1916 for the Liverpool Engineering Society about the use of electricity in the slate industry, almost certainly using the Penrhyn system anonymously as example.[40]

Smaller quarries that were were not too remote from the system took supply over the subsequent two decades but the more remote quarries never had a supply. However, most of the latter were in severe decline in the early 1900s.

Dorothea was a deep open pit working like Pen-yr-Orsedd but apparently with very different management views and they seem to have been late to adopt electricity. They experimented early with electricity but had well developed power systems based on water or steam and had access to rail-borne coal close at hand. As an open pit working, steam and water power must have suited their methods better than was the case of the underground mines. They seem to have had some sort of hydro scheme in 1895, possibly for lighting or pumps, and an 80 kW oil engine driven AC system by 1938 but they did not take a public supply until 1956.[41]

Subsequent developments

Maenofferen's was another particularly interesting system, not least for its longevity. It was still largely in working order in the early 1990s. With Llechwedd's, it was probably the last remaining large DC industrial system in working order in the UK, possibly in the world. Recent research indicates that they added a second rotary converter in 1929.[42] At that time they also renewed their power station equipment, using a more efficient Turgo impulse turbine in place of a Pelton wheel. In 1935 they signed up with the North Wales Power Company (formerly North Wales Power and Traction), for a medium voltage AC supply and the quarry provided a building for use as a NWP substation.[43] Previously the only AC on the site had been the bulk feed at 10 kV to the transformers feeding the converters. All subsequent development at Maenofferen relied on small AC motors but the DC system remained in use for the main loads until closure of the mills and underground workings in about 1997. The DC power station and rotary converters continued in service, exporting to the grid, until the power station plant was replaced by modern AC equipment for that purpose, a function it continues to perform using the original civil works with their subsequent developments.

Votty relied on a DC supply from Dolwen power station and interconnection to Llechwedd and Maenofferen, which had gone by the 1930s. The mills were not electrified until 1920 and in 1926 two oil engines of 250 hp were purchased

---

[31] Thomas, *op. cit.* (n. 9 above), p. 53.

[32] Woodward, *op. cit.* (n. 11 above), p. 220, describes the use of rotary converters in North Wales to prolong the life of public DC systems.

[33] Woodward, *op. cit.* (n. 11 above), p. 215.

[34] *Electrical Review* vol. 59 (Dec. 1906), pp. 911–919 and 955–958. Almost the whole article is devoted to Oakeley. It is part 3 of a serial article about the Cwm Dyli project, starting the previous October.

[35] Gwynfor Pierce Jones, pers. comm. and papers, based on information from documents in Caernarfon Record Office.

[36] Thomas, *op. cit.* (n. 9 above), p. 53.

[37] John Crosskey, unpublished report on Maenofferen Slate Quarry Co. Ltd. company records at Companies House, 1978, Plas Tan y Bwlch Archive.

[38] Woodward, *op. cit.* (n. 11 above), p. 215.

[39] Eric Foulks, pers. comm. (from local press Aug.? 1912).

[40] G.K. Paton, 'Electric power in slate quarries', *Transactions of the Liverpool Engineering Society* 37 (1916): Gwynedd Archives, XM/4046/36. This reference gives much interesting detail on mill drives and cost comparisons as well as being a good snapshot of developments at that date.

[41] Notes by Alun Richards in the Plas Tan y Bwlch Archive (primary source unknown).

[42] Crosskey, *op. cit.* (n. 37 above).

[43] Crosskey, *op. cit.* (n. 37 above).

to supplement the DC electricity supply.[44] There was a new agreement with the Yale Co. and the North Wales Power Company in 1932. Power was supplied as AC in 1937, when Dolwen power station began to generate AC instead of DC and rectifiers were installed at the quarry, the main plant in the quarry remaining DC. The converter station was set up at the top of Tuxford incline. That date probably indicates the date when the town was beginning to be converted to AC too, but large rotary converters were still in use in the town at nationalisation in 1948.[45]

In 1916 G.K. Paton's paper gave the following analysis (Table 1) of the units of electricity consumed by the most important divisions of three unnamed quarries though one of them is almost certainly Penrhyn and the author suggests that the other open quarry is likely to be Pen yr Orsedd.[46]

Table 1   Electricity consumed in three unnamed quarries

% of units used by	Underground quarry	Open quarry A	Open quarry B
Mills	15.0	8.6	20.5
Haulage	50.0	77.0	51.2
Compressors	10.0	4.4	16.5
Pumps	25.0	10.0	11.8

After Paton

In 1933 there was talk of amalgamating Oakeley, Llechwedd and Votty so an inventory of the equipment in each quarry was prepared. That included a list of all the electric motors in the quarry and their usage (Table 2), so it allows us to compare electricity use in the three quarries in a snapshot which probably represents the peak of electrical development in the industry. The author can only speculate as to the differences in three very similar quarries but one might suppose that they are mainly geological. However, the apparent low percentage for mill driving at Oakeley is strange.

Table 2   Installed motor horsepower at three quarries

	Oakeley	Llechwedd	Votty
Installed capacity	2076 kW	900 kW	848 kW
Mills	9%	15%	14%
Haulage	40%	38%	45%
Compressors	28%	24%	15%
Pumps	20%	21%	23%
Other	3%	2%	3%

Conclusion

There is no doubt that the building of the 4 (later 6.5) MW Cwm Dyli power station, the first in Wales, possibly anywhere, to be built primarily for the industrial quarry load, stimulated electrical development from water resources throughout North Wales which continued with the building of stations at Dolgarrog (26.5 MW, by stages from 1908 to 1944) and Maentwrog (18 MW in 1928, later 24 MW, now 30 MW).

North Wales Power became the principal generator and distributor of electricity throughout North Wales and as far east as Crewe in Cheshire. Important customers from an early date included the Marconi Wireless telegraph station at Waenfawr and the Penmaenmawr granite quarries. They also took over the private power station of the Aluminium Co. at Dolgarrog, supplying power to the works when it re-started and developing the station as a major source of supply. In the 1920s, following re-organisation of the industry under the 1923 Electricity Act, they provided power for much of the heavy industry in Crewe, including the LMS railway works, as well as the coastal towns in North Wales. Their hydro supply was supplemented by Mersey Power's steam plant in Runcorn and later from grid connections near Chester and Crewe. Initially distribution to the quarries was at 10 kV but, as loads developed, these lines were upgraded to 20 kV and many subsequently to 33 kV. An interesting paper of 1946 published by North Wales Power about their system shows the extent of their 20 kV system, much of it the original lines built to serve the quarries.[47]

After 1906 many of the communities along the power line routes were connected to the NWP 10 or 20 kV system and so were early beneficiaries of the supply to the quarries; communities such as Dolwyddelan had electricity supplies long before similar communities in other rural areas and the coastal towns benefited from bulk supplies of the cheaper hydro source of power. Blaenau Ffestiniog, thanks to the presence of the quarries, had a public electricity supply in 1906 for all its major industries, its lighted streets, its public buildings and for those residents who could afford it, well before many parts of London had any supply at all and were still crying out for it as late as the 1920s.[48]

Sadly, all the DC schemes are now extinct but the smashed remains of the Maenofferen scheme, the victim of copper thieves in recent times, can still be found above and below ground and the Llechwedd DC plant at Pant yr Afon has been preserved intact.

---

[44] Graham Isherwood, pers. comm., based on information from documents in Gwynedd Archives, mostly company reports.

[45] Emile Garcke, *Manual of Electrical Undertakings*, vol. 45 (1948/9).

[46] Paton, *op. cit.* (n. 40 above).

[47] 'Generation, transmission and distribution in North Wales and south Cheshire', NWP internal paper, reprinted in *Electrical Review* (Dec. 1945 – March 1946).

[48] Leslie Hannah, *Electricity before Nationalisation* (London: Macmillan, 1979).

Appendix I

Quarry Electrical Equipment

DC or AC?

As intimated in the paper, in the early electricity supply industry there was a heated battle between those favouring the DC system of electrification and those promoting the AC system.

DC appealed to railways and tramways largely because of its ease of control of motors to develop full torque at starting, a characteristic required for traction. A similar characteristic is also ideal for incline winding. DC was also easy to understand by municipal councillors requiring local domestic lighting schemes in their patch and it also provided employment in the many small, local power stations required for a DC system. It was backed by a powerful salesman, Edison. The serious disadvantage of DC is that either the power station has to be within about a mile or so of the point of use or it needs excessively heavy cables if uneconomic transmission losses are to be avoided.

Tesla, a Serb from Vojodina, espoused the AC system in America but he was no salesman. Ferranti did likewise in the UK but met determined opposition from the DC camp, particularly municipal authorities.[49] That resulted in DC equipment development forging ahead in Britain while AC stagnated. Matters on the continent of Europe were different; the advantages of the AC system were, by 1900, well understood and there were several manufacturers who could supply equipment.[50] In the early 1900s one of the Bruce Peebles directors, M.T. Pickstone, toured Europe and discovered how far ahead they were in design and manufacture of AC equipment; in 1902 Peebles formed a trading alliance with the Hungarian firm of Ganz of Budapest. They then headhunted knowledgeable staff from Europe and employed W. Maurice Georgi, then working for Siemens Halske. Georgi read several papers to British institutions and also designed the Oakeley system.[51] It may well be significant that when Oakeley came to prepare a specification for their AC system, they employed a Maurice Georgi from Newcastle on Tyne.[52]

The principal advantages of the DC system are:
1. simple to understand
2. compatible with use of a battery for peak loads and after hours supply
3. ideal motor torque characteristics for winding and traction with simple control

The disadvantages at that time were:
1. inability to change the voltage without great expense, so generation, transmission and utilisation voltages must equate

2. practical distribution distances severely limited by losses due to 1
3. the need to use commutators and brushes on all rotating machines, incurring expense and higher maintenance costs

The advantages of AC are:
1. easy to change transmission voltage using transformers, thus minimising losses to give almost unlimited transmission distances
2. cheaper and more robust single speed motors, ideal for constant speed drives e.g. mills or static machines, the so-called squirrel cage motor
3. the ability to use rotating field generators more suited to higher voltages and consequently greater power

The main disadvantages of AC are:
1. it is more difficult to provide the right motor torque characteristics for starting under load e.g. traction or winding
2. the great difficulty of providing any sort of storage medium for use in time of very light load so generators need to run at any time power is required

Power stations

Both the quarry and the public electrical equipment was often state-of-the-art for their time. The quarry DC stations, however, were typical for the time, with Pelton wheel turbines driving dynamos directly coupled or via belts. A simple switchboard was provided with fuses for protection.[53]

The Croesor AC power station was not as revolutionary as Kellow wanted people to believe and was typical of designs that were well established on the continent of Europe. It has indeed been suggested that Kellow just used the Thompson text book. However, it was revolutionary in the slate industry.

Cwm Dyli on the other hand was a considerable achievement much written about at the time.[54] The harsh conditions high on the flanks of Snowdon and the size of the project, remote from rail communication and probably the largest hydro station to that date, meant that the engineering world took great interest.[55] Brief details of the plant are in the body of the paper and full details will be found in the references.

Subsequently, small generation schemes were provided in several small quarries and to supplement the generation in larger ones. Oil engines seem to have been the prime movers, in most cases probably driving DC dynamos through a belt.

Transmission lines and substations

The use in 1906 of 10 kV for transmission was also innova-

[49] Hannah, *op. cit.* (n. 48 above).
[50] Thompson, *op. cit.* (n. 19 above), pp. 210–216.
[51] Isherwood, *op. cit.* (n. 10 above).
[52] Determined engineers in the North East did much to promote AC, as their priority was electricity supply to collieries over considerable distances, for which AC was vastly superior. Two of those engineers went on to found the consulting engineering firm Merz and McLellan.

[53] Extant switchboard at Maenofferen and photographs.
[54] 'Electric power distribution in North Wales', *The Electrician*, 26 Jan. 1906 (pp. 578–580), 9 Feb. 1906 (pp. 622–625, 660–663), 16 Feb. 1906 (p. 699), gives a good description of the Cwm Dyli scheme.
[55] Both *Engineering* and *Electrical Review* had articles but *The Electrician* (*ibid.*) seems to have the best.

tive in the UK though similar voltages were in use on the continents of Europe and America. Transmission lines used almost exclusively wood poles, either single or in A or H formation depending on the weather conditions expected and the number of conductors.[56] Steel masts were used in the Llanberis Pass. Subsequently, as loads grew some 10 kV lines were upgraded to 20 kV then to 33 kV; others were converted to 11 kV.

The lower voltage surface distribution, both for public supplies and the internal quarry supplies, was mostly by means of overhead lines as cable development was still in its infancy and there were reliability doubts, especially as many would have to pass through made up ground consisting of slate debris. Also, overhead lines were easy to repair with local labour. As a result a typical specialist substation building design developed and is found in many quarries. They often had an overhanging roof or small towers at each end partly protecting a gantry, one for the insulators of the incoming HV supply and the other for the local distribution. They usually had insulating bushes through one end gable for the HV supply and earthenware pipes for cable or bare conductor on insulators at the other. On the HV side of the power company's transformer, protection was by fuses with open busbars on porcelain insulators in wire mesh cages and manual isolation switches operated with hand-held insulated rods and oil immersed circuit breakers with over current trips. All access to the HV side of the substation was restricted to power company employees. Substations built from the 1930s onward used standard metal clad oil circuit breakers or ring main units for HV switching. Kellow and probably the early DC systems paid close attention to lightning protection, as did the Cwm Dyli engineers; water jet lightning arresters were used on the main busbars at Cwm Dyli.[57]

Metering would normally be carried out on the lower voltage side of the transformers in the incoming substation at the quarry. In the case of the DC system studied at Meanofferen it was on the DC side of the rotary converters.

Local distribution

On the DC schemes this was at 500 volts nominal using three conductors with the centre one earthed and the outer two at + and − 250 V to give 500 volts across the outers and 250 volts to the centre for lighting and small motors. Distribution was usually on overhead lines, with bitumen insulated cables underground as rubber was said to perish quickly in the damp environment.[58] Protection was usually by means of fuses or hand-operated contactors with over-current trips at the manned locations. They also had an earth leakage indicator on the underground cable system.

On AC systems, all quarries except Croesor (which used 40 Hz) used what is now the AC standard of 50 Hz, three-phase, 4 wire 440/415 volts, giving a nominal 230 volts to the earthed neutral for lighting and small motors.[59] Protection was by air break trips with backup fuses in the

smaller sizes and oil immersed circuit breakers for higher powers.

Rotary converters

As the AC system came to dominate the electricity supply industry, rotary converters were often used to link older DC systems to bulk AC supplies and dispense with local DC generation. In the case of the quarries, as generation was by water power with most of the cost already committed to civil works, rotary converters were used to supplement local generation of DC rather than replace it.

A rotary converter is in effect a rotating switch, synchronised to the AC frequency. It ensures that the DC circuit is always connected to an appropriate point on the AC waveform to ensure as far as possible a steady flow of current from one to the other. Rotary converters can be used to pass power from AC to DC and vice versa. The frame of the machine need only be sized to keep the machine turning synchronously and does not need to be rated for the full power to be transmitted, as would be needed in a motor-generator set, but the armature winding and brush gear needs to pass the full current. They are characterised by having six or more slip rings at one end and a commutator at the other.

Rotary converters were normally fed from dedicated six-phase transformers to make flow of power as smooth as possible. The peak output voltage of the transformer equates to the DC voltage so it would be 380 volts RMS for a 500 volt DC system. The Llechwedd unit has been preserved at the National Slate Museum at Llanberis.[60]

A rectifier does the same job but can only pass power in one direction. Votty and Bowydd quarry used rectifiers rather than rotary converters as they had no generation of their own, always relying on the Yale generators at Dolwen until they were converted to AC in 1937. They too used dedicated six-phase transformers.

Boosters

Boosters were common in early DC schemes, where batteries were used, in order to maintain the supply within close voltage limits. They consisted of a motor, an exciter and a generator on a single shaft. Ingenious interconnection of the windings allowed them to work automatically taking power from the incoming supply and generating a voltage adding to or subtracting from the incoming supply to keep the distribution busbars at or near constant voltage. That compensated for the big variation of voltage of a lead acid battery between charge and discharge. All the quarry DC schemes are believed to have had boosters; the one at Maenofferen was of the Highfield type. A full description of their operation will be found in the reference and other text books.[61]

Winding motors

DC winding motors were compound with a strong series ele-

56 'Electric power distribution in North Wales', op. cit. (n. 54 above).

57 ibid.

58 Paton, op. cit. (n. 40 above).

59 Isherwood (pers. comm.), based on his research in the Oakeley archive, asserts that Oakeley used 500/280 volts.

60 Cadi Iolen, 'Llechwedd rotary converter', Welsh Mines Society Newsletter 61 (Autumn 2009), pp. 22–24.

61 Simmons & Avery, Electrical Engineering (London: Cassell & Co., 1920), pp. 780–785. This reference is a mine of technical information on early schemes and equipment; it also covers telephones and wireless. Also useful is A.E. Clayton with N.N. Hancock, Performance and Design of Direct Current Machines (London: Sir Isaac Pitman & Sons, 3rd ed. 1959).

ment and were controlled by a liquid resistance connected in series. Typical power rating for underground inclines was of the order of 90 hp (68 kW). The liquid resistances at Maenofferen were quite crude consisting of copper plates lowered into wooden barrels (latterly plastic) filled with a sal-ammoniac (ammonium chloride) solution. (Brine could not be used for that purpose as chlorine is generated.)

Those on AC were wound rotor induction motors, usually with liquid resistance starters. Typical power rating for underground inclines was of the order of 90 hp (68 kW). The multi-track surface inclines at Oakeley required ratings up to 200 hp (150 kW) though many engineers would now think that 200 hp was a bit excessive as in practice only one track on the incline is wound at once, but the duty rating (the actual winding time per hour) would be higher on a multi-track incline.

Mill drive motors

Mill systems were usually conversions of a drive from a central water wheel or steam engine through line shafting with individual machines driven by belt from the shaft, so a low speed was required to drive the shafts. DC mill motors were shunt machines with resistive starters; those surveyed at Maenofferen drove the shafting through worm reduction gear boxes. Typical power rating for this purpose, as far as current research goes, was 30 to 40 hp (22 to 30 kW) with a few smaller ones.

Mill driving motors on AC were usually squirrel cage induction motors with star-delta starters or sometimes wound rotor with resistive starters. They usually drove the line shafting through either speed reducing belt pulleys, a combination of gears and pulleys or worm reduction gearboxes.[62]

Compressor motors

All the electrified quarries used electricity to drive air compressors for air power, mainly for rock drills but also for air winches and small ventilation fans. On DC schemes, shunt wound motors with resistive starters were the norm; 10 to 20 kW would be typical. On AC, the smaller sizes used squirrel cage motors with star-delta starters. However, there were larger units, mainly in the AC-electrified quarries, which were housed in dedicated compressor rooms, some underground. They used wound rotor motors with sizes which could be as much as 100 to 200 kW with resistive or liquid starters.

Oakeley had five in use post war; all of which except that on L and P floor probably went back to the original electrification.[63] Latterly they were on Middle Quarry, C floor, DE floor and underground on L and P floors. Underground units were moved around to suit development. Power rating varied widely depending on the size of the compressor.

Pump motors

Pump motors followed a similar pattern to compressors with sizes up to 125 hp, 93 kW, recorded in Oakeley.[64] The

larger sizes were wound rotor machines with resistive starters to obtain good torque for starting against a large head of water. The research also records that for pump motors operating underground in a damp environment, Bruce Peebles supplied special motors with increased electrical clearances and larger frames.

Locomotives – trolley wire powered

At least two quarries, Croesor and Llechwedd, used electric traction on their main levels. The loco at Croesor was part of Kellow's original scheme and included in the original specification.[65] It was designed and manufactured by Kolben, not designed by Kellow as he claimed. Nor was it the first in mining in Britain as one was known to be in use in Lucy Tongue level at Greenside mine in the Lake District prior to 1904. Siemens made mine locos commercially from 1881. The Kolben machine contained two 220 V DC motors with a series/parallel control arrangement and 4 notches on the controller. It was designed to haul 30 tons on the level. It was to be supplied with DC from the AC system through a motor-generator set. Current pickup was by means of a pantograph. Current supply was by means of a single overhead trolley wire with return through the rails.

Lechwedd had three electric trolley wire locomotives. The first, in 1924, was called *Welsh Pony*. An uncaptioned photo in the Llechwedd archive may be this loco, which looks like a Siemens unit without any body work. Another photo of *Welsh Pony* shows a rather crude body which might have been fitted at the quarry. Llechwedd used a two-wire trolley system, presumably to avoid having to bond the rails.[66] *Welsh Pony* survived intact until 1967 but had been out of use since the 1950s. In 1927 they converted one of their steam locos to electricity by removing the boiler, lowering the cab to give clearance for the trolley gear and fitting electric drive to the chassis; it was called *The Eclipse*. A second steam loco was similarly converted in 1931, becoming *The Coalition*. Both locos survive and are currently at the Welsh Highland Heritage Railway, Porthmadog, awaiting restoration.

Locomotives – battery powered

At least five quarries had battery powered locos, Maenofferen, Llechwedd, Votty, Aberllefenni and Braich Goch.[67]

The Maenofferen unit was purchased, possibly in 1935, as part of improvements to the underground transport following commissioning of the B31 incline.[68] A machine extant, derelict in the Maenofferen mill, was a later replacement by Wingrove and Rodgers. It was photographed at work underground in 1982 by the author.

A Votty unit worked on L floor and is pictured in *Caban*;

---

62 Paton, *op. cit.* (n. 40 above).
63 'Power from the air grid', *Caban* (Oakeley house magazine) (July 1957), p. 17.
64 Unpublished research by Graham Isherwood and the late Rodney Weaver; also 'Pumping and power', *Caban* (Oct. 1951), pp. 3–8; 'Floor to floor', *Caban* (May 1955), p. 4; *Caban*

(May 1957), pp. 17–18.
65 Kellow, *op. cit.* (n. 23 above).
66 Isherwood, pers. comm., based on Industrial Locomotive Society NW handbook. The locomotive *The Coalition* can be briefly seen working in 1962 at https://www.youtube.com/watch?v=aoCHbq1JF5g (accessed Aug. 2014).
67 The Aberllefenni and Braich Goch locomotives are detailed in V.J. Bradley, *Industrial Locomotives of North Wales* (Industrial Railway Society, 1993).
68 Gwynfor Pierce Jones, pers. comm., papers and an insurance document of 1950 record the date of purchase of a motor-generator set to charge it from the new AC supply but the loco may pre-date that.

another worked on K floor but no technical details are known to the author.[69] Llechwedd are thought to have had two or three battery locos in 1921.[70] The BEV units currently working on the Llechwedd Quarry Tours operation were purchased for that; their history is not known to the author but may well be in the public domain.

Motor-generator sets

Motor-generator sets were occasionally used. Only two positive references and one probable have come to light so far. Croesor had a set to provide 220 volts DC for the locomotive from their AC system.[71] That was included in the original specification. Maenofferen purchased one in 1935 to charge their battery loco operating on B floor.[72] Another is reported extant in Llechwedd but the author has not had a chance to examine that. Reports indicate that it is a Mather & Platt unit probably used to provide low voltage lighting from 440/230 volts AC, or possibly their DC system. Others will no doubt be found with on-going research.

Ventilation

The author knows of only three quarries that used ventilation systems driven by electricity. Croesor always had ventilation problems, possibly due to the lie of the veins in relation to the mountain slope. Kellow was prosecuted for allowing underground fumes from his Robey steam winder to affect workers. He installed a large ventilation fan driven through gearing by a very high speed Leval steam turbine. When electricity became available that was replaced by an electric motor. The remains of the fan casing are extant near the adit entrance.

Llechwedd are known to have experimented with an electrically driven ventilation fan in 1890.[73]

Maenofferen must also have had poor ventilation as it had few openings to surface, but it was not until 1948 that they installed an extraction fan pulling air from the tops of some of the chambers east of the B31 incline, their main production area at the time.[74] Floor B was closed beyond the B31 incline and various baffles constructed to make it into an airway to the 60 inch fan driven by a 35 hp AC motor discharging up to floor A by a roofing shaft in chamber 31.

Lighting

Kellow specified arc lamps in all working chambers but it seems they were more trouble than they were worth and most quarries continued to use individual candles underground until electric cap lamps were introduced. Lighting was provided in mill work places by 'Glow Lamps' (sic) over individual splitting or sawing pitches. It is reported that the workers were reluctant to use artificial light as it affected their traditional working hours.[75] Lighting was provided in tunnels, pass-byes, and underground winder and compressor rooms where a supply was readily available.

Offices and *cabanau* on the surface were usually lit, at least in the larger quarries, as were some of the managers' houses.

Wiring, certainly in early days, was with single insulated wires carried in ceramic cleats on wooden battens, a standard system for industrial buildings at the time. The remains of that wiring system may still be seen in the Maenofferen mill and winder house. Voltage was certainly 250 for DC schemes and probably 230 for AC ones until workplace legislation required a maximum of 110V which necessitated step-down transformers.

Electric cap lamps

Electric cap lamps came late to the underground quarries. Oakeley only had them post Second World War and they were not in general use in the quarry until the early 1950s.[76] Maenofferen only started to use them in 1960.[77] There is no record known to the author for other quarries.

Winches

Kellow specified enough electric winches for all the working bargains. They were to be capable of lifting 3 tons and were to have two motions to lift blocks and transport them across the floor of the chamber.[78] It is thought that one of the original winches was used as the winder for the C-D incline sunk at a later date. More details are not known to the author.

There is a record in 1939 of an electric tugger winch in Maenofferen to move wagons from chamber B8 to the Back Vein incline.[79] It is likely that the extant winch in chamber B8 is the one used for that purpose. No further research has been carried out to date; no doubt there were others but most power winches were driven by compressed air.

Telephones

Simple point to point telephone systems must have been used quite extensively in the underground quarries. The instruments surveyed extant in 1981 at Maenofferen were all wooden case types with hand generators for ringing of 1920s origin and there are many insulators underground that may well have been for communication circuits.

Llechwedd latterly had a small Private Automatic Exchange (PAX) which the author was called upon to repair after a lightning strike. Their last working underground chamber on B floor had an extension off the Quarry Tours PAX, which the author maintained, for emergency purposes.

Several quarries had private circuits to wharf offices or management houses.

Miscellaneous equipment

The quarries must have been tempted to buy second-hand electrical equipment and this may mislead the industrial archaeologist. A transformer is extant on floor 2 in Maenofferen with a rating plate indicating 1000/440 V. There is no other indication at the quarry of use of 1000 V and it was possibly a second-hand colliery unit, where

69 'From floor to floor', *Caban* (Jan. 1954), pp. 4, 8, 9.

70 Isherwood, pers. comm.

71 Kellow, *op. cit.* (n. 23 above).

72 Charles Warren Roberts letter book, *op. cit.* (n. 5 above).

73 Unpublished research, Plas Tan y Bwlch Practical Industrial Archaeology course, *op. cit.* (n. 5).

74 Crosskey, *op. cit.* (n. 37 above).

75 Paton, *op. cit.* (n. 40 above).

76 'Ffestiniog slate', *Caban* (May 1949), p. 5, records that candles were still in use by rockmen in many chambers; 'Pumping and power', *Caban* (Oct. 1951), p. 7, mentions that electric cap lamps were in general use.

77 Crosskey, *op. cit.* (n. 37 above).

78 Barrell, *op. cit.* (n. 22 above).

79 Crosskey, *op. cit.* (n. 37 above).

1000 volts is a commonly found distribution voltage. It was probably used to provide 110 volt lighting from 440 V. There is also extant in the same location a 500/550 V winch probably with similar provenance.

Kellow was enquiring in 1913 for a 'Mechanical Navvie' that was to be electrically powered but there is no indication of purchase.[80]

---

[80]　Barrell, *op. cit.* (n. 22 above).

Appendix II

Electrical Contractors to the Quarries

Many firms were involved with electrical matters in the quarries; the following are just some of those who appear most regularly in early days.

Bruce Peebles

Peebles and Co., the original firm, started in 1866, manufacturing gas appliances. They started to produce DC motors and generators in 1898 and converted to a public company, Bruce Peebles Ltd, in 1902. They formed a trading alliance in 1902 with Ganz and Co. of Budapest, pioneers in the development of AC equipment, and by 1904 were supplying AC equipment in Britain to Ganz designs, some of it imported. They diversified into civil engineering work and in that way were able to undertake all aspects of the Cwm Dyli project. An ex Peebles man, E.W. Beutell, was the Chief Engineer of NWPT.

Bruce Peebles Ltd carried out all the installation work at Oakeley and Pen-yr-Orsedd and used the latter as a publicity platform. They also got heavily involved with the Portmadoc, Beddgelert and South Snowdon Railway project which failed in 1908, possibly connected with the failure in the same year of the first Dolgarrog aluminium project, in which NWPT and Peebles had interests. That in turn led to the failure of Bruce Peebles Ltd which was reformed as Bruce Peebles & Co. Ltd.[81]

The Bruce Peebles archive is understood to be very complete and contains many full plate publicity photographs of Cwm Dyli, Oakeley and the Pen-yr-Orsedd electrification, many of which are available from Gwynedd Archives. The author has failed to make contact with any archive still available and has had to rely on secondary sources.

Johnson & Phillips

J&P, as they were often known, were a south-east London firm with factories in Charlton. They were founded by the two partners in 1875, specialising in undersea cable and cable laying machinery as well as supplying telegraph and telephone equipment and cable of all kinds. They diversified into lighting and electric power equipment and were large-scale industrial electrical contractors, manufacturing many items but also buying in and rebranding items for sale that they did not make themselves. They were involved in the modernisation of the electrical equipment in Maenofferen in the 1920s and the extant mill motors came from them.[82]

The author has, in spite of searches on the internet and contact with a local history group, been unable to trace any possible archive.

Mather & Platt

This firm supplied both AC and DC motors and pumps to the quarries. A Manchester firm, their origin was in the textile machinery business and they diversified into electrical manufacturing. They supplied equipment for several early electric railway schemes including the first electric London Underground line. The firm was taken over by Weir Pumps and is now part of Wilo Pumps, Germany.

The author has not investigated any possible archive.

The North Wales Power Co. Ltd

The company started life as the North Wales and District Light Railway and Electric Power Syndicate Ltd. To start with, they concentrated on railway activities. They were replaced by the North Wales Power and Traction Company in 1903, who took over all their powers, still pursuing some railway activities but concentrating more on the electrical side with the building of Cwm Dyli power station. They must have been severely hit by the collapse of the Portmadoc, Beddgelert and South Snowdon Railway project and also of Bruce Peebles, a close partner, and were taken over as a wholly owned subsidiary by the Dolgarrog Aluminium Company who also acquired all their railway interests. They continued to trade under their own name until 1919. In 1923, as a result of several more Acts and Orders they became North Wales Power Company Ltd with a greatly extended area of power supply. They were nationalised in 1948 and their area of supply became Area 4 of the Merseyside and North Wales Electricity Board.[83]

It is not known what may have become of any archive since privatisation, when it went to the Electricity Council whose fate is unknown to the author.

Sandycroft Foundry

The company seems to have had its origins in 1837 with a foundry owned by John Taylor at Rhydymwyn supplying equipment for the Alyn lead mines.[84] When the mines declined in the 1840s they turned to producing mining equipment for Spain and in 1862 moved to the site that had been the Cram shipyard on the river Dee at Sandycroft near Queensferry. They then expanded their activities in the mining equipment market, mainly overseas. They supplied the equipment for Dolwen power station, then motors for Maenofferen and Llechwedd and probably many other quarries. A quirk of many of their machines is that they carry order numbers in place of serial numbers.

Their archive is in Flintshire Record Office Hawarden but does not go far enough back to be of interest to students of early electrification.

Yale Electric Power Co.

The moving spirit behind Yale, one T.P. Osborne Yale, was a

---

[81] Bruce Peebles & Co. Ltd continued to trade until in 1969 it merged with Reyrolle Parsons, Newcastle, to become Parsons Peebles Limited, Motor & Generator Division, which itself in 1977 was absorbed into the Northern Engineering Industries Group. This then (1989) merged with Rolls Royce. The company is now owned by Clyde Blowers. http://www.parsons-peebles.com/about-us/company-history; http://www.gracesguide.co.uk/NEI (both accessed 26 Nov. 2014).

[82] Report (in preparation) of surveying at Maenofferen 1981/2012 for Plas Tan y Bwlch Archive.

[83] More details can be found in Woodward, *op. cit.* (n. 11 above).

[84] Woodward, *op. cit.* (n. 11 above), p. 207. See also http://www.gracesguide.co.uk/Sandycroft_Foundry_Co (accessed Aug. 2014).

son of a Votty and Bowydd director (there were three other directors common to both Boards).[85] It is reasonable to suppose that formation of the Yale Electric Power Co. was on the initiative of Votty and Bowydd quarry. It is believed that Yale had a contract for pumping at Votty, and probably for power as well. The contract for pumping let to an outside contractor seems to be unique in the industry. It was of considerable advantage to Yale, allowing them to pump when other loads were low giving a better utilisation factor on their plant. (Oakeley had a similar arrangment but arranged by telephone between Cwm Dyli power station and the quarry as required.)

[85]   Isherwood, *op. cit.* (n. 7 above).

Quarrying in Wales: Borrowed Technology

Ian A. Thomas

Abstract: Say 'Wales' and 'quarry' and the word 'slate' almost invariably follows. Yet extraction of other materials in Wales for building and industry has long exceeded slate – over time, from ten thousand quarries. In tonnage terms, this mundane sector outstripped coal production in the 1960s. This paper can only skim through an industry which was active 230,000 years ago, underpinned the Industrial Revolution, in recent years exported to many European industries, whose output peaked at over 28 million tonnes in 1994 and even provided curling stones for the Olympic Games. The changing technologies in quarrying, processing and transport, from manual input to computer controlled plant, will be reviewed.

Introduction

This account concentrates upon stone extraction and focuses upon operations in Wales. After a short resume of developments prior to the Industrial Revolution, it considers extraction, processing and transport, as well as change within the markets for stone and 'knowledge transfer'. Equipment, ideas and materials in most cases have been imported. Slate is largely excluded, as in many instances that sector developed separately and was frequently technically more advanced; it had a product commanding higher selling prices and a much wider market, and hence often had better access to capital. As such it was typically managed in a more corporate fashion (Richards 1995).

The question arises as to whether there have been any innovations employed by the industry that were initiated from within that sector. One is hard pressed to come up with any robust responses. In retrospect there might have been a handful for the industry as a whole such as 'blondins', self acting inclines, static hook-up unloading winches and tunnel blasts, but it is unlikely that any of these was first deployed in the Principality. Quarrying, being an endeavour to extract relatively low value, bulky materials, has rarely had the access to capital, such as that utilised in gaining metal ores or coal, sufficient to drive technical ingenuity. So operators have only had recourse to adapting or borrowing ideas and equipment – not only from such better endowed extractive neighbours, but also from civil engineers ('in a rush to make things happen on a grand scale'), the military (with short term objectives, no expense spared and equipment readily pensioned off) and the New World, where mechanisation was forced by the availability of labour often being at a premium.

However, south Wales can claim firsts in respect of at least three advances which, although possibly considered tangential to the local quarrying industry, had worldwide implications. Richard Trevithick was the first to build a successful rail locomotive, which started running in 1804 from the limestone quarries at Penydarren to the company's ironworks. In 1855 Bessemer patented a novel method of producing relatively cheap bulk steel, much of his experimental work having been conducted in south Wales, but it was not until 1879 that Gilchrist and Thomas, again working in south Wales, perfected a method of using dolomite linings to enable most UK iron ores to be employed. These

last two innovations created an ongoing demand for high purity limestone and dolomite respectively, both locally and internationally.

Early historical context

Wales, unlike England, can only track stone working back a mere 230,000 years. In this regard, the Neanderthals' activities in Pontnewydd Cave, Denbighshire, are remarkable in two respects. Firstly the site lies isolated, more than 70 miles (110 km) north-west of the otherwise recorded limit for hominid occupation in western Europe, and secondly the tools found included flint – surely geologically anomalous in north Wales? Apparently the flint was fortuitously introduced by Irish Sea ice flows, presumably from Co. Antrim. Other tools accompanying the flint ones had been formed out of local rocks by the application of similar 'borrowed' knapping techniques, but they were crude by comparison (Green 1984).

Probably the most widely acclaimed early 'export' from Wales, at least in the public's mind, is that of the so-called 'blue stones' (spotted dolerites) from Preseli area to Stonehenge. Did the transfer to Salisbury Plain rely solely on human intervention, or was it largely assisted by east-flowing glaciers? The controversy rolls on but, interestingly, those slogging it out are not universally divided professionally into archaeologists and geologists; some eminent archaeologists, notably Aubrey Burl, are in the pro-ice camp. Less contentiously, stone was often dug and used on the spot, an excellent example being at Din Lligwy on Anglesey (a less sophisticated version of Orkney's Skara Brae), in which fourth-century AD hut bases and platforms depended on levering out stone that was appropriately proportioned by the bedding and jointing of the underlying Carboniferous limestone. In contrast, possibly the first, or at least the best, early indisputable example of concerted 'industrial scale' stone extraction occurred at such sites as Craig Llwyd, an obvious contender for Britain's longest (albeit intermittently) operational quarry. Perched at 1500 ft / 500 m and overlooking Penmaenmawr, this microdiorite outcrop supplied almost 10% of the 4000 provenanced UK stone implements, to locations across southern Britain (Clough & Cummins 1988). Recent work at Hyssington, on the border east of Montgomery, has revealed highly selective quarrying of the localised picrite rock. These two sites, and half a dozen others, notably on the Lleyn Peninsula and in Pembrokeshire (in common with many examples elsewhere in the UK), imply a very advanced level of geological discrimination. Presumably this was the result of centuries, if not millennia, of trial and error to locate the material best fitted for tool-making, driven by market forces, effectively based on inherited knowledge of product quality.

Although the Romans introduced a level of sophistication and organisation in construction on a scale not seen previously, it is understood that not a single verifiable Roman quarry site has been investigated archaeologically in Wales. Local source sites have been suggested for the stone employed at Segontium, Caernarfon, and Sudbrook has been put forward for some of the building work at Caerwent and Caerleon based on petrographic affinities (Lott & Barclay 2005). The lacuna in our certain knowledge of Roman quarries probably relates to obliteration by subsequent extractive activities and to the fact that there were virtually no changes in technology in winning building stone until the late nineteenth century, particularly in tool form. Import of stone, notably red sandstone – from the Wirral and possibly from an identified Roman quarry at Handbridge, Chester – and buff Dundry limestone from near Bristol, set a trend that was apparent in building design right through to the 1930s. Ostensibly this added colour or contrast to the fifty shades of local grey stones characteristic of much of the country. In the mediaeval period this polychromic approach may have had religious connotations; it was revived by the nineteenth-century Arts and Crafts movement.

The intervention of the Normans brought the first phase of large-scale stone building, almost immediately in the case of Chepstow Castle (1067 – although most of the stonework there is much later), later in that of Tintern Abbey (1131). The latter depended upon stone from the nearby Barbadoes Quarry, which continues to be active intermittently. Castle building extended across the south and coastward into mid-Wales, but techniques remained virtually unchanged.

In terms of constructional enterprise in Wales, Edward I's castle-building programme was not excelled until the Railway Mania of the nineteenth century. The logistics deployed for Edward's thirteenth-century enterprise were of World War II proportions and have been recorded in detail (Colvin 1963; Taylor 1986). With largely conscripted craftspeople, labourers and others, the workforce peaked at about 2000 individuals. Although the structures built reflect a number of design advances, particularly the application of defensive strategies witnessed in the Near East by returning crusaders, methods of extraction, carriage and shaping appear to have changed imperceptibly, if at all.

Contemporaneous and later building of castles, for example by the Welsh princes, of great abbeys or churches and, following the Dissolution, of grand country houses again displayed little evidence of technical advance.

Unlike slate working or the extraction of stone for major building projects, material for vernacular buildings, or such material as aggregates or cobbles for foundations and roads, was initially effectively gathered rather than conventionally quarried. In the south-west of England this would have been termed 'moorstones'. In upland areas many of the older buildings, for example in Dolgellau, display such large, unhewn blocks. Screes were a favourite source in this respect and were still targeted, for example at the head of

the Talyllyn pass (Bwlch Llyn Bach), until well after World War II. Beaches and sea cliffs were another prominent early source. Those exploiting limestone between Abergele and Colwyn Bay began in a similar manner. Although 'quarry' leases were recorded here in 1284 and 1696 (and may have referred to cliff workings), the 'modern' trade here appears to have taken off prior to 1800 when beach collectors began to supply Cheshire farmers for lime burning. The operations at Penmaenmawr began in the same way, quarrying of in situ bedrock, as such, not commencing until several decades later, in about 1830. At both locations the key economic driver was the need for ballast to trim general cargo ships returning to the Dee or Mersey. In these cases, of course, the ballast had the advantage of being eminently saleable. Meanwhile, in the south the ancient rights of 'cliffage' were exercised, as documented in 1672 on the Gower Peninsula and possibly also operated in Pembrokeshire. In both areas much of the coast, greatly appreciated now as 'natural', is in fact the product of quarriers nibbling away over centuries.

Industrial Revolution to the present

With remarkably few exceptions, the Roman or medieval worker would have been totally familiar with the surroundings of most quarries active in 1800. Furthermore, the differences – the growing use of gunpowder and tramways – were still relatively limited in extent. In particular, the hand tools were more or less universal and simple; many were almost identical in form to the basic implements wielded by sculptors and monumental masons today at some stage of their work. It was only their metallic compositions that changed, to tougher alloys, starting at the end of the nineteenth century.

Innovation was strongly concentrated in the period from the 1870s to the 1930s, so much so that by the middle of the latter decade almost all the technology in use today had emerged in principle, with two notable exceptions, namely hydraulics and computer controls (Thomas 2014; Thomas 2015). This period will now be covered in more detail and, by way of example, many of the descriptions of developments are based on contemporary accounts of activities at a number of the more advanced operations, notably Penmaenmawr (Fig. 1; Davies 1974). Changes were evident in all aspects of the industry – extraction, processing, transport and products. However, the lags in applying some of the innovations, particularly at smaller sites, often ran into decades.

Extractive techniques

The use of picks, hammers and wedges to open up fractures, and levering out rock with crow bars were the traditional methods of 'breaking ground'. They were the stock techniques and tools in Roman quarries and were still those most commonly used in 1800. Workers had to provide their own hand tools (a continuing requirement at some units until after World War II), which were made and sharpened by on-site blacksmiths.

Although gunpowder, generally known as black powder, or simply 'powder', had been used for quarrying in continental Europe since the fifteenth century, probably its first recorded application in British quarries was not until the late seventeenth century on the Isle of Portland. This was almost certainly facilitated by an almost unique set of cir-

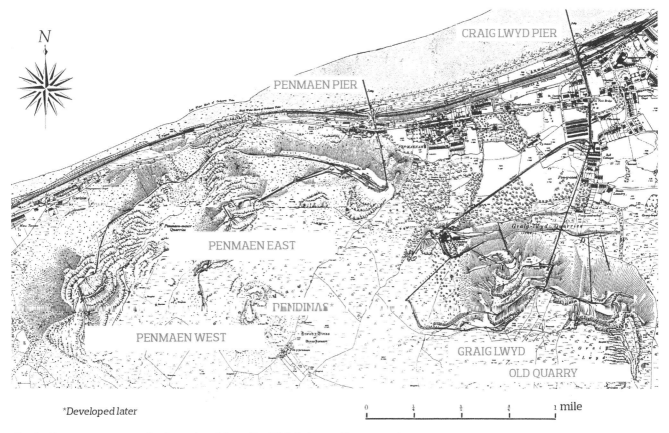

Fig. 1   Penmaenmawr quarries (reproduced from the 1913 Ordnance Survey map)

cumstances, so it was not until a century or more later that its application in quarries (as opposed to mines, some of which were using powder before 1700) became more widespread. Cilgwyn slate quarry, Penygroes, was most unusual in employing black powder only a few decades after Portland. The main slate operations were certainly using powder by about 1800 with stone extraction following a decade or two behind.

Records of early usage of powder in stone quarries are extremely sparse. A brief examination of inquest reports also confirms this view of the delayed introduction of its use for blasting in quarries, as most of the deaths before 1830 were due to falls of rock (including being crushed by 'stone of no use' – i.e. overburden or waste), implying that working was entirely by hand, effectively 'baring-out' rock, unaided by explosives. The other significant cause of death, incidentally, was associated with lime-burning. The availability of powder in this period was most probably conditioned by the nation's state of war or peace.

Handling powder was, of course, always potentially hazardous. Although safety generally improved following William Bickford's widely used 1831 patent fuse, well into the late nineteenth century it was not uncommon for children of quarry workers to be tasked with gathering straws or reeds, filling them with powder as fuses and, to keep them dry, storing them under their beds. The Gunpowder Act 1860 outlawed storage of amounts of more than 200 lb (91 kg) in non-specialist facilities and the Explosive Substances Act 1875 required local authorities to regulate stores, heralding the widespread building of magazines associated with quarries.

Metal rods, known as steels or jumper bars, held and turned by one man and hammered into rock by a partner, constituted the main form of drilling in quarries for centu-

ries. Initially these holes were for prising rock apart physically (forming openings to take plugs and feathers – as used from the medieval period), later as charge holes for blasting (Stanier 2000). These were only superseded by mechanical drills after the 1880s or '90s (hand held or on rigs). Steam driven rock drills were trialled in 1872 for example at Penmaenmawr, but not considered successful, although improved tripod-mounted steam rock drills were utilised there from 1895. Elsewhere compressed air began to replace steam for drilling in the 1890s. Drill design has continued to develop considerably to the present day, with rotary, top hammer/percussive and down the hole drills being applied to meet particular conditions. The addition of crawler tracks greatly increased the mobility of self-propelled rigs.

The construction of Holyhead's western breakwater, completed in 1873, was without doubt one of the UK's largest civil engineering fetes. Started in the early 1850s, the project needed to secure 7 million tons of stone – 6.5 million of which were drawn from the extremely tough quartzite on Holyhead Mountain. At first, in line with the conventions of the time, small shot holes were drilled and primed with gunpowder. As output targets were being missed, vertical shafts were dug then filled with powder, but this still proved insufficient so a third method was tried. In 1856 a tunnel blast was initiated. (This method had already been used in Scotland in 1852.) This comprised an adit driven at right angles into the foot of a face. At a calculated distance inwards, tunnels were driven at right angles (i.e. parallel with the face), in plan forming a 'T' shape. The ends and other points along the cross-bar of the 'T' were then opened up as chambers and packed with powder. In a single blast, over 60,000 tons were released. This was exceeded in 1857 by a blast which produced 130,000 tons (Fig. 2). The 4 km long Holyhead breakwater was largely complete by 1868.

In an attempt to reduce production costs to compete with Staffordshire quarries delivering limestone to ironworks, in 1867 early experiments were conducted using chamber blasts at Pant Quarry, just over the English border. This required a 60 foot shaft, at the base of which a chamber was hollowed out and packed with 1.55 tons of powder; the blast brought down 8–9000 tons of limestone. The following year a tunnel blast was carried out; 6.6 tons of powder was employed using electrical detonation. The total volume released was not reported, but the explosion was heard 10 miles away and the practice was not repeated. Tunnel blasting was also tried with black powder at Yr Eifl in July 1902 and achieved a rock fall of 150–200,000 tons of 'granite'. Even this scale of blast was exceeded, although using high explosives, in the 1960s at Raynes (Llysfaen) limestone quarry, Abergele. Although the drops of material produced were impressive, fragmentation was generally

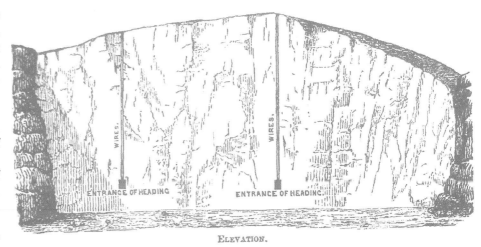

ELEVATION.

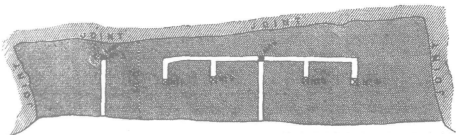

PLAN.

Height of face, 120 feet.   Length of face, 250 feet.
Length of heading, 120 feet.   Grip of heading, 40 feet.
Depth of sink, 15 feet, being 3 feet below the level of quarry.
Length of chambers—No. 1, 12 feet ; No. 2, 12 feet ; No. 3, 12 feet; No. 4, 12 feet ; total 48 feet.
Charges—No. 1, 5,000 lbs.; No. 2, 4,000 lbs. ; No. 3, 4,000 lbs. ; No. 4, 5,000 lbs.; No. 5, 3,000 lbs.;
total, 21,000 lbs.
Line of least resistance, average 23 feet.
Produce, 130,000 tons.

Fig. 2   Section and plan of tunnel blast preparations at Breakwater quartzite quarry, Holyhead, 1857 (Hayter 1876)

very uneven, requiring considerable secondary breaking, a cumbersome and potentially dangerous procedure. Until relatively recently this has necessitated small-scale blasting of individual blocks, also known as 'popping'. Most of the spectacular historic blasts were detonated simultaneously. However, it was found that introducing millisecond delays between the initiation of each explosive charge produced better rock breakage, and this method is now used routinely. In the later twentieth century, popping was displaced by the use of drop balls swung from cranes, but now, apart from better fragmentation from initial blasts, jib-mounted peckers are employed.

High explosives, notably in the form of Nobel's gelignite, became available in the 1870s and the slightly less potent TNT some decades later. However, even by 1909 their use, and that of myriad other patent explosives, by quarries in the three 'Welsh' Inspectorate Districts was less than a third of the weight of black powder used. These new agents were unsuited (as they still are) for use in winning building or dimension stone; also leading writers considered fragmentation was too flaky to produce good aggregates (Greenwell & Elsden 1913).

Apparently early quarry high explosives, especially TNT, were produced from ingredients which had originally been prepared for military use and become available from the replacement of time-expired charges in shells and warheads. For many years nitro-glycerine was the most important sensitiser for commercial explosives. As late as 1930 black powder still accounted for almost 50% (by weight) of quarry explosives, but ammonium nitrate was growing

in favour. Ammonium nitrate / fuel oil (ANFO) mixes have accounted for most of the quarry explosives used over the last half century (White & Robinson 1995).

A number of powder works were established across the UK within a few decades of 1830, for example those at Pontneddfechan, Glynneath, dating from 1857. Cookes works at Penrhyndeudraeth began producing mining and quarrying explosives on a series of headlands during World War I and closed in the 1990s. Both operations were acquired by ICI.

Single quarry faces often exceeded 100 ft / 33 m in height by the 1960s. To increase safety, bench heights are now typically restricted to 15 m and Inspectors generally prefer a 12 m limit. In one case, Criggion near Welshpool, the working height was approaching 650 ft / 200 m in 1967. Here not only would conventional benching have proved problematic, but also the working plan would have retained a tortuous journey between the points of extraction and processing. A radical solution, a glory hole system, was adopted. The company drew upon expertise from its mining interests in South Africa and Cornwall. An almost vertical shaft was sunk from the high level quarry floor to provide a 'rock pass'. At its base, it was intercepted by a long adit housing a conveyor which leads to the main processing plant on the floor of the old quarry. Rock blasted in the new upper quarry is fed into a mobile primary crusher, then into the rock pass (Fig. 3).

Over 99% of stone extracted in Wales has been drawn from open quarries, rather than being won below ground. In exceptional circumstances the higher costs and hazards of mining have been considered justified. Three examples include the Dinas silica mine at Pontneddfechan, which produced exceptionally pure silica rock that was used for furnace lining bricks, the quality of which was highly regarded in Russia. The second was a much smaller undertaking near Mold, which supplied silica 'flour' to Lever Brothers for use in the domestic scouring powder marketed as Vim. In the third, the 10 mile / 16 km long Milwr Tunnel was designed to drain lead mines in the Halkyn area. When the mines closed the facilities were used as an industrial water supply. The tunnel encountered very high grade limestone which met Pilkington's demanding specification for use in the production of non-coloured glass; stone production was effectively a by-product of water management.

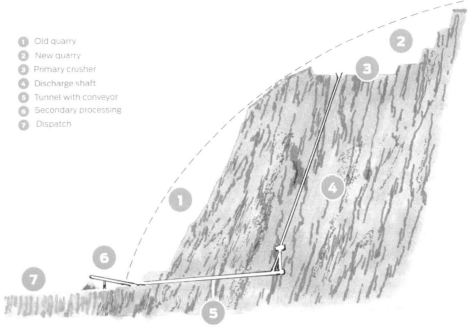

1 Old quarry
2 New quarry
3 Primary crusher
4 Discharge shaft
5 Tunnel with conveyor
6 Secondary processing
7 Dispatch

Fig. 3   Glory hole at Criggion Quarry, near Welshpool (I.A. Thomas / S. Chadburn)

Processing

Processing essentially involves reducing stone, sand and gravel to the desired shape and size and sorting into saleable product and waste. Currently, building and blockstone (e.g. for sea defences) only account for 0.002% of Welsh production; for all the remaining applications, stone is reduced to size, with a few exceptions, by crushing, then sorted by screening (sieving), sometimes accompanied by washing (Fig. 4).

The following section describes the evolution from manual processing to mechanisation between the 1870s and the interwar period. Automation followed from the 1950s and computerisation took hold from the 1970s to the present day. Nevertheless, it should be borne in mind that much of the stone industry was moving at a much slower pace. In particular, simple hand breaking by sledge hammer continued at some sites into the 1940s, if not even later. For example many customers, such as steel and chemical producers, considered that hand-broken and selected stone was cleaner than mechanically crushed material, and thus it was greatly favoured by lime-burners.

Whereas Cornish rolls were employed in British mines

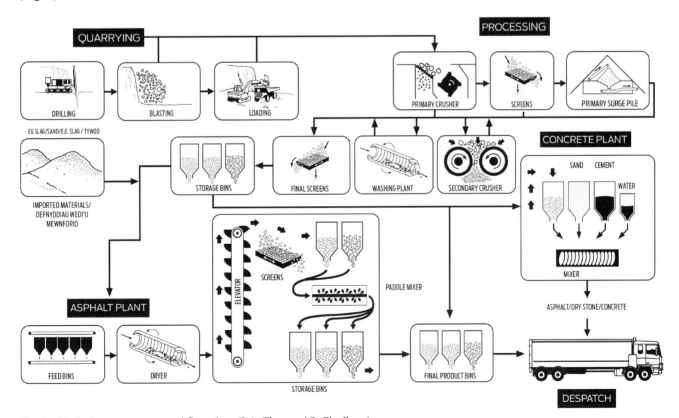

Fig. 4   Typical quarry process and flow chart (I.A. Thomas / S. Chadburn)

and in America by 1806, and drop hammers and impact crushers had been patented by 1840 (although not commercially produced), rock producers here did not generally follow suit until the late nineteenth century, when widely available, reliable crushers came onto the market. Best known were Eli Whitney Blake's jaw crusher (patented 1858), followed by Rutter's and Gate's gyratory crushers (developed 1869–1881). Roll crushers were further elaborated by Thomas in 1864 based on grain milling technology and Williams' impact crusher was patented in 1895. Mechanical crushers had been used, for example, in Leicestershire at Groby before 1848, but the wear-points degraded rapidly. Ten years later roll crushers were claimed to be viable at nearby Bardon Hill (Mountain 1860). William Lester introduced a steam powered crusher at Minera, probably in the 1860s. Although suited to many engineering applications, steel in general does not combine hardness and ductility, i.e. it lacks toughness. In 1882 Sir Robert Hadfield invented then utilised manganese steel for extremely tough applications such as crushers and excavator blades, thus resolving a number of long-standing shortcomings. By 1922, with the introduction of the Symons cone crusher, all the main conventional stone crushing techniques now in use – jaw, rolls, impactor/swing hammer and gyratory, had been developed (Mellor 1990). Technology from the USA still dominated the design field, but in the UK and Europe many crushers were produced under licence or applied in modified form; for example, Blake's jaw crusher was being sold in the UK under licence by Marsden of Leeds from 1862 (Mellor 1990).

The basic principles of separating out sizes of material by screening (sieving) go back to the Greek and Roman empires; indeed there were few modifications until the introduction of the rotary trommel screen, which achieved very wide usage from the late nineteenth century until the 1950s and, for sand and gravel, is still employed in modified form. Over the last century many other gravitational, cyclone and float/settlement systems, especially for sand and gravel separation, have been applied. The most frequently used technique, however, reverts back to inclined shaking screens, although with more sophisticated controls, polypropylene in place of metal decks etc.

One of the main trends over the last three decades has been to replace fixed processing plant with sets of mobile crushers and screens. Not only is this a more flexible approach in that machinery can be moved as quarry faces advance, but it often represents a more viable capital investment which can be switched from site to site in response to market changes.

The increasing use of vehicles with pneumatic tyres on public roads created a rapidly rising demand for 'bound' macadam road surfaces. Coal tar coated stone, alongside imported natural asphalt from 1900 onwards, effectively ceased to be used with the closure of 'town gas' works; it gave way to coating with bitumen (oil derivative). To ensure supplies of both tar and gas, some quarries ran their own distillation plants. Initially limestone aggregates proved more amenable to accepting coatings than granite, but unfortunately they developed slippery surfaces in use. The problem of coating stripping was resolved, which boosted the demand for igneous rock.

One of the few areas in which stone preparation was probably ahead of the slate industry was in respect of mechanical sawing. Cutting stone with indented saw blades combined with metal shot as an abrasive was apparently in hand in the first decade of the nineteenth century, and multi-bladed gang saws were operative about that time. In the 1820s powered circular saws were used in stone working, but not in the slate sector for ten years or more. However, most of these ideas were adapted versions of machinery seen in timber yards. It is likely that saws were mainly applied in shaping Pennant sandstone in the South Wales Coalfield, but little used in the early period for granite and limestone. A plethora of other machines were developed for turning, coring, polishing, buffing and routing stone. Before World War I various types of patent rock splitters were available to speed up sett and kerb making but, although these products accounted for important Welsh markets until the mid-1920s, no references to such mechanisation could be found. Routine hand-shaping of setts etc. certainly continued in the north Wales granite quarries until regular production more or less ended in the early 1950s.

Limestone was heated to produce lime for building mortar from Roman times onwards, and for agriculture from at least the sixteenth century. Kilns have developed from simple sod-covered piles to highly sophisticated, computer controlled operations – which constitutes a vast subject in its own right. Briefly, this sub-sector was an extremely important feature of the Welsh industry, which included the use of many kiln types. Pembrokeshire was a major early source from the thirteenth century onwards; indeed 250, mainly eighteenth- and nineteenth-century, kilns have been plotted along that coast. Similarly, the 'north crop' of the Carboniferous limestone, along the northern edge the South Wales Coalfield, in places supported dozens of kilns per square kilometre. Most of these were built of stone and often lined with firebricks or sandstone. Examples of the large, multi-chambered classic Hoffman kiln, patented in 1858 and initially designed for brick-making, were erected at Llanddulas (two kilns before 1872), at Raynes/Llysfaen (1875), at Minera (1868 and 1874) and at Llanymynech (c. 1900). Vertical 'patent' metal-clad kilns of various designs were introduced from the late nineteenth century and operated in some cases into the 1950s and '60s; they were to be seen as far apart as Dyserth and Minera in Denbighshire and Ifton in Monmouthshire (Ellis 1995).

From having been a major player in lime-making in the past, there is now no commercial production in Wales. Small amounts of specialist lime mortar are sold but not manufactured by companies in Wales. The most recent lime burning in the Principality was probably that carried out experimentally at Cornelly some years ago. High purity lime for steelmaking at Port Talbot is delivered from Batts Combe Quarry, Cheddar. Although demand from the steel industry for dolomite goods grew after the 1880s, there was no appreciable specialist production in Wales until Taffs Well Quarry was developed for this market in the 1920s. The industry is now served from Derbyshire and Co. Durham.

John Smeaton of Leeds, in searching for reliable mortars for rebuilding Eddystone Lighthouse in 1756, experimented with hydraulic limes (capable of setting under water), including that from Aberthaw, Glamorgan: part of the continuing history of lime morphing into cement. Although Aspdin patented Portland Cement in 1824, it took a further half century before a substance recognisable as the modern product emerged. In this respect the remains of old works at Aberthaw and, in the north, Afonwen near Caerwys are of considerable industrial archaeological significance. A works at Penarth produced cement from bottle kilns, now all demolished. Rotary kilns, dating back to the 1880s experimentally in England, were perfected in America and by the 1920s were used almost universally, the two current works in Wales, at Aberthaw and at Padeswood, Flintshire, being some of the most advanced in Europe.

Power and transport

The evolutionary trends in the movement of stone within quarries and beyond well illustrate the sequence of power sources deployed.

Humans, horses and occasionally oxen provided power for transport initially. (Incidentally, no examples of horse gins at Welsh stone quarries could be found although they were known in southern England.) In terms of general power sources, it is perhaps surprising that, apart from aggregates producers, in most building or dimension stone quarries and a substantial number of those supplying lime kilns, or fluxing material, stone was still man-handled many decades after other units had been fully mechanised; indeed in some instances all the activities were essentially manual, namely 'breaking, filling and dramming/tramming', until the 1940s or later. Creigiau Quarry near Llantrisant, which provided lump stone for the blast furnaces at East Moors works, Cardiff, in the early 1950s, is a good example (Fig. 5).

In more progressive enterprises steam was adopted gradually after 1850. From 1889 it was used to drive crushers and screens on a large scale in Braichllwyd mill, Penmaenmawr, and to an ever-increasing degree into the early 1900s in

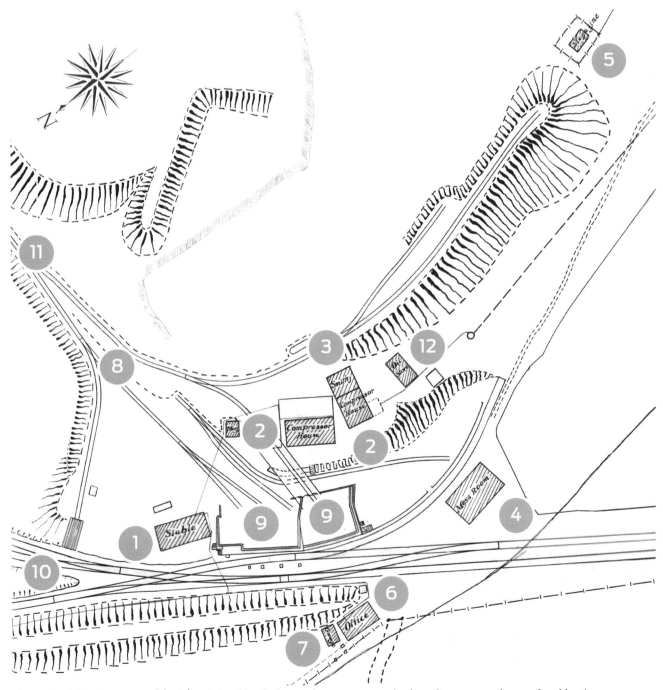

Fig. 5   Creigiau Quarry near Llantrisant. 1 stables for horses for narrow gauge haulage, 2 compressor houses, 3 smithy, 4 mess room, 5 magazine, 6 office, 7 garage, 8 narrow gauge lines to storage bins, 9 storage bins, 10 standard gauge main line, 11 working quarry, 12 oil store. Detail from 1937 quarry plan with revisions until 1954. (I.A. Thomas / S. Chadburn)

response to the growing market for aggregates, including rail ballast. It was typically supplied by large centrally located Lancashire boilers and dispersed via pipeline grids for various applications within quarries, including processing, drilling and locomotion.

However, compressed air (generated by steam-driven compressors, Fig. 6) rapidly began to replace steam for drilling in the late 1890s as pipelines of up to three miles in length lost little pressure, whereas steam losses through condensation were noticeable after a few hundred yards (anon. 1901). Such claims for compressed air transmission were disputed (Greenwell & Elsden 1913, 242). In 1901 at Craig yr Hesg Quarry, Pontypridd, air powered drills were estimated to be six times more productive than hand drilling. Almost as rapidly, electricity (albeit steam generated) began to supplant earlier means of energy distribution for processing and compressed air production in the 1910s and for excavation around 1930. Electricity was usually generated on site until higher capacity supplies from the National Grid became available, often as late as the 1970s. Unlike in slate operations, water power does not appear to have featured on any significant scale.

To a limited extent, petrol took the place of steam for three decades until reliable diesel engines became general in the 1930s, used for power generation, locomotives and trackless (non-rail) haulage. Gas engines were also briefly popular in the same period. Only occasionally were electrically powered locomotives used in open quarries.

Turning to transport in more detail, from about 1786 until the 1840s the new ironmasters of south-east Wales commissioned a rail and tramroad network of almost 100 km to deliver limestone flux to their furnaces (van Laun 2001; Hughes 1990). In the north, from 1801 the pre-mainline rail system was dominated by that serving slate quarries and, to a far lesser extent, stone producers (Richards 2001). However, despite Trevithick's pioneering 1804 locomotive, men and animals continued to propel wagons for a further 50 to 80 years, even in the larger advanced operations; at Penmaenmawr, for example, the first steam locomotives were only purchased in 1878. The cost of maintaining good draught animals and challenging gradients often forced change. On some particularly steep slopes, sledges were used in the early days.

Echoing the slate industry, and regardless of the motive power, integrated transport systems began to become more common from the 1860s and '70s. In stone workings these comprised a narrow gauge rail network with easily repositioned lightweight sidings laid alongside freshly blasted material at the foot of rock faces, connected to a spine track which delivered stone to bunkers (aka bins, silos, hoppers), kilns or crushers. Unconventionally, the rail system serving the quarry and breakwater construction at Holyhead inherited and maintained Brunel's broad gauge (Neale 1997).

Hand-loaded cranes were used to transfer stone to higher levels or fill wagons. Blondins (cableways slung between high points or towers) were first developed in Scotland in

Fig. 6   Central steam-driven compressed air plant, Craig yr Hesg Quarry, Pontypridd, 1901 (*The Quarry* (1901))

1872 and shortly afterwards applied in some Welsh slate quarries but, as far as is known, their use was not extended to stone working. Inclined bucket conveyors were widely used from the late nineteenth century for transferring between levels in plant, but rubber belt conveyors did not become reasonably reliable until the 1950s.

At some sites, hoists, tipplers or skips were used for the final part of the journey to processing. Occasionally, after 1900, buckets running on aerial ropeways were utilised, especially for sand and gravel or over difficult terrain, as between Twynau Gwynion and Morlais near Merthyr in 1914, or, as at Tan y Mynydd Quarry at Llanbedrog, mounted on pontoons for loading ships. The finished product was normally transferred to standard rail wagons or jetties. Steep sections within quarries were served by inclines, especially from the 1870s, using chains, then rope and finally steel cable. Gravity was an important factor; for example, self-acting inclines were widely used in north Wales. By about 1950, the Penmaenmawr complex had 42 such double-track planes.

The final conversions from manpower or powered rail carriage using small quarry wagons to rubber tyred vehicles were spurred on by lack of labour in World War II, although the engagement of prisoners of war delayed the transition in places. In most cases this move to 'trackless' stone quarrying started in the early 1950s, earlier than in most mines and many slate quarries. Ex-army lorries and equipment such as one-ton Muir Hill dumpers were put to use in many quarries after 1945 (Moody *et al.* 2003).

The first mechanical excavators were rail mounted, steam driven, had chain transmissions and were deployed almost entirely in civil engineering projects such as dock, railway and canal construction. In quarries their use was confined to working soft rocks such as clay, chalk and soft limestones. As such they were probably not used for stone in Wales, except possibly in the cement industry in the Vale of Glamorgan. For an example elsewhere in the UK, a rail-mounted Marion steam excavator from the USA is understood to have been trialled by ICI at Buxton in about 1929, but its progress was not regarded as satisfactory.

For excavation in general, steam began to give way to electric motors (the power being supplied by trailing cable from a central generator) or petrol engines in the later 1900s. The 1920s saw the introduction of diesel engines and, borrowing from tank development, crawler based excavators. Again, most of these advances were rarely applied in UK hard rock quarries until some years after 1925, when Bucyrus in America intro-

duced their 120-B electric, crawler mounted, cable operated shovel. This was the first production machine designed specifically for tackling hard rock. Indeed, some of these machines were so robust that they were still active in the 1950s and '60s. H.W. Darbyshire's exploratory visit to the USA in 1930 within a year resulted in him importing a 120-B machine with a 4 cubic yard bucket for Penmaenmawr Quarry. As a consequence, mechanical loading of 7 tons capacity standard gauge rail wagons there replaced hand filling of 400 two-ton tubs running on 70 miles of 3 foot gauge track. Incidentally, the slate industry had generally adopted a 2 foot gauge; the 3 foot gauge used here and at Llanddulas appears to have been inherited from the erstwhile owners' other operations at their Runcorn quarries.

The last major innovation in power transmission, that of applying hydraulics to excavation and articulation, did not fully emerge in the UK until the 1950s, again utilising experience gained from the military, this time in the form of aircraft retractable undercarriages. Although in the USA Euclid employed hydraulics to manipulate tipping in the 1930s, in the absence of hydraulics in the UK other ingenious approaches had to be adopted. In certain ICI quarries, for example, and at Penmaenmawr (in 1949), specially designed very large capacity hinged reinforced skips were attached to rubber-tyred semi-trailers hauled by upgraded road lorries. After being loaded by face shovels, they were unloaded at the crusher station by lowering a winch-controlled hook made to engage with a bar on one side of the skip. The load was thus side tipped into the crusher (Fig. 7). In 1950 Euclid established an assembly plant in Scotland, which was doubled in capacity in 1954 but initially largely

Fig. 7   Unloading a tipping truck at Penmaenmawr 1951 (courtesy Tony Brewis)

served the rapidly expanding civil engineering sector until about 1960. Their dumpers, and UK derivatives such as that produced by Aveling Barford, became universal in quarries from the 1960s, particularly as companies engaged in motorway construction integrated quarries into their portfolios.

With the exception of the rail systems developed by the ironmasters (restricted to south-east Wales), coastal marine transport represented the principal means of bulk carriage for stone, particularly in the north and west, into the 1850s; indeed, in the north ship-borne cargoes probably predominated up until World War II. Access to marine facilities was a highly significant determinant of the location of major quarries, such as the cluster between Abergele and Colwyn Bay (Fig. 8), those at Penmon (Anglesey), Penmaenmawr and around the Lleyn and Pembrokeshire coasts. Some sites, notably on the Lleyn Peninsula, were totally dependent upon the sea; indeed, at Nantgwrtheyrn this virtually applied both to quarries and the community (Webb 1997). One novel practice, which had origins predating nineteenth-century trade, was that of scuttling small incoming craft on the sandy beaches of the Gower Peninsula; limestone blocks were loaded into water within a boat (to minimise damage to the hull); boats were drained on the outgoing tide, then the sea cocks were closed to enable the boat to be floated off on the next incoming tide.

The later spread of rail had it own positive impact on quarry viability at sites such as Hendre Quarry near Rhydymwyn, the otherwise very remote Arenig Quarry west of Bala, operations around Old Radnor and those near Llandybie.

Knowledge transfer and its implications

The most remarkable influx of labour and presumably skills into Wales took place in the thirteenth century under Edward I when he conscripted stone diggers, masons and carpenters from virtually every English county to create his 'Ring of Stone' defences. Of particular relevance, county sheriffs were required by writ to supply the following numbers of stone masons: Shropshire and Staffordshire, 30; Derbyshire and Nottinghamshire, 30; Rutland, 20; Yorkshire, 20; Lincolnshire, 20. (Colvin 1963) All were instructed to report to Chester, with similar arrangements in respect of Bristol for southern counties. Supervision of much of this unprecedented logistical challenge was assigned to a Frenchman from Savoy, Master James of St George.

More conventionally, there are many instances of knowledge transfer from other areas and other sectors, but almost invariably the traffic was incoming. For example, records of the north Wales hard rock industry include references to men coming from Aberdeen, Kirkudbrightshire and Leicestershire to work as sett makers in the first half of the nineteenth century. Many of the managers were also drawn from elsewhere, particularly from Scotland, the slate industry and metal mining, including from overseas. In the north, capital support was mainly derived from Merseyside and Lancashire whereas south and mid-Wales depended more upon the Midlands and, later, the Bristol area. At Llanddulas, for example, and initially Penmaenmawr, Liverpool and Runcorn merchants were key investors and managers were dominated by Scots, whereas the ironmasters in the south hailed from the West Midlands.

By the end of the twentieth century the vast bulk of

Fig. 8   MV *Arklow Viking* at Raynes jetty, Llysfaen (CEMEX)

production in Wales was concentrated in only a handful of international companies, but all effectively based in the UK. Fifteen years later, all these groups have transferred to the control of French, German, Swiss and Mexican concerns and, at the time of writing, the industry is in an unprecedented state of flux as divestments have been required.

One event in Wales, which was to have implications for the quarrying industry internationally, took place in 1917 at the Prince of Wales Hotel, Caernarfon. Thanks to the drive and determination of Simon McPherson, manager of two quarries near Trefor, the Institute of Quarrying was inaugurated. The Institute represents professionals in the industry through thirteen branches in the UK and affiliated bodies in five other countries.

In 1878 C.H. Darbyshire took control of parts of what became the Penmaenmawr complex (see Appendix below). Although the family had existing ties with the area, his innovatory involvement is exemplary in many respects. He brought with him civil engineering experience in railways, of building the Mont Cenis railway in Italy, and in slate through working with his brother, manager of Penyrorsedd Quarry, Nantlle. Within three or four years of his arrival he paid fact-finding visits to examine crushers at Mountsorrel Quarry in Leicestershire and Clitheroe, Lancashire, then in 1887, sent batches of stone to Mountsorrel for crusher trials to determine the most appropriate types and settings to introduce. Within a year of his father's death in 1929, H.W. Darbyshire visited the USA on a fact-finding tour (as mentioned above) and in 1931 imported to Penmaenmawr a 56 in. x 72 in. Buchanan jaw crusher, probably the largest crusher on the market at the time (shortly afterwards Raynes Quarry followed suit with a slightly smaller machine, 48 in. x 72 in., which was only decommissioned about 2007). On the same trip Darbyshire Jr ordered one of the first heavy duty rock excavators to be put in service in the UK.

In the south, Alfred Lewis was another pioneer deserving mention. At his Pontsticill, then Vaynor, quarries near Merthyr he used engineering experience gained at the Crawshaw foundry to design and build crushing and screening equipment in the 1900s, then in 1912 developed and commissioned innovatory tarmacadam mixing plant. He continued to finesse techniques until shortly before his death in 1955.

Traditionally the main manufacturers of quarry plant in the UK have been heavily concentrated in the area between Leicester and Leeds, be they makers of cranes, processing plant or transport systems. Two areas in Wales also made a distinct contribution. During the last half of the nineteenth century the De Winton foundry of Caernarfon made a significant technical input to the slate industry. Less well known is their interaction with stone quarrying more generally: in the supply of locomotives and engines used to power processing plants, and in designing and installing integrated crushing and screening machinery, notably at Penmaenmawr. In the south, probably the two largest makers of mine and quarry rail wagons in Britain were based in Cardiff, later joining the Powell Duffryn group, itself a significant quarry operator. Hymac, which started as Rhymney Engineering, Cardiff, in 1946 and which became a world pioneer in hydraulic excavator design, especially 360° turntable mounted tracked machines, also became part of the Powell Duffryn group.

The technical advances described, coupled with radical market changes, were to have a major impact on employment and communities. Detailed statistics are not available in series form. Information for Penmaenmawr shows that the workforce was 910 in 1894, 1082 in 1913, fell back then peaked at 1100 (almost all men) in the late 1920s. By the end of 1932, following extensive mechanisation and economic depression, employee numbers had plummeted to 388, rose slightly, then in 1963 were recorded in the quarry as 227, halving by the 1970s. In the industry as a whole such changes were accompanied by a more than commensurate decline in accidents.

In the late 2000s about a quarter of Welsh stone production was exported to England, mainly limestone from the Clwyd area to the north-west, but there are also growing quantities of Pennant sandstone from the south for high specification roadstone. Meanwhile the uptake of recycled aggregates in Wales, as in England, had risen to percentages higher than for virtually all other developed economies.

References and further reading

anon., 1901. 'Pennant Stone: Macay and Davies' quarries', *The Quarry*, pp. 78–86

Burl, A., 2007. *A Brief History of Stonehenge: a complete history and archaeology of the world's most enigmatic stone circle* (London: Robinson)

Clough, T.H.McK., & Cummins, W., 1988. *Stone Axe Studies, 2: the petrology of prehistoric stone implements from the British Isles*, Council for British Archaeology Research Report 67

Colvin, H.M. (ed.), 1963. *The History of the King's Works*, vols I and II (London: HMSO)

Davies, I.E., 1974. 'A history of Penmaenmawr quarries' *Trans. Caernarvonshire Historical Society* 35, pp. 27–72

Ellis, B., 1995. 'Quarrying and limeburning', in J. Bennett (ed.), *Industrial Minera: the lead mines and quarries of Minera* (Wrexham Maelor Borough Council), pp. 29–36

Green, H.S., 1984. *Pontnewydd Cave: a lower Palaeolithic hominid site in Wales – the first report* (National Museum of Wales)

Greenwell, A., & Elsden, J.V., 1913. *Practical Stone Quarrying* (London: Crosby Lockwood)

Hayter, H., 1876. 'Holyhead New Harbour', *Minutes of the Proceedings of the Institution of Civil Engineers*, minute 1454, pp. 95–112

Hughes, S., 1990. *The Archaeology of an Early Railway System: the Brecon forest tramroads* (Royal Commission on Ancient and Historical Monuments of Wales)

Lott, G.K., & Barclay, W.J., 2005. 'The geology of building stones in Wales', in M.R. Coulson (ed.), *Stone in Wales: materials, heritage and conservation* (Cardiff: Cadw), pp. 6–13

Mellor, S.H., 1990. *An Introduction to Crushing and Screening* (Institute of Quarrying)

Moody, I., Jones, S.K., Jervis, E., Jenkins, A., & Hopkins, B., 2003. *Wenvoe and Twyn-yr-Odyn* (Wenvoe History Group/Tempus)

Mountain, C.G., 1860. 'Description of machinery for crushing stone for macadmising roads' *Proc. Inst. Mech. Engineers*, pp. 234–47 + pls

Neale, A., 1997. 'Broad gauge at Holyhead', *Industrial Gwynedd* 2, pp. 18–25

Richards, A.J., 1995. *Slate Quarrying in Wales* (Llanrwst: Gwasg Carreg Gwalch)

Richards, A.J., 2001. *The Slate Railways of Wales* (Llanrwst: Gwasg Carreg Gwalch)

Stanier, P., 2000. *Stone Quarry Landscapes: the archaeology of quarrying in England* (Stroud: Tempus)

Taylor, A.J., 1986. *The Welsh Castles of Edward I* (London: Hambledon Press)

Thomas, I.A., 2014. *Quarrying Industry in Wales – a history* (Wirksworth: National Stone Centre)

Thomas, I.A., 2015 (in press). 'Bulk minerals', in P. Newman, *Research Framework for the Archaeology of the Extractive Industries in England* (National Association of Mining History Organisations)

van Laun, J., 2001. *Early Limestone Railways* (London: Newcomen Society)

Webb, E.M., 1997. *This Valley was Ours* (Llanrwst: Gwasg Carreg Gwalch)

White, T.E., & Robinson, P., 1995. *The Use of Explosives in Quarrying* (Nottingham: Institute of Quarrying)

Appendix

Chronology of the Penmaenmawr Quarries

To augment the references already made in respect of the Penmaenmawr group of quarries, which led the way for almost a century from the 1850s, a selective chronology of their progress is particularly instructive. It is largely drawn from Ivor Davies' 1974 account. (It should be noted that two competing companies were active here until their merger in 1911.)

1830s	self acting inclines, tramways and jetties installed
1848	Chester to Holyhead railway completed to Penmaenmawr, after which much of the quarry output was sent by rail
1878	first locomotives introduced
1878	C.H. Darbyshire's arrival; Graigllwyd Co. set up by Darbyshire family
1880s	(early in the decade) C.H. Darbyshire's fact-finding visits to examine crushers at Mountsorrel Quarry in Leicestershire and Clitheroe, Lancashire
1884	16 in. x 8 in. Baxter jaw crusher installed to produce macadam
1887	batches of stone sent to Mountsorrel for crusher trials to determine the most appropriate types and settings to introduce
1888	Braichllwyd mill (steam powered) started producing rail ballast on a large scale; similar mill established by rival company – doubled in size in 1893
1895	mechanical rock boring began
1897	Concrete product plant set up
1902	Penmarian mill commissioned (steam)
1911	the Darbyshire and Brundrit companies merged and Eifl Quarry joined the group
1912	tarmacadam coating plant started
1913	change of main power source from steam to electricity
1913	electrically driven compressors for drilling
1929	Traylor gyratory crusher installed plus two jaw crushers and cone secondary and tertiary crusher replaced rolls
1929	Vibrating screens replaced revolving perforated trommel screens
1929	C.H. Darbyshire died; W.H. Darbyshire took over
1930	W.H. Darbyshire visited USA on fact-finding tour
1931	56 in. x 72 in. Buchanan jaw crusher imported from USA, probably the largest on the market at the time
1931	Bucyrus 120B excavator (electrically powered) imported from USA
1943	additional Buchanan crusher installed
1948	rubber-tyred dumpers began operating
1958	removal of rail infrastructure completed; replaced by dumpers and belt conveyors

Other Papers Presented at the Conference

The following papers were presented at the conference but were not submitted for publication in this volume.

The Welsh Slate Industry: archaeological evidence for development and change
Louise Barker

Development and change are inevitable for an industry that dates back to the Romano-British period, which dominated the world market in Victorian times and remains active, albeit on a much reduced scale, today. Whilst this is clearly evidenced in the documentary record, is the same true for the surviving remains on the ground? As part of its thematic study on the Welsh Slate Industry, the Royal Commission has undertaken archaeological survey at a series of slate processing complexes. Interpreting and understanding the resulting data has in some cases proved challenging without documentary sources to hand; but the archaeology does tell the story. Using specific case studies this paper will look at the archaeological evidence on a number of themes including power systems, processing and transport; it will also look outside the quarry at the wider impact of an industry through the development of settlements and their communities.

Mechanisation on the Coal Face: a history
Darran Cowd

The mechanisation of coal mining, specifically at the coalface itself, led to the development of equipment almost unique to the coal industry. Early ideas such as Firth's 'Iron Man' of 1862 mechanically imitated the action of a miner and his pick. However, it was the development of three technologies, the bar cutter, disc cutter and the chain cutter, which moved away from human imitation, that influenced the design and development of the large double ended ranging drum shearers that everyone now recognises as the de facto coal mining machine of today.

This paper looks at the contributions of companies such as Mavor & Coulson, Gillott & Copley, British Jeffry Diamond and Anderson Boyes, and individuals such as Sir William Garforth and John Anderton and his NCB colleagues.

Splitting the Mine: the effect of Buddle's panel method on extraction rates in nineteenth-century coal mining
Mia McCabe

Accounts of coal mining in the nineteenth century regularly recognise the working and 'winning' practices of engineers of the north-east England coalfield as a leading example of coal extraction. Particular credit is given to John Buddle, a colliery viewer and mining engineer whose development of a zoned approach to working became the de facto standard for the industry.

This paper analyses Buddle's plans, records and public testimony and examines technical aspects of his work, particularly his contributions to mine ventilation and illumination and advancements in pillar working, during the period 1801 to 1835.

Dating the Introduction of Gunpowder in the Central Wales Orefield
Robert Protheroe Jones

The beginning of the utilisation of gunpowder in hard rock mining in Europe in the seventeenth and early eighteenth centuries constituted a technological step-change in the non-ferrous mining industry. This paper summarises the diffusion of this new technology from its Central European beginnings, and within Britain from its initial adoption in Derbyshire lead mines. Datable documentary and field evidence is examined for the early use of gunpowder in the lead-silver mines of the Central Wales orefield. It is suggested that early gunpowder use underground constituted gunpowder assisted mining, being an adaptation of the preceding mining technique of hand picking. A suite of characteristic features is identified as being potentially useful in distinguishing and dating this phase of mining technology in the region.

Work on this paper has developed further areas of enquiry not covered in the original paper as delivered at Bangor. It is now intended to publish the work as a separate publication covering the diffusion of gunpowder-assisted mining, with special reference to Britain and the Central Wales orefield.

Contributors

Louise Barker has worked as an archaeologist since graduating from Newcastle University in 1996. She started her career working as a field archaeologist for the Archaeological Practice Ltd in North England and then moved to Cambridge in 1999 to work for English Heritage as an Archaeological Investigator. Louise joined the The Royal Commission on the Ancient and Historical Monuments of Wales as an Archaeological Investigator in 2004 and since April 2011 has also taken on the role of Team Leader for the Recording and Investigation section of the Commission. Much of her work at the Commission involves the survey and interpretation of archaeological sites and landscapes, and the presentation of this to a wide ranging and varied audience.

Tim Colman worked as an exploration geologist in Tasmania, Western Australia, Galway and Clare. After a period teaching geology at Forest Fields College Nottingham he became an economic geologist for British Geological Survey Minerals Group working on (amongst other things) the Minerals Incentive Scheme, Mineral Reconnaissance Project, Snowdonia Regional Mapping Project, East Midlands and Northern England Metallogenic Models and Exploration Criteria Projects, Metallogenic Map of Britain and Ireland, Exploration Guide for Metalliferous Minerals in Britain, EU Mine Waste Directive plus short-term overseas mineral development projects in Angola, Falkland Islands, Mozambique, Turkmenistan and Zambia. He retired in 2007.

Darran Cowd is Collections Officer at the National Coal Mining Museum for England at Caphouse Colliery. While growing up in Cornwall he developed a strong interest in mining, engineering and transport heritage as an active volunteer with a number of groups, including the Cornwall Mining & Caving Club and Bodmin & Wenford Railway before pursuing a career in the heritage sector.

Darran has subsequently held a variety of curatorial positions in national museums such as the Imperial War Museum and RAF Museum as well as the NCMME, specialising in engineering and technology collections.

His current personal research interest, the remains of the West Yorkshire coalfield, is informed by the discovery of a set of standard mine plans formerly held in the surveyors office at Denby Grange Colliery.

Andrew Davidson is Chief Archaeologist for Gwynedd Archaeological Trust. Andrew has worked within Welsh archaeology for some thirty years, and between 1998 and 2011 was responsible for managing the Contracts section of the Trust. He has supervised several projects undertaken at Parys Mountain, and takes a keen interest in its archaeology.

Steve Grudgings is an 'accidental expert' in the history and archaeology of the UK coal industry, having visited and photographed (both at surface and underground) over 200 of the UK's active and closed coal mines since 1980. Actively involved in archaeological assessments and conservation of mining sites in the Bristol region, he was one of the founders and previous Chairman of South Gloucestershire Mines Research Group (SGMRG).

One of Steve's particular areas of interest is the development of the technologies and skills required to construct and operate early engines and he believes the 'fire engineers' of the pre-Watt era were more skilled and knowledgeable than is generally recognised. Steve has had a number of papers published in the journals of the Newcomen Society and the Bristol Industrial Archaeology Society.

David Gwyn After a first career in teaching David worked as an archaeologist for Gwynedd Archaeological Trust and is now a freelance consultant and lecturer specialising in industrial, post-medieval and landscape archaeology and research and heritage management, conservation advice and planning issues. Amongst his other interests are the narrow gauge railways of north Wales – he is a director of both the Ffestiniog and Welsh Highland Railway and the Bala Lake Railway. David is the author of *A guide to the industrial archaeology of North West Wales*, *Dolgarrog: an industrial history* (with Eric Jones), *Gwynedd: inheriting a revolution: the archaeology of industrialisation in north-west Wales* and *Welsh Slate: Archaeology and History of an Industry* and has been the editor of *Industrial Archaeology Review* and *Industrial Gwynedd*.

Graham Isherwood became interested in narrow gauge railways and the industries that spawned them while at school. In the early 1970s, both the Llechwedd (Quarry Tours) and Oakeley (Gloddfa Ganol) quarries in Blaenau Ffestiniog opened their doors to the public. With a background in maps and plans he was drawn to the incredibly complex surveys of the quarries that he found as well as the technologies that made them possible. For twenty years he acted as historian to Gloddfa Ganol until it closed when the quarry was taken over by McAlpines. He also acted as historian for a time to the Red Rose Live Steam Society in Lancashire, who were engaged on the restoration of the Astley Green Colliery winding engine. He has written various articles on aspects of winding engines, including the Astley Green engine, as well as books and booklets on Welsh slate quarries: *Candles to Caplamps: the story of Gloddfa Ganol*; *Slate from Blaenau Ffestiniog*; *A Walk into the Slate Mountain* and *Cwmorthin Slate Quarry*.

David Jenkins is a retired Senior Lecturer in Soil Science at Bangor University with a particular interest in geochemistry, mineralogy and pedogenesis and is intrigued by their application within archaeology. He has now reverted to his lifelong fascination with the underground and has focused on the mines at Mynydd Parys in Anglesey, on their Bronze Age and industrial history and on their heritage. He is a founder member and Trustee of the Amlwch Industrial Heritage Trust and the Parys Underground Group, and is also a Trustee of Gwynedd Archaeological Trust. He escapes underground when possible.

Mia McCabe is researching innovations in coal mining technology in the North East at Newcastle's Northumbria University, with particular focus on the work and legacy of John Buddle. The project is sponsored by the AHRC and is conducted in collaboration with the North of England Institute of Mining and Mechanical Engineers.

Mia's background is in cultural and industrial heritage, and her previous research was sponsored by the Croatian Ministry of Science and Education, and the UK Foreign and Commonwealth Office under the Chevening scheme. Her work continues to focus on regional identity and how this copes with a decline in local industries and the communities they support.

Catherine Mills is a lecturer in modern British environmental history at the University of Stirling. Her main research interests are in the historical creation, management and perception of post industrial, particularly mining, landscapes. She currently is working on a series of interrelated projects exploring the unrealised environmental impacts and associated cultural and health legacies of rural industrialisation.

Catherine has published on the occupational health of Cornish miners, urban air pollution and the health and safety regulation of the British mining industries.
E-mail: c.j.mills@stir.ac.uk

Tim Oulton was evacuated from the Wirral to the Lledr valley in the Second World War which stimulated a lifelong interest in narrow gauge railways, slate quarries and mountains. He served his apprenticeship with Metropolitan Vickers (later AEI) in Trafford Park, Manchester, and after qualification worked for AEI as a railway signal engineer. Much of his working career was spent as an engineer with the Merseyside and North Wales Electricity Board in the Chester and Wirral areas. He is a Member of the Institution of Engineering and Technology. Tim has a long-term record of volunteering on the Ffestiniog Railway. His more recent interests have been underground photography in slate quarries, hill walking and collecting, and especially showing, the toy train products of Meccano Ltd as illustration of British toy manufacturing at its very best.

Robert Protheroe Jones took a degree in geology at Aberystwyth University and initially worked for Welsh Water Scientific Services in central Wales, including monitoring mine water pollution alleviation schemes. In 1990 he joined the staff of the Welsh Industrial and Maritime Museum, Cardiff, where he was responsible for the metalliferous collections. Now Principal Curator of Industry in the National Museum of Wales Department of History & Archaeology, he is based at the National Waterfront Museum, Swansea. He has been surveying and recording Welsh metal mines on surface and underground for 30 years. Email: Robert.ProtheroeJones@museumwales.ac.uk

Rick Stewart Having gained degrees in town & regional planning and coastal management Rick chose to follow a career in the museum/heritage sector. Since 1995 he has been employed at Morwellham Quay in Devon where he is currently mine manager. In 2013 decade-long research project focusing on the history of Devon Great Consols culminated in the much anticipated publication of *Devon Great Consols: A Mine of Mines*. Current research is focused on eighteenth-century copper mining in south-west England. Rick is a very active mine explorer and a member of his local cave rescue team.

Ian Thomas's ancestors in England were quarry operators and builders, and in Wales, master mariners. He served his time in printing long before computers and graduated in geology from Swansea. After working in 'mineral intelligence' at the forerunner to the British Geological Survey, he joined Derbyshire County Council undertaking strategic mineral planning. With others, he promoted his concept of the National Stone Centre, being its Director from 1988 until retiring in 2012; he continues as an associate consultant and its Honorary President. In 2013 he was appointed NAMHO Chairman. In addition to researching quarry history, he is a freelance designer and painter.

Simon Timberlake is Excavations Director of the Early Mines Research Group. A geologist and former museum curator, he has undertaken archaeological excavation and research on ancient mining sites since 1986. Since 1996 he has worked at Bangor, Manchester and Coventry universities on projects funded by the Leverhulme Trust, and now works as a field archaeologist for the Cambridge University Archaeological Unit. He has an interest in experimental archaeology and the reconstruction of prehistoric mining and smelting processes and has published (either singly or jointly) more than 40 papers on early mining related topics. He is a director of the Welsh Mines Preservation Trust.

Rob Vernon was a geologist for 24 years in the coal industry (deep mines). For much of this career he was heavily involved with drilling boreholes. With the industry's demise, he researched and gained a doctorate on the archaeological prospection of smelting sites. Currently his main interest is Spanish mining, particularly the operations of British companies. He has written various papers and given talks on the subject at international conferences. He is also an honorary member of the Colectivo Proyecto Arrayanes, a Spanish mining heritage organisation based at Linares, Spain. As a geologist, the history of mineral exploration has always been more than a passing fascination, and several of his more recent papers and talks reflect this interest.